Practical
CLOCK ESCAPEMENTS

Practical
CLOCK
ESCAPEMENTS

Laurie Penman

Published by:
Mayfield Books
Matherfield House, Church Lane,
Mayfield, Ashbourne,
Derbyshire, DE6 2JR, England
Tel/Fax 01335 344472

Published in the USA by:
AutaMusique, Ltd
Summit Opera House, Two Kent Place,
Summit, NJ 07901 USA
Fax (908) 273 9504

British Library Cataloguing in Publication Data:
A catalogue record for this book is available from the British Library.

Printed in Spain by
Keslan Servicios Graficos

Normal workshop safety practices must be observed at all times and the author and publisher of this book accept no liability for any accident or injury, no matter how caused, by following the procedures presented here, which are given in good faith.

Contents

Preface

My intention in writing this book was to describe the repairing, making and designing of clock escapements in a practical manner. So far as can be managed, dimensions that cannot be measured with normal engineering tools have been ignored. In other words the dimensions used are linear — they can be measured using a rule, micrometer, vernier calliper or even by making marks on a piece of scrap metal. Wherever possible specifying small angles in either degrees or radians has been avoided because most clockmakers (amateur or professional) do not have the means of measuring these accurately. What utility is there in quoting the locking of an escapement as 'half a degree' when the only instrument generally available to the ordinary clockmaker cannot show the difference between 0.5 and 0.4 degrees ?

Though this is a book on *practical* clockmaking, many readers may not want to take it into their workshop. For this reason the steps in making some of the more usual types of escapement are summarised, so that these particular pages may be copied and used for reference on the workbench.

It should be noted that, although some of the workshop techniques described here may seem rather obvious to the experienced clockmaker or model engineer, they might not be to newcomers. As this book is intended for those with all levels of experience and expertice, it is hoped that all those concerned in the practical aspects of clockmaking and clock repairing will find something of interest.

In some instances there is repetition of both text and diagrams where they are of relevance to more than one chapter. This is quite deliberate, to avoid the need for constant cross-references to other sections, and though this is necessary in some cases, it has been kept to a minimum.

Alternative methods of construction are sometimes given, depending on the equipment available. Not all clockmakers possess a lathe or dividing equipment, and though these are desirable for may tasks, some can be done entirely by hand.

As the author is no mathematician the reader will not find any erudite and scholarly discussions of the more abstruse characteristics of balance wheels, balance springs or the effects of mass and lubrication on pallets and detents. I hope that this will not be a disappointment.

A glossary has not been included, as I have always found them tedious to use; instead an appendix includes diagrams of typical clock movements and their parts. Most technical terms have been explained as the chapters progress or their meaning should become clear by the way that they are used.

The first of these technical words of course is 'escapement' and if you will just turn the page I will make a start. Enjoy yourself.

Laurie Penman
Totnes, Devon, England

CHAPTER 1

Introduction to Escapements

1 What is an Escapement?

The escapement is the device in a clock that allows the gears to rotate in a regulated fashion. Not like a clockwork motor that runs fast when fully wound up and gradually becomes slower, but evenly, so that it can be used to mark time. It does not actually *measure* the intervals of time, but doles them out so that the gear train turns in a predictable manner.

The measurement of these intervals is handled by an oscillator of some description: a foliot (**Fig 1/1**), a pendulum (**Fig 1/2**) , a balance wheel (**Fig 1/3**), a crystal and even more exotic oscillators than these. For most clocks the time interval is the length of time taken for one 'beat', or swing from one side to the other, of the pendulum, balance or foliot. (Note that the period of oscillation, as used in scientific work, is from one extreme of swing *and back again*, ie twice the beat.)

The other important function of an escapement is to feed energy from the power source (ie the weight or spring) via the gear train to the oscillator, to replace the energy lost by friction, and so keep it swinging. Hence the oscillator is impulsed.

Fig 1/1 Foliot with a crownwheel and verge escapement

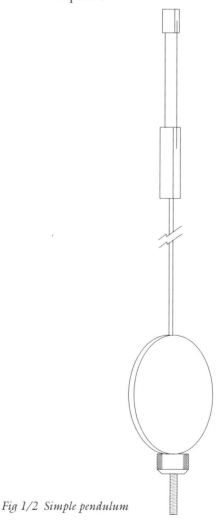

Fig 1/2 Simple pendulum

2 Types of Clock Escapement

The escapements popularly used in clocks can be divided into two broad types: recoil and deadbeat. A recoil escapement actually causes the train to reverse its motion and wind back on itself a small amount — the deadbeat escapement however, introduces a 'dead' face which eliminates this reversal and allows the movement to progress in one direction only. Since clock gear trains only run efficiently in one direction, the recoil action produces more friction than the forward running of the movement. Also the amount of friction during recoil is more variable, and this results in the straightforward recoil escapement being generally less accurate than deadbeat escapements. However they are accurate enough for most domestic purposes — a longcase or grandfather clock with a recoil escapement for instance, can keep time to within ten or fifteen seconds a week (provided the temperature is reasonably constant) — and they are usually more robust than deadbeat versions.

Most of the popular escapements (verge, recoil anchor, Graham and Brocot deadbeats,

and all their variants) allow half a pitch of the escapewheel to move through the pallets for each beat of the oscillator and so it 'ticks' at each beat. A few allow the escapewheel to move a complete tooth pitch in one go after two beats of the oscillator, and so the escapewheel only rotates every other beat.

However in either case, the functions of both impulsing the oscillator and the management of the escapewheel, are handled by one device: the recoil anchor, the deadbeat anchor or the verge. These essentially consist of two pallets mounted on a body.

There is a complete class of escapements that split these two functions, having different devices for impulse, and for locking and unlocking the train. These escapements include gravity escapements, the more delicate detent escapements used in very precise mechanical chronometers, and, of course, electronic clocks where the oscillator is a crystal or a radioactive material. The mechanical versions will be found in Chapter 8; I do not intend to deal with electronic and atomic clocks at all.

3 Oscillators

The foliot is probably the earliest of the oscillators to have been used in a mechanical clock and it is simply a T-shaped bar, pivoted on its upright and adjusted by moving weights along the horizontal arms. This was later modified into an upright with a wheel as the horizontal component, ie a balance wheel (**Fig 1/3**), but it should not to be confused with the balance wheel and hairspring assembly that came into use much later for watches and small clocks.

Simple oscillators like the foliot and early balance wheel are not good at keeping to time as they have no constant restoring force, and hence tend to move faster or slower according to how much power is delivered to them. The power varies because the efficiency of a gear train alters under the effects of changing lubrication, heat and cold, the movement of

each tooth as it drives its meshing partner, and one or two much smaller, natural effects.

The Foliot
The foliot keeps time by balancing the amount of energy fed to it by the gear train against

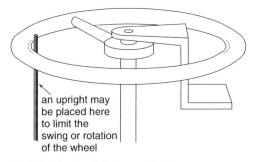

an upright may
be placed here
to limit the
swing or rotation
of the wheel

Fig 1/3 The simple balance wheel

the energy needed to rotate its masses at different velocities. If the weights are moved out along the arms the system slows its rotation because the amount of energy being fed to it has not increased — and more energy would be required to keep the rate of rotation constant. More energy is not forthcoming unless more weight is hung on the driving wheel.

The angle that the foliot turns through is limited by the escapement. Since it is a recoil escapement the foliot presses back against the train after each tooth of the crown wheel escapes beneath it and consequently *lifts* the driving weight until its own energy has been used up. Only after this point can the driving weights resume their downward movement and the foliot then rotates in the direction that will release the next escapement tooth.

The Simple Balance Wheel

A simple balance wheel has no means of altering the energy needed to drive it (I do not know of an instance where weights were added to the rim of a wheel) and its period of rotation or beat is limited by a springy bar that interferes with the rotation of the single spoke of the wheel. By moving this bar (known as a 'hog's bristle regulator' in the case of a watch)

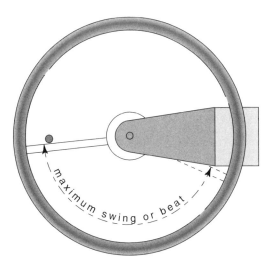

Fig 1/4 A single limiting bar (banking pin) will make the beat uneven, ie the verge will not lift evenly on each side of the crownwheel

the angle of rotation may be decreased or increased within the limits of the mechanics (**Fig 1/4**). The minimum rotation is decided by what is necessary for the teeth of the crownwheel to clear the flags of the verge, and the maximum rotation by the fact that 180 degrees is about the maximum swing that a verge can make without both flags losing contact with the escapewheel teeth. Due to the practical difficulties of making a cock to reach from outside the rim of the balance, on clocks such as early balance wheel lantern clocks the cock is set within the rim as shown, acting as a second banking pin. Some gothic clocks have two hog's bristles on an adjustable arm for regulation.

The Pendulum

The pendulum introduced a much more reliable method of measuring time; it employs a moving mass (the pendulum rod and bob) and a restoring force (gravity). The two together — an unchanging mass and an invariable restoring force — are much more stable and not affected by changes of lubrication, heat, etc. The actual time interval measured can be adjusted by moving the mass in relation to its pivot (ie moving the bob up or down its rod).

As the first pendulums were short and the mass of the bob was relatively small, they were not good quality oscillators — though much better than the simple balance wheel. An improvement was made by increasing the mass of the bob and the method of suspension. At the same time the pendulums that were used on longcase or tall clocks were made very much longer, until most were about a metre long from the middle of the bob to the pivoting point and measured out intervals of one second per beat.

Balance Wheel with Hairspring

A restoring force was given to the balance wheel by fitting a spiral spring, commonly known as a hairspring. This is the oscillator that is seen in mechanical watches and many small clocks. In this case the intervals are adjusted (rated) by altering the effective length of the spring by sliding a piece of metal around the outermost coil — effectively the spring finishes at the place where this contact takes place. A few examples (the suspended balance for instance) alter the rate by mechanically moving two small masses in relation to the centre. Most balance wheels do not have their mass changed after leaving the manufacturer,

and rate adjustment is achieved by just altering the stiffness (ie the length) of the hairspring alone.

Pendulums and balances are dealt with in detail later because the operation of an escapement is intimately involved with the type of oscillator that is used.

4 Recoil Escapements

So far the oscillators alone have been discussed, but now we can consider the actual escape mechanism attached to these oscillators.

The Crownwheel-and-Verge Escapement
The crownwheel-and-verge (often just called the verge) and the anchor are the main types of recoil escapement. The verge is, as its name suggests, a staff or rod with two pieces, called pallets or flags, sticking out from it at an angle (**Fig 1/5**). It can be seen from the drawing that a wheel with saw-shaped teeth (the crownwheel) rotates under the staff, which is parallel to the wheel face. The flags lie over the teeth of the crownwheel and one of the teeth is in contact almost all the time with one of the flags. Its action is similar to that of the anchor escapement discussed in the following paragraphs, but as more illustrations are required than is necessary in this introductory section, detailed descriptions follow in Chapter 2 'The Verge Escapement'.

The only time that there is no contact be-

tween the teeth and one or other of the flags is the fleeting moment when the clearances — needed to make any mechanical device work — allow the wheel to make a small movement entirely free of the verge flags. This is called the 'drop' of the escapement.

Verge escapements (other than foliot or balance examples) are commonly associated with short, light pendulums pivoted on a knife edge or a round pivot, rather than hung on a spring or piece of silk. As a consequence the pallets do not press down severely on the crownwheel if the clock is moved carefully while it is still going, Hence verge escapements were used for many decades in clocks such as early bracket clocks, that were made to be moved from room to room.

The Anchor Escapement
The anchor escapement employs a piece of

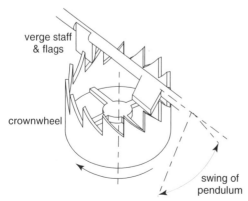

Fig 1/5 The crownwheel-and-verge escapement

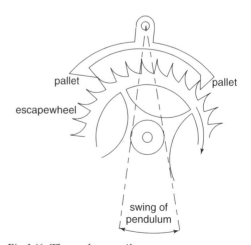

Fig 1/6 The anchor recoil escapement

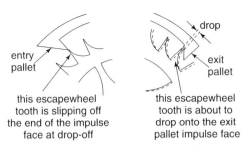

this escapewheel tooth is slipping off the end of the impulse face at drop-off

this escapewheel tooth is about to drop onto the exit pallet impulse face

Fig 1/7 An anchor escapement showing drop

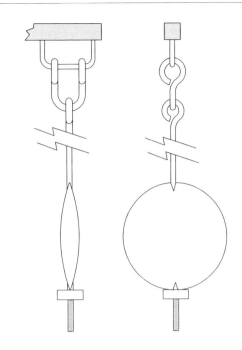

steel that, with some imagination, can be said to have the shape of a ship's anchor, and its arbor or spindle lies parallel to the arbor on which the escapewheel is mounted (**Fig 1/6**). Once again the wheel is in contact with one or other of the two pieces of steel (pallets or nibs) that engage with it, except at the instant of drop (**Fig 1/7**). Pendulums associated with this escapement are usually heavier than in clocks with verge escapements and are of all lengths, from very short to very long. They are hung on spring steel or silk threads — or in the case of many Black Forest clocks, on two rings and a staple (**Fig 1/8**). Because of the relatively large mass of the pendulum and its bob, clocks with anchor escapements are not designed to be moved about while still working.

It is somewhat easier to see the staged movement of the escapewheel through its escapement than it is for the verge escapement. **Fig 1/9** shows the pendulum swung over to the left and the anchor tilted so that the left-

Fig 1/8 A pendulum suspension using two rings and a staple, as used on some Black Forest clocks

hand pallet (the entry pallet) is just on the tip of a wheel tooth. The pallet on the right (the exit pallet) is fully bitten into the space between two teeth and one of these is pressing against the incline plane or impulse face. The wheel is clearly rotating clockwise.

The pressure of this tooth raises the right-hand side of the anchor and consequently causes the pendulum to accelerate a little faster to the right than it would do purely under the effect of gravity. This additional force, which

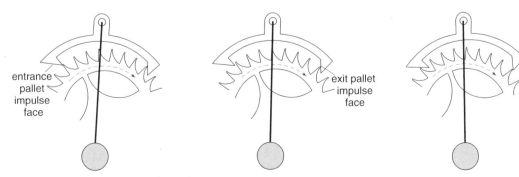

entrance pallet impulse face

exit pallet impulse face

Fig 1/9 Simplified action of the anchor escapement

is what keeps the pendulum swinging instead of gradually coming to a halt, is called the impulse. When the pendulum has swung right over to the other side and the anchor has changed its tilt so that one of the teeth of the wheel 'escapes' by a measured amount, the action is reversed and so the pendulum is kept swinging in a regular fashion. This will be dealt with at length in Chapter 3 'The Recoil Anchor Escapement'. The actions of all the escapements are dealt with explicitly in their respective chapters.

5 Deadbeat Escapements

The Graham Deadbeat Escapement

This is the most well known and well used of the deadbeat escapements — it is also the earliest, speaking historically.

If those parts of the pallets of a standard recoil anchor escapement that only comes into operation at the time of recoil are removed and replaced with a surface that is a true arc based on the centre of the pallet arbor (**Fig 1/10**) there will be no recoil. The surface that the escapewheel now rubs on does not force the train backwards, nor does it allow it to move forward. The escapewheel tooth is in contact with a 'dead' face at the time when a recoil anchor would be moving the train backwards. When the swinging of the pendulum exposes the rest of that surface (the impulse face) to the pressure of the wheel, the action is the same as in the recoil anchor escapement. This is the essence of a deadbeat escapement and it relies on there being a sharp delinea-

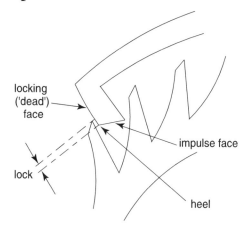

Fig 1/11 The demarkation between the impulse and locking ('dead') faces at the heel of the deadbeat escapement

tion of impulse and dead faces at what may be called the 'heel' (**Fig 1/11**). When this heel wears, the escapement pallets begin to impose recoil on the train, more energy is needed to work the clock and it usually come to a stop because no additional energy is available.

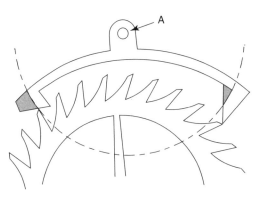

Fig 1/10 A Graham deadbeat escapement differs from a recoil. The shaded area is removed to reduce the length of the impulse faces and to create two new locking faces that are concentric with the pallet pivot centre A

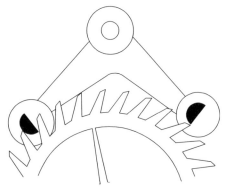

Fig 1/12 The Brocot escapement

The Brocot Escapement

Th Brocot escapement (**Fig 1/12**) is almost a deadbeat escapement, for though there is a slight amount of recoil, in most configurations it *is* very small. It will be found that in most clocks the difference in timekeeping between a Graham deadbeat and a Brocot escapement would not be noticed.

The big advantage of the Brocot escapement is that since the pallets are halved cylinders set into holes in a brass body, the escapement can be controlled and manufactured by reference to the centre positions of four holes. Thus it is easy to make jigs for batch production.

The Pinwheel Escapement

The pinwheel escapement (**Fig 1/13**) is another deadbeat escapement, but it should not to be confused with the pin-pallet escapement, which is a cheap version of the lever escapement. As the escapewheel has no teeth, but is simply a wheel with pins mounted in one or both of its faces, it can be easy to make if accurate drilling facilities are available and it is certainly easy to repair. There are advantages too in the design of the escapement as will be seen in Chapter 7, for its time keeping is good and it is often found in skeleton clocks with deadbeat escapements.

Most professional clockmakers seem to have preferred the Graham deadbeat for good timekeeping and the impression is that the pinwheel escapement is usually made by amateur clockmakers and designers, presumably because its manufacture lent itself to normal engineering, rather than clockmaking, techniques.

Fig 1/13 The pinwheel escapement

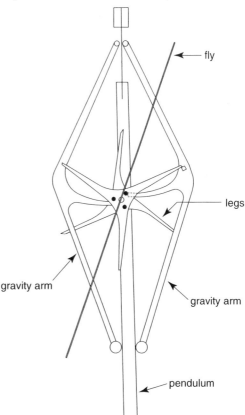

Fig 1/14 Grimthorpe's double three-legged gravity escapement

6 Gravity Escapements

This family of escapements relies upon the force of gravity to impulse the pendulum, rather than the power of a weight or a spring via the gear train. Friction of the train, due to increasing friction caused by the deterioration of the lubricant and pivot wear, and/or the weakening of a mainspring will cause the impulse to vary. This produces changes in pendulum swing and hence timekeeping errors. Since gravity is invariable (within the considerations of most clock mechanisms) timekeeping of a clock with a gravity escapement should be equally invariable. During the eighteenth and nineteenth centuries there were several attempts to design a gravity escapement, but none were really successful until Dennison (Lord Grimthorpe) designed the double-three legged escapement for the Westminster clock (**Fig 1/14**).

Though sometimes used for regulators, gravity escapements found great favour in turret clocks, where enough power has to be supplied to cope with adverse conditions (such as ice, snow, or even birds, on the hands), yet the impulse is still constant.

7 General Comments on Making Escapements

Though the verge escapement is the oldest it is not necessarily to easiest to quantify, but it can adjusted while it is being made. If a mistake is made it is relatively easy to recoup the error. Flags that are a little too short can be corrected by decreasing the angle between them. Other escapements are not so forgiving.

In the chapters that follow various geometries are shown for the anchor, Graham, Brocot and one or two other escapements and an important point should be made that is rarely referred to in books dealing with making or repairing clocks.

In practical clockmaking there are errors present in the rest of the movement that affect the operation of the escapement. For instance, the parallelism (in two planes) of the escapewheel and pallet arbors and the clearance on the pivot holes for both arbors. *As a result it is almost impossible to produce an escapement that is precisely 'right' from its geometry alone, unless the rest of the movement is made to tolerances far higher than are usual in clockmaking.*

Pallets that have no means of adjustment ***must*** *be finished off in the clock they are intended for. The geometries that are illustrated in this book will not produce a working escapement on their own, because they cannot take account of these errors. Always treat any method of marking or making the pallets as a guide to producing working surfaces that are close to their finished form, and leave a small amount of metal to be removed when the operation has been studied in the movement itself.*

The Brocot and the Vulliamy-style deadbeat escapements are both made with inbuilt adjustment; the anchor and the solid-type Graham deadbeat escapements are not.

CHAPTER 2

The Verge Escapement

1 Description & Operation of the Verge Escapement

The verge is the earliest mechanical escapement (excluding Su Sung's eleventh-century waterwheel clock), and for this reason it seems to be regarded as a simple one. In fact it is at least as complex to describe geometrically as any other and its original simplicity of manufacture lay purely in the ease with which the flags could have their angles modified by twisting the staff, and the ability of the device to work (given enough power), in a variety of badly made versions. **Fig 1/1** (page 7) shows a typical verge escapement fitted to a foliot — a horizontal bar pivoted at its centre and with weights hung at the end. The position of these weights is adjustable and used for setting the rate of the clock.

Timekeping of the Verge Escapement

The frequency of the foliot's swings or beats (given a constant energy input from the rest of the movement) is dependent on the rotating mass and the radius at which the masses operate (radius of gyration), see **Fig 2/1**. The arm remains constant in shape of course, so the variation in beat is related to the change in position of the weights alone. If the weights are moved towards the centre the arm will rotate faster — move them out and it rotates slower.

The change in rate or beat is more or less directly proportional to the change in the radius of the weights' position. If the weights of a foliot clock that is running slow by five minutes per hour are moved inwards two inches (for instance) with a resulting increase of ten minutes per hour in the rate, moving them one inch only will increase the rate by about half that and produce the correct rate.

However the foliot is strongly affected by the energy delivered to it by the train (and that in turn is varied by changes in temperature and lubrication), and the method of suspension of the foliot staff. Hence the foliot is not a good timekeeper.

A variation on the foliot is the early balance wheel with no associated restoring force (**Figs 1/3** and **1/4**, pages 8-9). The beat of the balance wheel cannot be changed by altering the radius of gyration of course — or by changing the mass of the rotating wheel. Hence the change of beat is achieved by using a pin or a 'hog's bristle' to interfere with its rotation and restrict the angle through which the balance wheel can swing (**Fig 1/4**, page 9). Clearly this cannot be less than what is needed for the verge flags to clear the crownwheel teeth, but the rotation that the wheel makes can be altered from the minimum needed to operate the escapement to a maximum of about 180 degrees, above which both flags will lose contact with the escapewheel teeth.

It is not known which came first, the foliot or the balance wheel. Both forms of the foliot — balance wheel and weighted arm — can be adjusted for rate by altering the driving weight or the energy delivered by a spring.

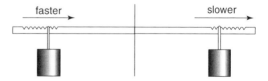

faster   slower

Fig 2/1 Adjusting the foliot for time rate. A foliot with the weights at a short radius rotates faster than with the weights at a large radius

An interesting point about the type of early verge clock that has its foliot or balance wheel suspended from a cord, is that as the foliot or wheel rotates the cord tends to lift it and acts as a spring, giving some restoring force. A balance wheel with a spring is a much better time-keeping device than a balance alone. It would be interesting to know how early cord-suspended verges compares with balance wheels with a pivot and cock at the upper end of the arbor.

As stated in Chapter 1 the introduction of the pendulum improved timekeeping considerably and the verge escapement used with a light pendulum was used widely in bracket clocks. The combination of verge escapement and pendulum is the one usually referred to in the rest of this chapter, though of course the same principles of operation also apply to the foliot and balance wheel.

Operation & Geometry of the Verge Escapement

The types of verge that have been used in antique clocks vary greatly from century to century and from nation to nation. Speaking very loosely, one can say that verges with wide angles (about 90 to 110 degrees between the flags) were used in Britain from the early seventeenth century to the late eighteenth century, narrower ones (less than 75 degrees) in the nineteenth century. Most British clocks had short pendulums associated with this escapement. On the Continent both short and long pendulums have been used and the crutch (the rod attached to the verge arbor that contacts the pendulum rod and transmits energy to it) can be horizontal or vertical, al-

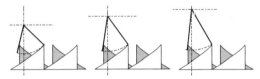

2/2 The angle between the verge flags becomes narrower and the 'bite' shallower as the height of the verge arbor increases. Also the swing of the pendulum is smaller

though vertical is much more common,

Three statements are important when considering the verge escapement:
• When the height of the verge above the teeth of the crownwheel is small the angle between the flags is large, and it becomes smaller as the height is increased. The 'bite' of the flags between the teeth becomes shallower at the same time.
• If the height of the verge remains constant, a wide angle between the flags requires long flags and a small angle of swing for the pendulum.
• For a given height of verge above the crownwheel the angle of swing of the pendulum increases as the angle between flags decreases — and *vice versa*.

The first statement is demonstrated in **Fig 2/2**. As can be seen. the angle between the flags becomes smaller as the centre of the pallet arbor is raised (as long as nothing else changes). The bite (the amount that the pallets sink into the crownwheel) becomes shallower too, which results in the escapement becoming more critical, with less tolerance for poor manufacture and wear.

Fig 2/3 illustrates the progression of the verge escapement through one beat of the

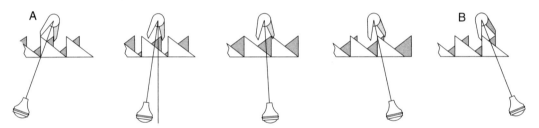

Fig 2/3 The operation of the verge escapement over a period of one beat

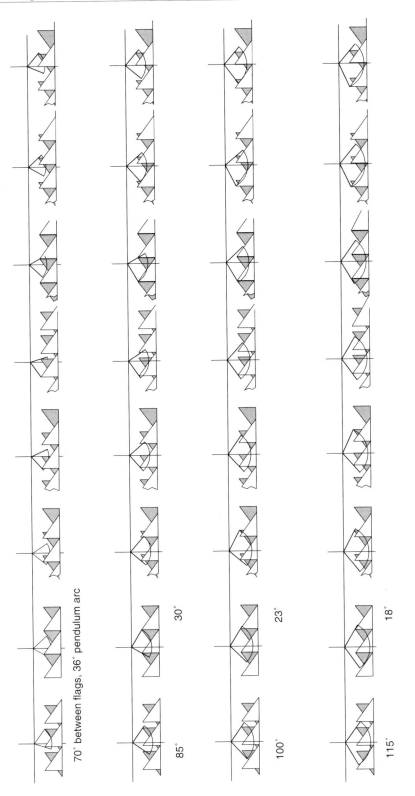

70° between flags, 36° pendulum arc

85°

30°

100°

23°

115°

18°

Fig 2/4 A comparison of four verge escapements with the verge arbor at the same height above the escapewheel, but with different angles between the flags

pendulum. The crownwheel (which usually has an odd number of teeth, but see Section 3) is shown rotating in steps of one eight of a tooth pitch (one unit). At **A** drop-off occurs when the existing tooth is four units from the centre line of the crown wheel, ie midway between adjacent teeth. At **B**, at the other end of the pendulum arc, the flag drops off the rear shaded tooth in the same position relative to the centre line.

A comparison between the operation of four different escapements is shown in **Fig 2/4**. Each has the verge arbor set at the same height above the crownwheel, but with angles between the flags of approximately 70, 85, 100 and 115 degrees respectively.

The effects of changes in the flag length and the pendulum arc can be seen, and since circular error (see pages 19-20) decreases with a smaller pendulum arc, wide flag angles should produce better timekeepers than narrow flag angles. Unfortunately, with wide flag angles there is a wedging effect and very large frictional losses during recoil. The best flag angle for general use is about 90 degrees, certainly no more than 110 degrees. This effect is particularly important when repairing verges, because it is quite possible to reduce the timekeeping quality of a clock by carrying out an apparently good repair to the flags that alters the flag length and angle.

The four different verges shown in **Fig 2/3** progress through one complete oscillation (two beats) of the pendulum. Each verge is at the same height above the crownwheel, and again intervals of one eighth of the pitch have been used. It is clear that all these verges operate correctly, despite their differences. If the first drawing in the top line of verges, the second in the next down, the third in the third and the fourth drawing in the bottom line are examined, it will be seen that each one represents the verge at the drop-off of the rearmost tooth. Eight different verges at intervals of one sixteenth of the pitch could have been drawn and all would have worked.

In fact, as long as the angles of the flags are kept within reasonable limits (60-110 de-

grees), there is no angle that will not work — it is simply a matter of adjusting the length of the flags to suit the angle!

This makes the repair or replacement of a verge easier than any other escapement, simply make sure that the verge flags are long enough after repair or making and that the angle between them matches the original or a typical specimen of the same period and nationality. This is discussed again later.

Referring to **Fig 2/4** it can be seen that the length and spread of the verge flags was established by setting one of them vertical (and on the centre line of the wheel), while the other was just about to drop off. (This assumes a crownwheel with an odd number of teeth and a pallet arbor that crosses the centre line.) As can be seen, the angle between the flags is narrow compared with the flags in **Fig 2/3**. So which method is the best?

It rather depends on what the clock needs. The amount of 'bite' that is obtained in **Fig 2/4** for each of the verge flags is (in relative units): 2.6, 3.5, 4.3 and 5.2 reading from the top row, whereas setting one verge flag upright (**Fig 2/3**) produces only 1.8 units of bite. A good deep bite makes the escapement easier to manufacture and less prone to 'skipping' as the flags wear. On the other hand there is a pronounced upward pressure on all four wide-angled verges at the moment of first impulse — the moment when recoil begins. The second method gives little or no upward pressure at first impulse, but has a much smaller bite, as has been seen.

In clocks with a knife-edge suspension, any upward movement will lift the knife edge off its bed momentarily and timekeeping will suffer. To offset this action a piece of brass (a keeper) is placed over the top of the knife edge, so that it cannot lift out of its seat. However contact with this strip will give rise to frictional losses and since the upward force will be a proportion of the force developed at the crownwheel tooth, any variations in train efficiency will lead to variations in the friction produced by this keeper. As it happens, this loss tends to decrease the swing of the pendulum or balance when the variation in the driving force from the train tends to increase it, but this is not a nicely balanced opposition that improves timekeeping — it varies considerably.

The older style of wide-angled verge has the greatest upward component and suffers the greatest interference with the action of the escapement. Only a minority of British verges have round pivots at each end, and it would be expected that their timekeeping would be unaffected by this upward component when the bearings are in good condition. Unfortunately, as soon as there is any wear on the pivot holes (allowing upward movement of the staff and flags), wide-angled verges will be more badly affected than narrow ones.

Circular Error
When a pendulum swings through a given arc it describes a path that is either a part of a true circle if it is suspended on a knife edge, or nearly circular if it is hung on a cord or spring. Any increase or decrease in the angle that it swings through produces an increase or decrease in the time taken for one beat. If the path could be made to conform to a cycloidal curve, then different angles of swing would not produce alterations in the time taken (however other errors due to temperature and barometric pressure changes will still affect the length of beat). *The Science of Clocks & Watches* by A. L. Rawlings deals with the mathematics of these errors in detail.

The differences produced are called circular arc errors, and in practice changes in swing have a proportionately greater effect on timekeeping when the average swing is large than when it is small. Hence the tendency for inherently good timekeepers to have pendulums with a small semi-arc (the arc on either side of the vertical).

Large swings are typical of balance wheels and light-bob pendulums and these are usually found on early clocks. A balance wheel may have a swing of at almost 180 degrees. A light bob is frequently seen in those bracket clocks that have a curved slot in the dial for a 'false pendulum' to show through and indicate that the clock is going. A small swing is not appropriate for such a clock.

If there is a small swing and a verge escapement is still in situ, it is very probable that it is either badly worn or it has been modified and a more modern verge staff substituted for the original. Where the clock has been converted to an anchor escapement the swing will be very small (3 degrees either side of the vertical). Before repairing such a clock it is always a good idea to asking if the owner has considered having it converted back to verge operation. There are several specialist clockmakers who can carry this sort of work out and if it is done well the value of the clock can be increased, though current thinking is to leave such changes as being a part of the clock's 'history'.

Regional & Other Variations
The differences of construction between early clocks having foliots or balance wheels, light bob pendulums, heavy bob pendulums and crutches, and watches with balance wheels and hairsprings are not due solely to the technology of the day, but due more to the purpose that the clock was designed for. A clock with a light pendulum can be moved about while it is still ticking without causing any damage. In consequence it is not unusual to find a verge clock with a wide swing to its light bob pendulum dating from a period long after the introduction of the long pendulum on a suspension spring. The angle of the verge flags and the type of pendulum employed is not a reliable guide to the clock's date.

The angle between the verge flags also depends upon the country of origin, since it remained a popular escapement in certain areas after the long pendulum had been generally adopted for wall and standing clocks. The Comtoise clock is probably the best known one from France, but Black Forest clockmakers also made great use of it until the end of the eighteenth century and Austrian makers did so too. Not that the verge escapement died abruptly at that time, but it did decline in fa-

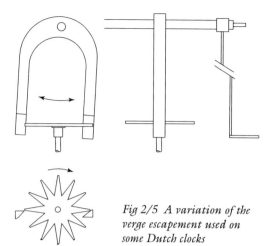

Fig 2/5 A variation of the verge escapement used on some Dutch clocks

vour of the various versions of the anchor recoil and the Graham escapements.

Clockmakers in Holland used the verge extensively, usually with a vertical verge oscillated indirectly by a long pendulum. But a variation has been seen that is much more suited to a long pendulum and a great deal easier to

make and repair (**Fig 2/5**). The flags were turned through 90 degrees and extended so that they bore on either side of the wheel (not a crownwheel as in **Fig 1/1**) — only a slight modification was needed to produce the Paul Gautier escapement some 150 years later. The starwheel is shown with an even number of arms, simply because the only illustration that I have appears to have twelve — however it could be an odd number, in which case the pallets would lie on the centre line of the wheel.

Design of Pallets

There are two methods of arranging the flags of a verge and they can be defined by their operation. In the first method the exit pallet is released when the entry pallet face is inclined with regard to the crownwheel tooth. Alternatively the exit flag or pallet may be released when the entry flag is normal (ie at right angles) to the face of the crownwheel. The latter is particularly suitable for verges with a

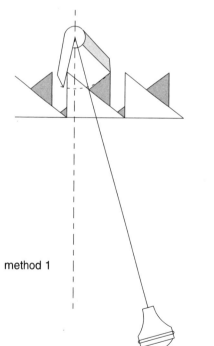

method 1

Fig 2/6 First method of designing verge pallets. Exit pallet released when the entry pallet is inclined to the crownwheel tooth

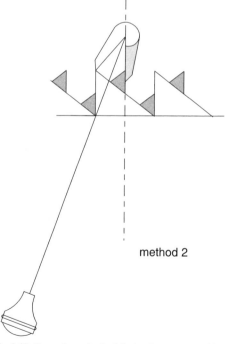

method 2

Fig 2/7 Second method of designing verge pallets. Exit pallet released when the entry pallet is at right angles to the face of the crownwheel

knife-edge bearing because there is less of an upward component to the impulse (**Fig 2/7**).

(It should be pointed out that the second method is really one end of the possible arrangements of flag length and angle. Because the verge is so flexible in design one can start with this condition of a vertical flag at first contact and by lengthening the flags and widening the angle between them it converts to the first of method.)

In the diagrams the shaded teeth are on the furthest side of the crownwheel, and those drawn solid are on the nearer side. Clearly they move in opposite directions when viewed from the side — viewed from the top the wheel is rotating clockwise.

An interesting point about the vertical flag style of verge is that if the teeth of the crownwheel are raked there is actually a small downward component on the staff at recoil (**Fig 2/8**). The wear tends to be distributed around the periphery of a pivot hole rather than in one direction. Since downward wear does not lift the verge flag away from the wheel tooth, there is only a part of the impulsing and recoil action that has a damaging effect on the escapement. A verge with a wider angle experiences wear of this type at all stages of the impulse and recoil.

The important factors in deciding the shape of a verge arbor and pallets may be summarised as:

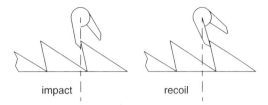

Fig 2/8 A verge with a narrow angle between the flags can produce a very small downward force during recoil if the teeth are raked

- The flags must be of equal length.
- The flags may be at any angle that the maker has found convenient.
- The length of the flags (or a given crownwheel and height) is determined by the angle between them.
- Pallets that bite deeply require a definite hollow back for the escapewheel teeth, otherwise they will foul the tooth after drop off (**Fig 2/9**).

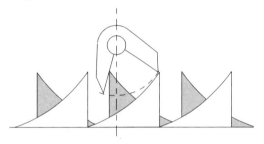

Fig 2/9 It may be necessary for the wheel teeth to have hollow backs so that the flags do not foul them

2 Making a Verge Staff & Pallets

A replacement verge staff for an antique clock should be made by traditional methods; the easy system of separate flags is only acceptable for clocks with no history. Though the making of the staff, verge flags and the pivots is dealt with in different sections, all these tasks affect each other, so *all* these sections (pages 22-27) should be read before starting on any of them.

The arbor and flags are made first, with the flags overlong but of equal length. The front pivot and rear knife-edge are then formed, and finally the flags brought to their correct length for satisfactory operation of the scapement.

Traditional Methods
There are two generally recognised traditional methods — if the use of forgings and castings is excluded as neither are available today. The oldest method is to use a strip of flat steel, the second method described below would not have been used until the late nineteenth century at the earliest. This latter method relies largely on turning a blank, but it can repro-

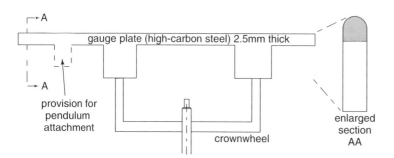

Fig 2/10 Making verge
flags from carbon-steel strip

duce the type of result obtained by the use of forgings and castings, in particular the type of flags that have sides raised higher than the thickness of flat metal would allow ('book' pallets). My own preference is for the strip method, it seems simpler, quicker and more in keeping with the type of clocks that can be expected to have verge escapements.

• **The Flat Strip Method**

Take a piece of annealed flat ground stock (gauge plate) thick enough for the diameter of the staff or arbor. This varies from clock to clock of course, but the average bracket clock verge arbor has a diameter of about 3/32in, or just over 2mm. Assemble the crownwheel in the clock plates before proceeding to the next step.

File the steel blank for the verge to the shape shown in **Fig 2/10**. The positions for the flags are obtained by laying the blank over the crownwheel and scratching marks for its diameter and then marking the shoulders of the

pivots from the clock plates and back cock. It is usual to make the width of the flags about four times the thickness of the crownwheel teeth. Sometimes a rectangular piece is left for attachment of a pendulum rod with a clevis (see also **Fig 2/18**).

The blank is prepared by filing the long straight edge to a semicircular section. This long edge must be straight and the section must be as constant as possible because it will later act as a register for straightening the verge. This is easier to achieve if the work is moved against the file, rubbing it lengthways along the cutting surface and rolling the steel piece over as you proceed (**Fig 2/11**). Finish off with coarse emery paper — about 150 grit — mounted on a flat metal surface. When the edge has been finished then the twist is put into the verge between the flags.

Hold one end of the flat strip (including the flag) in a vice and heat the middle portion of the strip until it is just bright red. Using

---

Annealing Gauge Plate

Heat to bright cherry red, allow the metal to soak in this temperature for at least five minutes, but do not let the edges give off sparks and burn. This should be a long enough soaking for metal that is just over 2mm thick. Now allow to cool very slowly by turning down the heat. It should drop steadily from bright cherry red to the point where the red disappears, over a period of about five minutes, anything faster will leave the steel tough and with hard spots. At this point the work can be put into dry sand or chalk to allow further slow cooling.

The best way to heat-treat steel is in a small muffle furnace with accurate temperature control, but this rough and ready method should give good results. If the steel is still hard afterwards (and it is not a nickel/chrome steel) try again with a longer 'soak' in the heat and a longer cooling time. Bright cherry red is 730-750°C. The actual annealing temperature is 760-780°C.

Fig 2/11 File the straight edge into a semi-circular section

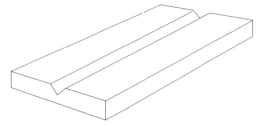

Fig 2/12 Jig for straightening verge

pliers, grip the other flag and twist the flag and arbor through 90 degrees, or whatever flag angle has been decided on. Be careful to produce as long a length of bright red metal between the flags as possible, so that the twisting of the strip is spread evenly along the length between flags. The direction of twist will depend upon how the crownwheel revolves — it is important to check this before starting to make the verge.

Most of the English bracket clocks with verge escapements that I have seen have a flag angle of 90 degrees, mainly because it is easy to twist the flag until it is horizontal while the other is gripped vertically in the vice.

While the staff is still held in the vice use heat and a straight edge to make sure that there is no bow from end to end. The staff must be soft at this stage and it is possible that the cooling effect of the vice jaws may have hardened it somewhat. Take the rough staff out of the vice and test the steel with a file. If you cannot persuade the file to cut easily, then the staff must be softened or annealed again.

Begin filing the staff to produce a round section between the flags, trying to make it as cylindrical as possible but do not touch the semicircular section of the long edge that has already been produced. File the ends of the verge staff to ease the task of turning the pivots afterwards. Again be careful not to touch the surface of the long edge. Now the rough verge must be straightened and to do this a simple jig is needed.

This straightening jig is a piece of brass or steel with a straight and evenly depthed V-groove in it (**Fig 2/12**). This is easy enough to make on a milling machine, but as most clockmakers will not possess one, an alternative is to fabricate the jig. The method shown on pages 24-25 is useful for producing accu-rate grooves in metal without the benefit of machine tools.

Lay the verge staff in the V-groove, with the semi-cylindrical edge seated in it and the flags sticking up in the air. Gently tap along the length of the staff with a light hammer to make the staff conform with the groove. If the curve is such that it does not bow upwards and allow you to flatten the bow, take it out of the jig, place it on a piece of soft wood and curve the staff freehand to make the centre stand high — and then lay it down in the groove again. It is not necessary to obtain a dead straight staff, but it must appear so to the eye and it must be straight enough for it to be held true in the lathe and drilling machine.

File the working surfaces of the flags so that the thickness is reduced to half the diameter of the arbor. Early verges usually have flat faces, but later verges are finished so that the flags have raised sides and the flat impulse faces are radial to the centre of the staff (**Fig 2/13**). The sides give a little added strength to the escapement and in particular make it much less likely that a crack will develop at this point when the flags are hardened.

File the flags so that they are, when checked with a vernier or micrometer, of equal length,

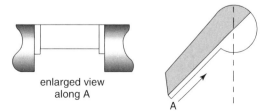

enlarged view
along A

A

Fig 2/13 The shape of the finished flags

Producing Accurate Grooves in Metal Without Machine Tools

A length of brass or steel rectangular bar twice as long as the required jig is chamfered along one edge. Scribe a line along one face of the bar by laying it on a flat metal surface, placing a steel straightedge alongside it and using this to guide the scriber (**Fig 2/14**). The size of the chamfer will depend upon the thickness of the straightedge (or any straight and flat piece of metal). Scribers may be made from pivot steel or silver steel by filing the point while rotating the rod in a lathe or a drilling machine — this keeps the sharp point on the centre line; the scriber is heat treated afterwards to harden it. The scribed mark should be about the same distance from the edge of the material as half the thickness of the verge staff.

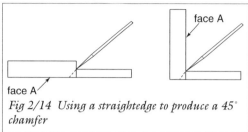

Fig 2/14 Using a straightedge to produce a 45° chamfer

Repeat with the bar standing upright and presenting what was the under face to the straightedge. Use the scriber again. By carefully filing to the limits of these two scribed lines an accurate chamfer is produced along one edge of the bar.

However, it is possible to establish a firmer control when filing. Find a piece of flat metal

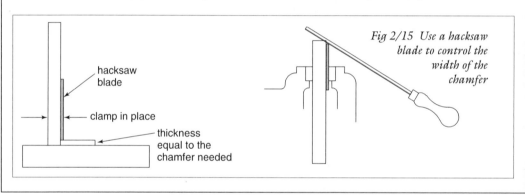

Fig 2/15 Use a hacksaw blade to control the width of the chamfer

though too long to operate correctly. Use a small chuck to hold the staff in the lathe. A small chuck (2in diameter) usually has jaws that are short enough to reach between the flags and grip the staff (**Fig 2/17**). Use a wrapping

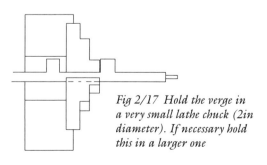

Fig 2/17 Hold the verge in a very small lathe chuck (2in diameter). If necessary hold this in a larger one

of cartridge paper around the staff to give a good grip on the surface, as it will vary a little from completely being round and parallel.

If the jaws are too long to fit into the space between the flags, or if a very small chuck is not available, the blank can be held with a split bush. A simple brass bush is made with an outer diameter large enough to lie outside the swing of the verge flags (**Fig 2/18**) and a drilled hole that is slightly larger than the filed diameter in the mid-portion of the staff. This bush is then sawn along its length to make two semi-cylinders. This split bush is then fitted around the staff and the assembly held in the jaws of a larger chuck.

as thick as the face of the chamfer that is required, and a hacksaw blade. Follow **2/15** and stand the bar on a flat surface so that it is resting on its edge. Cut the piece of flat metal in half and place the two halves alongside the bar to support the saw blade. Then clamp the latter in place using a clamp or hand vice at each end of the bar. This hard blade now defines another boundary for the chamfer — and one that the file cannot obscure or wear away without a deliberate effort on your part. (Do not try to file into this hard blade, as it may damage the file.)

Put the assembly in a vice with the scribed line uppermost and file the chamfer carefully. It should be easy now to let the file work down to the hard boundary of the saw blade on the side of the bar that you cannot see readily and gradually extend the chamfer until it touches the whole length of the visible mark. Finish by laying a flat file along the length of the rough chamfer and sliding it back and forth without rolling it over (**Fig 2/16**).

The bar now has a parallel chamfer along one edge. Cut the bar in half and cramp both halves together to form a groove of the chamfers. The bars can then be drilled and pinned while still clamped together or even glued with an epoxy resin. If it is intended to use this straightener for arbors very often make it of high carbon steel, harden it and then temper to a straw colour.

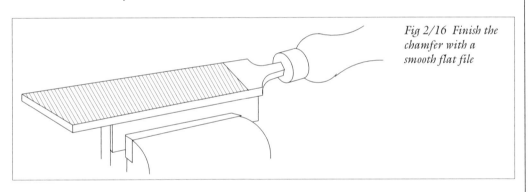

Fig 2/16 Finish the chamfer with a smooth flat file

Verge staffs are either fitted with one cylindrical pivot and a knife edge or both are cylindrical pivots. In the first case the cylindrical pivot is formed relatively close to a flag and

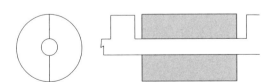

Fig 2/18 A bush of turned brass a little larger than the height of the flags. Drill a hole the same diameter as the staff and saw in two. Wrap the staff with paper when gripped in a chuck

consequently near to the support of the chuck jaws. The pivot can be turned easily without causing the protruding part of the staff to vibrate significantly. The other end will carry the pendulum rod (or very occasionally a crutch) and may either be turned to accept a rod with a bush, or left square for a clevice or a forked rod (**Fig 2/19**). A flat strip staff will not have enough thickness to allow it to be drilled for the attachment of the rod. Enough length beyond the pendulum attachment must be allowed for the pivot.

However, if the verge staff has two cylindrical pivots, it is quite likely that one at least is formed on the end of a section of staff that

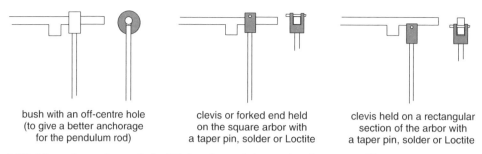

bush with an off-centre hole
(to give a better anchorage
for the pendulum rod)

clevis or forked end held
on the square arbor with
a taper pin, solder or Loctite

clevis held on a rectangular
section of the arbor with
a taper pin, solder or Loctite

Fig 2/19 Three alternative methods of fixing the pendulum rod to the verge staff

is too long to turn without vibration. In this case a fixed lathe steady may have to be used. Alternatively, the problem can be overcome by drilling the end of the staff and inserting a piece of pivot steel.

Make a centring jig (a bush with a hole of two concentric diameters) as shown in **Fig 2/20**. Since the verge at this point has been filed more-or-less round, or is rectangular, the centring jig is only intended to make sure that the hole to be drilled is not too close to the sides of the metal. The length of the flags will be finished after the pivot is made and any inaccuracy in the centre can be corrected later. The parallelism of the pivot and staff is more important and care should be taken to hold the staff upright in a vice on the drilling machine table, using the jig to guide the drill. An inserted pivot may be used even if it is possible to turn a pivot, and this will make the task of future repairers easier. The pivot steel should be an easy fit in the hole and secured with Loctite.

Polish, harden and temper the front pivot (and the rear one if this is a round one turned from the staff) and polish again. Remember that the pivot are in now in the finished condition and while you work on the flags they are easily damaged. The reason for making the pivot first is that it is easier to try the verge flags with a finished pivot located in its pivot hole, than to try and manage with an unfinished one that is a tight fit in its bearings and, still being soft, is liable to bend.

If the rear pivot is a knife-edge (as is the case with most British verges, then this should be made at this stage (see pages 30-33).

The flags are now reduced to their working lengths. Using a vernier or micrometer to measure and maintain similar lengths for the two flags, gradually file them down until one flag is on the drop-off at the moment that the other touches the impulse face (**Fig 2/21**). Try the flags in the reverse condition, carrying out these two operations together, working on first one and then the other flag, until both behave in the same fashion with the same length of flag. It is no use concentrating on one flag at a time, as that will produce an uneven escapement. Before the escapement will work properly the edges have to be bevelled.

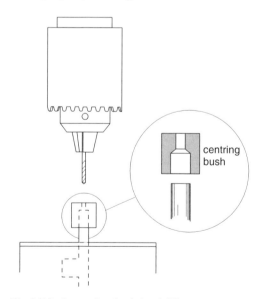

centring bush

Fig 2/20 A centring bush for drilling concentric holes in parts that cannot be held easily in a lathe chuck. If the end of the staff is of rectangular section the large hole in the bush is equal to the distance across the corners

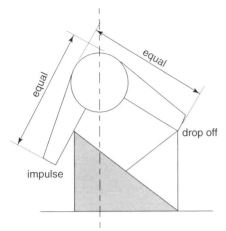

Fig 2/21 The flags should be of equal length with one flag at drop-off and the other just touching the tooth tip

• Turned Staff & Flags

This does not really require much in the way of description. Use a rod of high carbon steel such as silver steel (drill rod in the US) and machine it so that at the position of the flags there are two large diameters — and another one where the pendulum is to be attached. These diameters must be large enough to accommodate the length of the finished flags, which means that their diameters must be more than twice the distance from the pro-

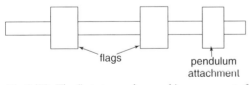

Fig 2/22 The first stage when making a verge staff by turning

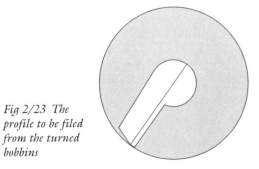

Fig 2/23 The profile to be filed from the turned bobbins

posed end of the flags to the centre line of the staff or arbor (**Fig 2/22**). Make the knife edge and/or pivot(s) as before, and finish them. The flags are filed from the large diameters, and the angle between them can be adjusted during this operation, there is no need to twist the staff. Note that the finished impulse face passes through the centre line of the staff. **Fig 2/23** is an end view showing the metal to be removed. This is the finished condition of course — until you are happy with the angle of the impulse faces simply concentrate on filing these. It is quite possible to make a series of impulse faces during the making of the verge and test them, before finally being satisfied with the action and filing off the metal that is not needed (**Fig 2/24**). The final form should be similar to **Fig 2/21**.

Fig 2/24 The almost finished flag

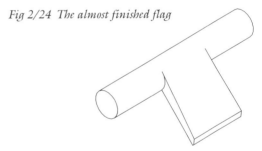

• Inserted Hard Surfaces

Many mid-nineteenth-century (and later) verge escapements had hardened inserts for the flags. This method of manufacture makes the use of separate pieces of hardened steel very convenient. The channel that is filed to form the impulse face in each flag is made a little deeper so that it no longer passes through the centre line and the side cheeks are left a little thicker. Since the arbor can readily be turned, the area which accepts the insert can be made a larger diameter than the rest of the arbor, strengthening it at this point. **Fig 2/25** shows how these cheeks are filed to produce an angle that makes part of a dovetail joint. The inserts are also angled on the sides to correspond with the cheeks, and they are are made to be a tight fit. Secure in position with a light tap with a brass hammer or a squeeze with

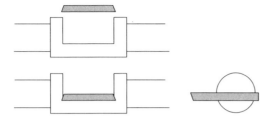

Fig 2/25 Inserted hard-steel flag. Do not make the flag too tight a fit in the slot or it will distort the arbor. About 0.005in (0.12mm) interference is about right

pliers to move them along their track between the cheeks.

The thickness of the hard material is sufficient to place the impulse surface on the centre line again. It must be obvious that this system also allows for adjustment of the length of the flags — the inserts are hardened in the same way as the flags of a solid verge and polished afterwards.

Modern Methods
• Separate Flags

This method is only suitable for a clock with no history, such as a new one or one with parts of so many different ages that there is no point to trying to work to any of the dates indicated. It also requires an escapement that has plenty of clearance under the staff and makes a relatively shallow swing. Although it offers the advantage of easy adjustment and a method of correction if too much metal has been removed from the length of the flag, I

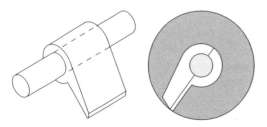

Fig 2/26 A modern design of verge flag. The central boss must be larger than shown in Fig 2/22 to allow for the bore for the arbor

do not care for the method very much as it is bulky and rather ugly. **Fig 2/26** shows the design of the flag, it slides onto a piece of silver steel and is locked in place with Loctite. In fact it is much the same as the previously described turned version, but allowance has to be made for the fact that it is drilled through for the arbor.

It does make a very simple escapement. Instead of filing the flags to suit, simply adjust the flag angle by twisting them on the staff when the Loctite becomes pasty. They can be hardened before fitting and the arbor can be treated separately to harden and temper the pivots. Stress relieve at 150°C.

Hardening The Flags

Cut a small potato in half and bury each pivot in one half; this will keep the pivots below their tempering temperature while the flags are heated to red heat. Hold the staff close up to one of the potatoes with a pair of old pliers and heat the flags to bright red, allow a soaking of about one minute and then plunge end first into a tin of oil that is tall enough to accept the whole length. Water will produce a slightly harder flag, but it also carries a greater risk of cracking the staff.

Clean the arbor, remove the potatoes and examine the pivots to make sure that they have not coloured above blue. If they have, re-harden and temper them — and then repolish. Otherwise just clean the pivots and polish with 1,000 grit paper. The impulse faces must be cleaned and polished with emery paper, beginning at 250 grit and progressing to 1000 grit. As a last precaution heat the whole piece to 150°C in a domestic oven; this is the stress relieving temperature and a ten-minute soak should be sufficient.

Putting in Beat

As long as the flags are made properly they will be in beat when used with a foliot or balance wheel. A pendulum, however, has to be put in beat by bending the pendulum rod or its crutch.

4 Verge Pivots

Verge Pallet Bearings

There are essentially four different ways of mounting verge pallets:

• Vertically with a round pivot and end bearing at the bottom and a thread suspension at the top. Usually used with a foliot or balance wheel.

• Vertically with a round pivot and end bearing at the bottom and a plain cylindrical pivot at the top. Used with a foliot or balance wheel, and in some Continental clocks with a long pendulum operated by a fork (eg Dutch *stoel* clocks).

• Horizontally with a round pivot at one end and a knife-edge bearing at the other, where a pendulum with a light bob is usually attached directly.

• Horizontally with round pivots at each end and transmission to a pendulum (usually with a heavier bob) through a crutch.

Round pivots are simple devices, and as long as they are hard, cylindrical and smooth they will operate well. Since this is a matter of either turning the pivot or drilling for an insert of pivot steel I shall do little more than illustrate them and make a few comments.

Round Pivots

Fig 2/27 shows a typical round pivot. To operate well on a verge it needs to be cylindrical because, either as a result of wear or adjustment, it may be moved along its length and a tapered pivot would alter the bearing clearances. The turning of a pivot for a verge and the drilling of one for pivot steel insert have already been described (pages 24-26), and the process needs no further comments. However, the vertical verge has an end bearing associated with the cylindrical pivot and that does need description. In clocks with a horizontal verge this same bearing is used to support the crownwheel.

The bottom pivot has a rounded end which rests on a hardened and polished flat surface, (**Fig 2/28**). Most commonly this is made of hard steel, but it is also seen as a 'jewel' in good quality late bracket clocks and even as hammered brass, though very rarely and only on the more lightly loaded contrate wheel.

Whether the supported wheel is the crownwheel or the contrate wheel, a small amount of adjustment in the height is desirable, and this is achieved by means of a screw or a wedge (**Figs 2/28-29**). The horizontal slot is to avoid having a blind end to the pivot hole and to provide for cleaning and lubrication, as blind holes are difficult to lubricate well with oils that deteriorate with age.

The important points to note are:

• The rounded end must be concentric with the cylindrical pivot otherwise the point of contact with the end bearing will be a *circle of contact* which will result in a much higher frictional torque than a produced by a true point contact.

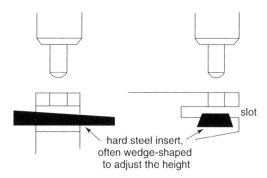

Fig 2/28 The lower bearing of a vertical verge, or the crownwheel of a horizontal verge

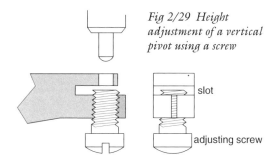

Fig 2/29 Height adjustment of a vertical pivot using a screw

Fig 2/27 Round verge pivot

• The supporting surface must be smooth and hard so that the relatively high pressures produced by the point load do not make a dimple. A dimple increases the area of contact and produces a higher frictional torque.

• A sloping support surface does not have any very bad effect unless it is extreme (say 10 degrees). Its only effect is to produce sideways thrust on the cylindrical hole of the bearing and although this does increase friction (friction equals load multiplied by the coefficient of friction for the material) it is a small increase.

As shown in **Figs 2/28-29** the block that forms the end bearing can be formed in a couple of ways. In the case of the dovetail and wedge it is simple to file up a piece of gauge plate and then harden and polish it. Where the end bearing is a screw there is the problem that there is often little room to make a new tapped hole with a modern thread form. The repairer will have to be prepared to remake the housing so that it can accommodate a new thread — and make a new screw from high carbon steel (silver steel).

The screw is hardened and the end polished in the lathe. **Fig 2/30** shows a detail of the tapped hole, with an alternative method of preventing the screw from coming loose. A saw

cut has been made across the hole after tapping and then the slot has been spread slightly with a screwdriver. This puts the two parts of the tapped hole sufficiently out of pitch to prevent the inserted screw rotating in use.

For a jewelled endstone, replacement jewels are often available from clockmakers' suppliers. But if a particular size is not obtainable, a 'jewel' made from silver steel and hardened and polished will prove quite satisfactory.

The Knife-Edge Pivot & Its Action

Note that since reference to the knife edge is made both here and in Chapter 10 dealing with pendulum suspensions, there is some duplication. This is intentional, as it is more useful to put information where it is needed by the reader, depending on whether the escapement or the suspension is being considered.

The knife-edge pivot has very low frictional losses but it is weak and so, except for some very specialised variations, it is only used for the light-bob pendulums typical of bracket clocks. However, it must not be overlooked that the weight of the bob should be sufficient to keep the knife-edge in contact with its bed at all times. It has been pointed out earlier that there is an upwards component to the forces acting on the horizontal verge and these must be overcome by the bob.

The pivots of any escapement must allow the pallets to oscillate about the centre that the escapement was designed for, ie the centre line of the arbor that carries the pallets. Since the knife-edge swings about its edge it is important that this edge coincides with the centre line of the arbor. The designed behaviour of the escapement will be altered if this is not so.

This edge must also be parallel to the cen-

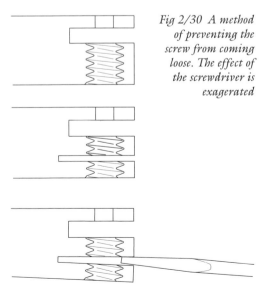

Fig 2/30 A method of preventing the screw from coming loose. The effect of the screwdriver is exagerated

Fig 2/31 The knife-edge should be formed on the centre line of the verge arbor

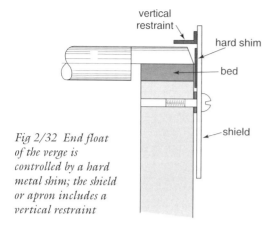

Fig 2/32 End float of the verge is controlled by a hard metal shim; the shield or apron includes a vertical restraint

tre line of the pallet, and the bed that it rests on should make contact along its full length (**Fig 2/31**).

• **The Design of Knife-Edge & Bed**

Fig 2/32 shows a side view of a typical knife-edge. The edge itself is on the centre line as stated above, it is parallel to the arbor and it makes contact with the full width of the bed. In addition the end is filed to a point (polished and very slightly blunted) that bears on a hard steel plate to control the end-to-end movement of the verge. Clearly if this point is not on the action line of the knife it will swing about that line and interfere with the correct oscillation of the verge and arbor.

The V of the bed and the cross-section of the knife-edge (**Fig 2/31**) must allow for the maximum swing of the pendulum. If the pivot flank comes into contact with the bed the knife-edge will lift, and apart from the interruption to the proper movement of the escapement, may allow the edge to drop down into a different part of the bed. The bed is made of brass and is soft, so it is possible for a lifted pivot to drop onto the flank of the bed V and cut a temporary resting place there.

Finally, a piece of brass is placed above the knife-edge to prevent it jumping clear of the bed if the clock is moved or jarred — this does not normally contact the knife-edge.

• **Making a Knife-Edge**

Measure the arbor or staff against the distance available (from front plate to the mounting

of the 'shield' or 'apron' which hides the end of the bed). Mark the arbor to define the finished length of the knife-edge, which should be a millimetre or two more than is necessary to take up the end-to-end shake and still leave the knife-edge in contact over the width of the bed. Do not make it too long as this will make it more prone to breakage — and it is already a delicate part of the verge.

The making of the knife-edge is assisted by turning up a small brass collar, whose inner diameter is a close fit on the arbor and its thickness shallow enough to allow it to be slipped onto the end and leave the unfiled knife-edge protruding (**Figs 2/33-34**). Since the collar is to carry guide marks on its face, it should be large enough to make these easy to use. This collar is also an aid to filing, as it will support the edge of the file (use the smooth or safe edge to contact the collar) so that a clean shoulder is produced between the arbor and the knife-edge.

Marks are made across the face of the collar to define a centre line and lines either side at half the included angle of the knife-edge. The collar is slipped onto the arbor and the flags are rested on a flat bar so that the centre line of the bush lines up with the vertical centre line of the flags. Since it is dificult to use an engineer's square for this with any accuracy, use dividers to place the line on the bush equi-distance from the ends of the unfinished flags (**Fig 2/35**). The flags should be of equal (but not their finished) length at this stage.

Although the angle of the cross-section is not very important, 60 degrees gives a relatively strong knife-edge and will allow a total

Fig 2/33 Fix a brass collar to the arbor to aid filing the knife-edge

Fig 2/34 The collar in position on the verge

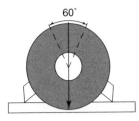

Fig 2/35 Mark the angle of the knife-edge at about 60 degrees

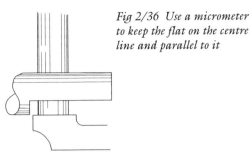

Fig 2/36 Use a micrometer to keep the flat on the centre line and parallel to it

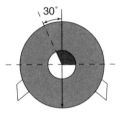

Fg 2/37 File one side of the hemi-cylinder at 30 degrees

swing of the same angle in a bed with a 120-degree V. It also positions the pivot without looking too constricting or so wide as to lose control of the knife-edge. Once the collar is in position lock it with a cyano-acrylate adhesive (eg Loctite).

File a flat on the underside of the arbor to give the position of the edge. Use a micrometer to keep it parallel to the outside of the arbor and to precisely halve its diameter (**Fig 2/36**). View the work from the side so that if the anvils of the micrometer are not flush with the metal, the light passing through the gap will give warning of this. Make sure that the last few thousandths of an inch are removed with a smooth file to give a good surface. Although this face will disappear when the sides are filed at an angle, a rough knife-edge will be left if the initial face is not smoothed off.

Having produced a semi-cylinder the first angled side is filed using the marks on the collar as a guide (**Fig 2/37**). A micrometer may be used again to ensure that the angled face is also parallel to the arbor centre line. Stop filing when the lines on the collar indicate that the working edge of the pivot have been revealed.

File the second face of the knife-edge in a

similar manner (**Fig 2/38**). Observation of the narrowing surface between the two angled sides will show if this last face is being controlled properly. The surface must have parallel sides as it narrows and the final strokes should leave the merest hint of the original surface as a hair's breadth line of even thickness along its length.

Finish filing by making the point at the end and at the same time reduce the overall length so that there is a little end-to-end shake. Rub lightly with fine emery paper to remove burrs.

• **Hardening the Knife-Edge**

Harden after the collar has been removed, otherwise there will be a sharp change in the state of the heat treated steel where the knife-edge joins the body of the arbor, and this will make it more liable to breaking. Rub the knife-edge in soap to limit the amount of scale resulting

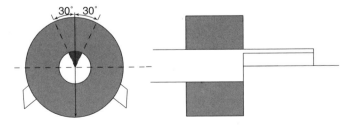

Fig 2/38 File the other side of the knife-edge

from the flame and then heat to bright red heat. Play the flame on the thickest part of the knife — the edge itself will burn very easily — and then quench in water or oil. Oil is preferred, for though the metal will be a little less hard than after water quenching, the thermal shock, and hence the chance of small cracks developing, is much less. After hardening brighten the metal with emery paper and then gently heat until the surface has turned a very light straw in colour.

The hardened and tempered knife-edge now needs a few strokes of an Arkansas stone along the sharp edge to produce a very tiny radius. Not too much or the edge will wander away from the true centre of the verge staff or arbor. Polish the point at the end with the stone at the same time.

The Bed

The knife-edge sits on brass (**Fig 2/39**) — steel will not do. The pressure developed between the edge and the bed when the pivot is working often produces a reddish 'gunge' that *may* be oxidation, but it appears even when the affected surface is apparently protected by an oil or grease film. Whatever it is, it is certainly solid and of no benefit to the pivot. Brass beds seem to last for about twenty years or so on most clocks.

Although the beds for most old clocks were made of as part of the backcock, they have all been replaced since they were first made. Clockmakers usually dovetail a new piece of brass into the backcock and then file the V in it. However I have seen one example at least of the V being made on a round insert, which, because of the difficulty of making a good round hole that 'breaks out' at the top of the

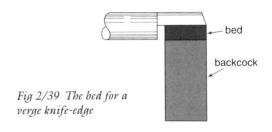

Fig 2/39 The bed for a verge knife-edge

cock, may have been done when the clock was first made.

Fig 2/40 shows the dovetail style and the manner in which the round type of insert was probably made initially. If a new backcock is being made then this technique is recommended, as it makes it very easy for the repairer who has to renew the bed — and with cyano-acrylate adhesives it is very easy to make sure that the insert does not rotate. It also allows a small sideways adjusment of the V (**Fig 2/41**); there is also a *very* small change in height.

Lay the verge flags on the top of the movement plates, if possible inserting the round pivot into its bearing — this will depend upon the clearance available and the amount of metal to be filed out of the bed to bring the knife-edge to its true level. Otherwise simply mark a point vertically over the pivot hole with a pencil and rest the round pivot there.

Move the knife end from side to side until the verge staff is directly over the centre of the crownwheel. It should be in line with the point of one tooth and exactly midway between two teeth on the opposite side of the crown. Scratch the edge of the plate with the knife edge to mark its position. For safety's sake also pencil a vertical line on the face of the plate from this mark so that when filing

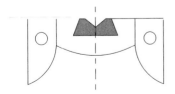 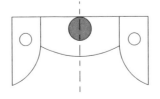 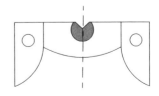

Fig 2/40 Replacement bed for the verge knife-edge dovetailed into the backcock (left). A round bed (right) and how it is inserted before the V is filed

Making a Traditional Type of Verge Using Flat Strip — Summary

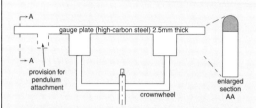

gauge plate (high-carbon steel) 2.5mm thick

provision for
pendulum
attachment

crownwheel

enlarged
section
AA

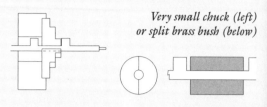

*Very small chuck (left)
or split brass bush (below)*

1 Saw a piece of high-carbon steel (eg gauge plate) about ³⁄₃₂in (2mm) thick to the shape shown, making the flag width about four times the thickness of the crownwheel.

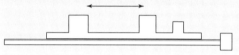

2 File the straight edge into a semicircle and finish with 150 grit emery paper.

3 Heat the middle port to just bright red and twist the flags through 90°. **Ensure that the twist is in the correct direction.**

4 File the arbor to a round section, but do **not file the top edge** that has already been rounded.

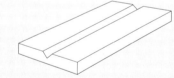

5 Straighten the verge using a bar with a V-slot as a jig.

6 File the flags to half the thickness of the arbor. Reduce their length, so that, though overlong, they are of exactly the same.

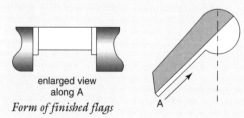

enlarged view
along A

Form of finished flags

A

7 Hold in a *very* small chuck or a split brass bush in a larger chuck to turn the front pivot.

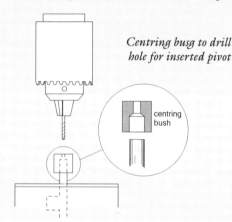

*Centring bush to drill
hole for inserted pivot*

centring
bush

8 If the pivot is too close to a flag to hold as shown, drill a hole using a centring bush and a drilling machine, then insert a pivot.

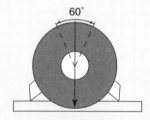

60°

9 To aid filing the rear knife-edge, turn a brass collar to slip over the arbor with a diameter larger than the flags. Mark a vertical line and lines 30° either side on the collar. Fix collar in position with Loctite.

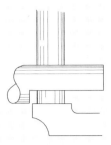

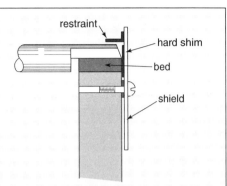

10 Use a micrometer to reduce the arbor to exactly a semi-cylinder and to keep it parallel.

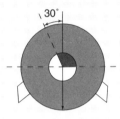

11 File one face of the knife-edge at 30° to the vertical.

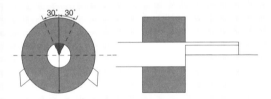

12 File the other face at 30° until a sharp edge is produced on the centre line, and smooth both faces.

13 File the end at an angle so that it just clears the end bearing of the apron or shield.

14 Remove the collar, harden and temper the knife-edge to light straw. Polish and produce a tiny radius on the knife-edge with an Arkansas stone.

15 File the V-bed for the knife edge about 120 degrees, making sure that the knife edge makes contact over its full length and that the verge staff is parallel with the face of the crownwheel.

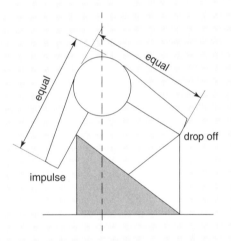

16 Fit the verge in the clock movement and test it against the crownwheel. File a little off each flag *in turn*, so that when one is at drop-off the other just touches the impulse face. Ensure that each flag is the same length and relieve front edge.

17 Smooth the impulse faces and harden the flags, stress-relieve at 150°C and polish down to 1000 grit.

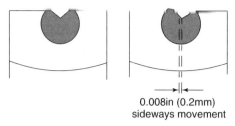

0.008in (0.2mm)
sideways movement

Fig 2/41 A round bed allows a small sideways adjustment of the V

commences you do not lose track of the correct position (**Fig 2/42**).

• **Filing the V**

(What follows assumes that the length of the flags has been provisionally marked, but they are not finished until the V has been completed, and these marks are placed close to their proper position.)

Use a three-square (triangular) file with a 4in long blade — these are often called Swiss files. Fit a handle to it and then proceed to file a V in the brass, keeping the point of the V on the line that was marked on the face of the movement plate (**Fig 2/43**). This requires careful judgement — keep trying the staff in the bearing as you make the V to check that the flags are being addressed correctly to the crownwheel. The staff should remain on the centre line of the wheel each time the knife is lowered into the bottom of the V. Stop filing the point of the V when the flags are a hair's breadth away from not clearing the teeth and the drop is even on each flag in turn.

Any serious discrepancy between the drop of the flags should be spotted during one of the test fittings of the verge staff. The aim is to place the staff parallel to the face of the crownwheel when the flags are just clearing the teeth. Play with the depth of the bed and the length of the flags to attain this. It will be

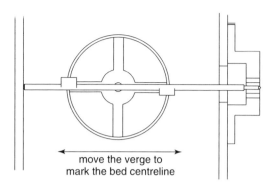

move the verge to
mark the bed centreline

Fig 2/42 Marking the centre line of the bed for the knife-edge

appreciated that there are two or three things going on at the same time. It sounds complicated, but if matters are taken carefully you will see which action is needed — whether to lower the V of the bed a fraction or shorten one or both flag lengths. Do not rush it. Look at the situation more than once before taking a decisive action.

• **Finishing the Bed**

When the V is almost deep enough it needs opening into a wider angle to allow the knife edge to swing from side to side without binding or lifting. The angle of the V needs the sum of the blade angle plus the maximum swing of the pendulum — plus another 20 degrees or so for 'freedom'. This often totals

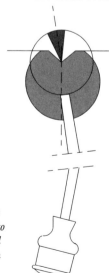

Fig 2/43 File the V with a triangular file, but do not widen the angle until the depth is almost correct

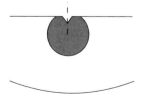

Fig 2/44 The V needs to be wider than the minimum to allow for the pendulum rod being bent when it is put in beat

about 120 degrees. Freedom is needed because when the pendulum is put in beat by bending the rod the vertical centre line of the knife edge will probably not coincide with the vertical centre line of the V (**Fig 2/44**).

While filing the V to this more open angle be careful not to lower it more than the whisker you left for accidents. As you work keep placing the knife edge in the bed (after painting the inside with a fibre tip pen), sliding it back and forth and then noting the bright mark that it has made in rubbing away the ink. It should stretch across the full thickness of the bed — if it does not, the knife edge is not in full contact with the bed. Adjust the filing of the V until the bright mark stretches from one face of the movement plate to the other. This is yet another point to be aware of as filing proceeds.

It sounds complicated, but if you take matters gently (the file has a rapid effect on the V), it will all come together. Make sure that:
• the verge staff is parallel to the wheel face
• there is complete contact of knife and bed
• the centre line of wheel is correct
• the open angle of Vee is sufficient.

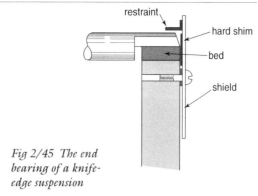

Fig 2/45 *The end bearing of a knife-edge suspension*

Finish with a fine file or emery paper (200 grit) folded over a piece of metal.
• **Knife-Edge End Bearing**
This is nearly always a simple piece of thin flat spring steel. It is drilled so that the apron and this steel shim are held in place with the sasme screw. The surface that the knife-edge end rubs on should be polished. There is a only a very light loading on this shim — unless there is something seriously wrong with the making of the escapement. Make sure that the verge staff can move end to end without the shoulder of the knife edge coming into contact with the inside of the clock plates (**Fig 2/45**).

3 Making Crownwheels

Types of Crownwheels
Almost all British verge escapements position the staff immediately over the centre of the crownwheel, which means that the wheel has to have an odd number of teeth. Some Continental verges however use even counts of crownwheel teeth and as a consequence the arbor has to be displaced to one side so that it will release half a tooth pitch at a time (**Fig 2/46**). Apart from this feature, which always seems to leave the escapement sounding out of beat, the making of a replacement staff and

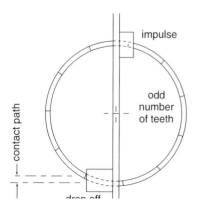

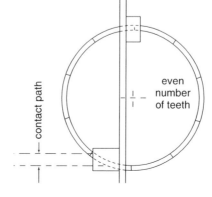

Fig 2/46 *Even-toothed crown-wheels need to have the verge staff off centre. Also the flags need to be wider*

verge flags is carried out in precisely the same manner for both British and Continental clocks. It will be seen from the drawing that the pallet needs to be wide enough to allow for the longer diagonal path of the tooth across the flag. This effect is worst for wide-angled flags. Whichever method of making crownwheels is used, *make sure that the teeth are angled in the correct direction*; if the teeth point in the wrong direction it cannot be turned over like an anchor or deadbeat escape-wheel.

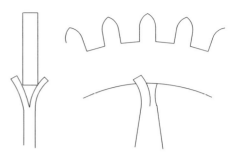

Fig 2/47 Very early method of fixing the crossings to an iron gear wheel or crownwheel

Strip Crownwheels

Old wheels were either made by forming a ring from strip brass, brazing the ends together and soldering to a separate crossing, or from a casting. It is unlikely that an iron crown-wheel will be found in any clock after about 1600, however if you do, the iron strip will be brazed (or more likely welded) into a ring as before and iron crossings sprung in and held by riveting or spreading (**Fig 2/47**). This technique is rather similar to the twisted lugs that were used to hold pre-World War II metal toys together. Each of the spokes of the cross-ing is split and one of the limbs so formed is bent until with a little wiggling the crossing can be fitted inside the ring and then the limb straightened to grip the ring tightly.

When this was the general practise the iron used was soft and very ductile and there was no danger of any of the limbs breaking when being twisted. Modern mild steels are often partially work-hardened when received — it is advisable to heat them to red heat and then allow to cool on a brick. They will definitely be softer after this treatment though the rela-tively slow cooling obtained by leaving them on a brick to cool is not, in theory, necessary. Mild steel should not be capable of harden-ing by heat treatment, but if metal is bought in small quantities it cannot be absolutely cer-tain that any piece is precisely what is asked for. It could be a medium-carbon steel and just within the heat-treatable range.

When making a crownwheel from brass strip it is easier to carry out the marking and the cutting of the teeth on a sheet of brass and then cut the strip off afterwards. A cold-working brass (70 copper/30 zinc) is best for this task, and this approximates to what would have been used in the original clock. Although this contains more copper than machining brass (nominally 60 copper/40 zinc) that is usually used for pillars and bushes, it is actu-ally a yellower brass than that. The UK speci-fication numbers are CZ106 and BS267.

Lay a sheet of 70/30 brass on the bench and with a ruler mark the length of the strip that will be used for the crown (**Fig 2/48**). This length will equal the circumference of the wheel and is equal to the crownwheel di-ameter multiplied by 3.14. Mark the position of the bottom of the teeth and the bottom of the crown with two parallel lines. (The top of the teeth will, of course, be one of the edges of the sheet.)

Draw another line at an angle from one end of the base of the teeth, and on that line meas-ured equal divisions with a ruler. This line is divided into as many spaces as the number of teeth on the crown (fifteen in the example shown). Join the end of the line to the end of the tooth base, closing the triangle.

The next task is a simple bit of school ge-ometry. Lay a set square down so that one edge lies along the line that you have just drawn. Make sure that it does not move and lay a ruler against its lower edge. Now the set square can be slid along the ruler and at every interval marked on the lower line (the one at an angle to the base), a parallel line can be

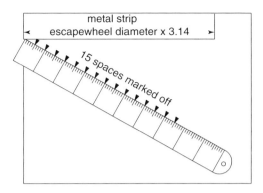
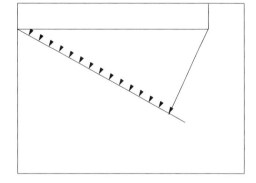
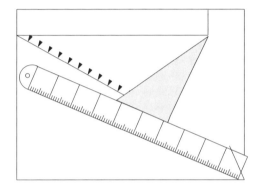
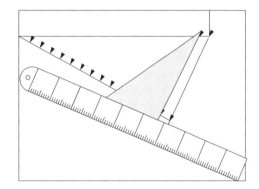

Fig 2/48 Marking out a strip crownwheel

scribed to cut the base of the teeth. In this manner the crown will be divided into as many equal parts as there are on the angled line. With the crown divided it only remains to outline the teeth (**Fig 2/49**).

Many crownwheels have no rake to the teeth, and if an antique wheel is being replaced then the same shape as the original should be followed. However a slight rake is of advantage for those clocks with a wide swing to the pendulum or foliot. In this case it is possible for the edge of the flags to touch the face of the teeth during recoil. A suitable slight rake

for teeth that are as high as their pitch is one eight of the height (**Fig 2/50**).

Cast Crownwheels
Castings for crownwheels are available, some with a boss instead of a collet and some in the form of a plain, shallow cup for a collet to be fitted. Neither is very easy to hold rigidly for

Fig 2/49 Marking the outline of the teeth for a strip crownwheel

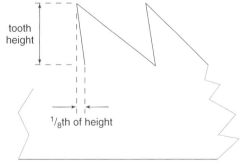

Fig 2/50 A slight rake to the crownwheel teeth is preferable

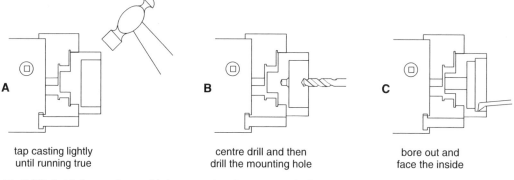

Fig 2/51 *Initial stages in machining a casting for a crownwheel*

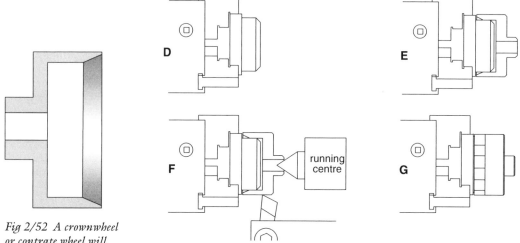

Fig 2/52 A crownwheel or contrate wheel will benefit from thinning on the inside

Fig 2/53 The casting with the inside machined is put on a brass mandrel (D) to turn the outside. The casting is divided and the teeth marked (G)

cutting the teeth on a machine; it is better to simply machine all over, mark a line for the base of the teeth and scribe the divisions by means of a dividing head if you have one, or a paper strip marked with the divisions if you have not. (See pages 41-42 for this method.)

Hold the outside of the casting lightly in the chuck, gripping the closed end of the cup as this is the stiffest part of the casting and it will not crush when the jaws are tightened after it has been set to run true.

Figs 2/51-53 demonstrate machining a casting. As the casting will be relatively uneven, tap it as the machine slowly rotates un-

til all the humps and hollows of the surface are balanced. You should be able to machine a complete cylinder removing all the original cast surface, and yet not desperately thinning any part of the finished work. Tighten the chuck jaws to hold it rigidly. Check that the casting has not moved before machining.

Make the hole for the collet or arbor with a centre drill followed by a twist drill, to ensure concentricity. Bore the inside of the crown and face that side of the crossing that is exposed.

If the crownwheel has fewer than twenty teeth they will almost certainly need thinning at the tip to improve the performance of the escapement. Thinning is simply turning a chamfer (**Fig 2/52**) on the inside of a cup-shaped wheel (the contrate wheel of a carriage clock for example) so that the tip of the tooth remains a single point as the wheel rotates. Although a crownwheel tooth is less critical in this than a gear tooth, when it makes more than a 10 degree rotation at each beat of the escapement the thickness of the tooth tip has a considerable effect on its operation.

A tooth tip that is thick has both an inner and an outer corner, and they impinge on the pallet surface differently as the wheel rotates. Upon entry the inner corner makes contact, changing to the outer corner at the mid to drop-off point. In effect this decreases the clearances available in a given escapement. The cure for that could be to reduce the length of the pallets of course, but thinning is better.

The casting can now be taken out of the chuck and a round brass bar put in its place. This bar must be large enough to be turned to fit the inside of the half-finished wheel and heavily chamfered to clear the corners inside the crownwheel (**Fig 2/53**). If a large hole has been made to accept a collet this can used to fit a screw and washer to clamp the casting onto the bar. Drill and tap the brass bar before fitting the part-machined crownwheel.

Otherwise the wheel must be held in place with shellac, a technique commonly used in clockmaking. A thin film of shellac is used as the interface between the work and the brass bar (commonly termed a chuck or mandrel), that has been turned for it. In other words, the work is glued in place with the shellac acting as a thermosetting adhesive. Warm the turned bar with a small gas torch and then rub shellac on to the hot surface. Press the wheel in place with a piece of wood and, if necessary, heat it too, so that the shellac melts (but does not bubble) and sticks to both the work and the bar. Hold it until it cools. If the metal is overheated this will take a long time — and serve you right!

Leave the shellac to fully harden and then face off the area immediately around the bore that has been drilled for the collet or arbor, using light cuts. As soon as a fully machined face has been produced, the tailstock and a live centre (ie one that rotates) can be used to help support the crownwheel. If the mandrel has been made ready for a screw and washer this can be put in place now instead of the running centre.

It is advisable never to place too much reliance on shellac attachments for machining. When the casting is securely and accurately held in the lathe the turning of the outside of the wheel can be carried out without any risk of chatter marring the surface. Face off the back of the crownwheel and chamfer it; finish the outside of the mounting boss if there is one and chamfer that too.

Measure the position for the bottom of the teeth and use the point of the tool to scribe a line around the outside of the wheel. If you have a dividing head or wheel cutting engine, or have prepared a paper strip for division (see below), now mark the tooth pitches around the circumference.

Dividing With a Paper Strip

This method of dividing the teeth can be used with a crownwheel made either from brass strip or a casting. Cut a strip of paper twice as wide as the tooth depth, wrap it around the crownwheel and cut through at the overlap so that it is exactly one circumference long. Pin it on a flat board and use the same marking out technique as discussed in 'Strip Crownwheels' (pages 37-39) for dividing the paper strip into the number of pitches that is needed. When the pitches have been marked on the paper with pencil, complete the form of the individual teeth and paste onto the outside of the wheel.

The teeth can be cut out using a piercing saw or jeweller's saw, but only attend to one tooth at a time, do not be tempted to cut across the full width of the wheel and produce two vertical faces at a time — it is unlikely to work. Do not forget to make the cuts on the waste side of the lines and leave some

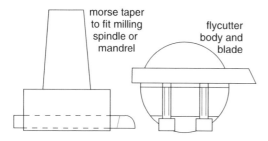

Fig 2/54 Fly cutter suitable for cutting the teeth of escapewheels

metal to file away to the pencil marks.

If you do want to cut the teeth by machine, use a fly cutter (**Fig 2/54**). The tool is made from gauge plate, a high-carbon steel that does not deform when heat treated. Harden and temper to a light straw, and use at high speed, anything between 2,000 and 5,000 rpm (revolutions per minute).

Making a Crownwheel From Solid Bar
New crownwheels for nineteenth-century clocks or modern reproductions may be turned from solid bar. It is simpler and more likely to produce a good result than fabrica-

tion from strip. **Fig 2/55** shows the machining sequence. There is no attempt to cut the teeth by machine, but merely to mark the uprights of the teeth using the dividing head and the base line. Even though the workpiece is more robust than a casting the size of the teeth is usually too great to cut in one pass.

For those skilled in filing accurately, it is as easy to cut the teeth by saw and file as before, and in the author's opinion, hardly worth the effort of setting up a suitable cutter. This is particularly true when the teeth are large, but it is a personal opinion only, and those with the appropriate equipment may wish to machine them.

The collet is made of a piece with the wheel and drilled to suit the nominal diameter of the arbor. If it is all machined at one setting (apart from cutting the teeth), there should be no difficulty in keeping the wheel true on its axis.

Pin Crownwheel
There is a version of the crownwheel that was used in the 'Columbus Clock' that was produced for the 1892 Columbian Exposition

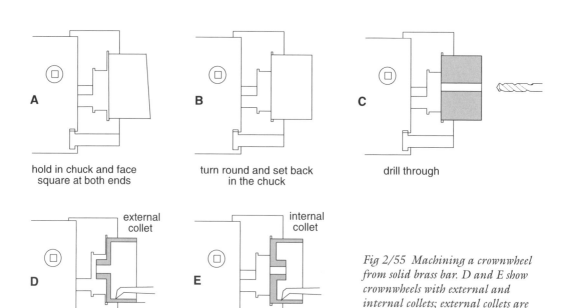

A hold in chuck and face
square at both ends

B turn round and set back
in the chuck

C drill through

D external collet

E internal collet

Fig 2/55 Machining a crownwheel from solid brass bar. D and E show crownwheels with external and internal collets; external collets are machined after the bar is turned round in the chuck

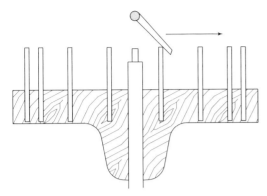

Fig 2/56 *Crownwheel with pins for teeth*

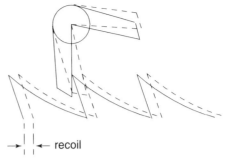

Fig 2/57 *The rake of the teeth should be large enough to prevent the edge of the flags biting into the teeth during recoil*

in Chicago.[1] A similar arrangement is also used in a modern wooden version of a medieval 'monastery' clock. This is a simple wooden disc with steel pins driven into its face.

The design is simple (**Fig 2/56**) and easy to manufacture, the upright pins take the place of the upright faces of the normal tooth and the escapement operates in exactly the same fashion as the common verge-and-crownwheel, with no apparent disadvantages. There is a slight dwell on the top of the pins if these are left flat as in the drawing. The Columbus clock had brass verge flags which were repaired in 1996, but there was no serious damage to the pins, which by then had been working for a century.

The Truth of Crownwheels

It is more important that the face of the wheel is true, than the outside diameter, although the beat will be affected if the wheel runs significantly out of centre. A slight rake to the front of the tooth will restrain the flags from putting pressure on their edges during the recoil (this only happens with flags that are vertical at first contact), and the curve at the back must be deep enough to clear the flag as it swings down.

The crownwheel and verge escapement is

a recoil type, so test the clearances by moving the crownwheel against its rotation a little after each drop off, and make sure that during recoil the lower edges of the flags do not scrape down the face of the tooth (**Fig 2/57**). The rake of one eighth of the tooth height mentioned earlier should be enough to keep the edges of the flags from biting into the teeth, but do not be afraid to alter this if necessary.

Excessive recoil will cause flags to bite into a raked tooth and excessive recoil is created by over-strong springs, weights that are too heavy or pendulum bobs that are too light. Check that springs, weights and bob are original before increasing the rake — and weakening the tooth tip.

Mounting the Crownwheel

This is carried out in the same manner as with any other wheel in a clock, but more attention has to be paid to the truth of the face than the diameter. If this is simply thought of as maintaining a constant path for the tooth tips, then it becomes exactly the same criterion as in all examples of toothed wheels.

If, after machining, the wheel does not run true, use a broach to make the bore slack on the arbor and then use Loctite or a similar cyno-acrylate adhesive to fix it in place on the arbor. (Winding a piece of soft wire behind the wheel will help to keep it in place longitudinally while the face is being trued up.) These adhesives pass through a pasty stage, so if the arbor is set up in the lathe it can be rotated as

---

1   This was brought to my notice by Steven G. Conover with the added information that it was associated with Henry de Vic (Vick) of Lorraine about 1370.

the adhesive sets and by lightly touching the teeth with a piece of soft material such as wood or plastic the wheel can be made to run true.

These light touches on the teeth are repeated until the adhesive is strong enough to retain the position that the wheel has been coaxed into. Leave the machine running for another ten minutes or so until it is in no danger of the wheel moving out of truth when the arbor is removed from the chuck.

5 Repairing Crownwheel & Verge Escapements

Repairing a Broken Verge Staff

It is unusual for the actual staff of the verge pallets to need any repair and when it does it is almost certain that the rest of the clock will be in pretty poor condition too, with damaged or worn flags and pivots. In that case a replacement verge is needed. However on the off-chance that, due to some flaw in the original metal or other occurance, the staff has broken in two without damaging anything else, here are a few comments on the repair.

If the staff has broken close to one or other of the flags it will be too difficult to hold the pieces together to make a repair worthwhile. Only if the clock is a top quality clock, where it is imperative that all original pieces be retained, is it reasonable to attempt the task. It involves pinning with high tensile steel and splicing new metal into the old so as to be not visible. This is not a subject that can be described easily, but is more suitable for a demonstration at the workbench.

A break that leaves lengths of staff attached to both flags will respond to a relatively easy repair. At first sight this will merely be the making of a sleeve or muff that slips over the diameters of both halves of the mid-portion of the staff. Each part is held in true register with soft solder or a cyano-acrylate adhesive (**Fig 2/58**), and if you can proceed in this way do so. Make the sleeve from steel, drilling it to a diameter that will allow the roughly cylindrical staff to enter and not rattle too much. The outside diameter should be about one and a quarter times that of the hole and the length about six times the diameter of the staff.

Unfortunately many verge escapements do not have sufficient clearance over the top support cock (**Fig 2/59**) to a repair quite as simple as this. Instead a modified sleeve should be made with the same diameters but the length increased by the width of the top cock plus a bit for clearance (**Fig 2/60**). The middle is now filed back to produce a partial cylinder. (This filing could be done after the sleeve has been installed but it would be difficult to hold the staff and sleeve in the vice without straining the repair.) It is only necessary to file enough from the sleeve to clear the top cock when the staff swings; the drawing indicates how much this is likely to be.

When the sleeve is locked onto the two halves of the staff with adhesive or soft solder, remember to position the portion that has been filed back immediately over the cock, (ie under the staff). Otherwise it will be a complete waste of time.

Fig 2/58 A broken verge staff repaired with a simple sleeve

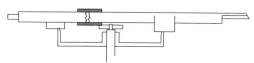

Fig 2/59 A simple sleeve will often foul top cock of the crownwheel

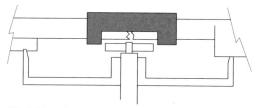

Fig 2/60 The sleeve needs to be wider and filed back to clear the top cock of the crownwheel

Repairing Verge Flags

A worn pallet flag has the same appearance as a worn pallet in any other escapement — it is pitted. Just as in the anchor escapement (Chapter 3) a certain amount of wear can be accommodated, but this eventually develops to the stage where a there is a definite pit at the point of first contact. The resultant steep edge between the original surface and the pit will tend to hold back the pallet and it will eventually become so bad that the clock fails for this reason alone. It is, after all, a recoil escapement and the crownwheel is pushed backwards at each beat of the pendulum. At that point the tip of the tooth is travelling *up* the impulse surface and the upper edge of the pit can become so sharply defined as to jam the action momentarily. Even without looking closely at the impulse surface, the hesitation and the lifting of the staff are sufficient to give notice of a badly worn flag.

If the flags are severely worn and there is other damage, it may be necessary to remake the whole verge staff and pallets. However this is unusual and a repair made by soldering spring steel 'slips' onto the worn faces is usually effective and acceptable.

It is not necessary to soften the flags and file back their working surfaces as you would on an anchor escapement. Unless the angle of swing is already very narrow (say 30 degrees) additional metal in the form of slips can be accommodated by shortening the length of the flags. There will be a shorter arc to the pendulum or balance but it should not have a significant affect. Slips of around 0.25mm (0.010in) thick are sufficient for bracket-size clocks.

The benefit of not heat treating an elderly piece of metal that is usually rather delicately made outweighs the small loss of arc. **Fig 2/61** illustrates the result of adding slips to the faces of the flags.

Thoroughly clean the surface of the flags with emery paper and then use a soldering iron to tin them. A good flux will be needed to successfully tin cast steel, either Baker's Fluid or a modern flux containing acidified

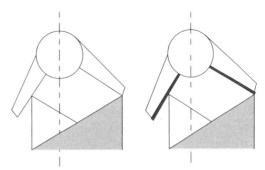

Fig 2/61 The addition of slips produces a slightly smaller flag angle and a slightly longer flag

zinc chloride. Put the flux on the clean surface first and then apply the soldering iron, scrubbing the surface with it until the molten solder has fully coated it. When the flags have both been tinned wipe off any excess solder while it is still molten using a cotton cloth, and put them to one side while the slips are prepared.

Old main springs are a fruitful source of steel for slips. Select one about 0.25mm (0.040in) thick and not corroded. Take the time to straighten out one of the coils so that the metal is fairly flat, tin it in the same manner as the flags, and then cut it with tin snips held in a vice, to form two rectangular pieces at least as big as the flags' surfaces. Some flags have raised sides (**Fig 2/62**), and in this case the slips must be made to fit between the sides, but overhang the original flag. Otherwise make the pieces both longer and broader than the flags.

Put flux onto all the tinned surfaces. Now hold the verge arbor in a small vice so that one of the flags is horizontal and lay one slip in place. Have a piece of wood and a length of pivot wire ready to pick up quickly. Using a

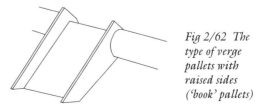

Fig 2/62 The type of verge pallets with raised sides ('book' pallets)

'soft' flame (blue, but without a well-defined pale blue inner cone) warm up the flag until the solder melts. Put down the torch and while supporting the flag with the piece of wood, use the pivot steel to press down firmly on the slip. If the joint is good there will be a bright edge of molten solder around the flag and the slip. If this is not achieved at the first attempt beat out a piece of solder to paper thickness, heat the flag again and touch the solder to the edges of the joint. It does not matter if any gets onto the top surface of the slip, as that can be cleaned off afterwards with emery paper. Now use the wood and pivot steel again while the solder is molten.

When the solder has cooled loosen the vice and turn the verge staff until the other flag is horizontal, tighten up again and repeat the process.

The verge flags are now repaired but are probably too long — they need to be adjusted to allow the escapement to operate with a minimum of drop (the movement of the wheel that does nothing). Looking back at **Fig 2/4** you will see that the drop-off in each set of drawings occurs when the tooth is at different distances from the centre line. As stated on pages 16-17, the correct length for the flags depends on the angle between them and the height of the arbor above the face of the crownwheel. Since, in the case of a repair, these are already fixed it is only necessary to cut back the length of the flags equally until the escapement works.

The length of the flags will also affect the total arc that the pendulum or balance swings through, being greater for longer flags. As stated earlier the addition of the thickness of the slips to the flags' impulse faces will narrow the swing of the verge. Unless the new slips are reduced to a sharp edge (**Fig 2/63**) the verge will behave differently. Reducing the slips in this way however also limits their life and negates the value of the repair. It is better to accept an alteration in the length of the flags and the swing of the pendulum.

Of course, if the original flags are sufficiently thick to allow the worn faces to be filed

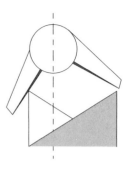

Fig 2/63 Thinning the slips will reduce any change in flag angle, but this is neither recommended or necessary

back far enough to allow for the slip thickness, the escapement can be made to perform exactly as before. However, those clocks whose value justifies restoration rather than repair, are also the ones which usually have the more delicately-made verges. You are left with the choice between slip repair (and the resultant changes in behaviour), and complete replacement.

Always relieve the ends of the slips as shown in **Fig 2/64**, it looks neater and makes the clearance more certain. As the steel of both the flag and the slip will be hard, use a stone (or a small diamond-coated file) to remove the excess and to make the relieving angle. A spring steel slip can be filed (just) with a saw-sharpening file which is harder than a normal one, but there is more likelihood of breaking the soldered joint with the pressure that is needed.

Since the repair involves soldering steel-to-steel the flux used will be at least a little corrosive (if it is Baker's fluid it will be *very* corrosive), so do not forget to wash well and neutralise the area with a solution of bicarbonate of soda (sodium bicarbonate), before polishing and oiling.

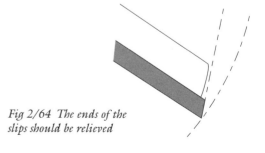

Fig 2/64 The ends of the slips should be relieved

Repairing Crownwheels

Failure in crownwheels is usually due to:
• damaged or bent teeth
• cracked crossings or rim
• or some accident that has resulted in the face of the wheel being bent out of truth.

A verge escapement can accept a certain amount of eccentricity for the rim (as much as 10 per cent of the outside diameter), but the face must run true, otherwise it will produce a varying drop as the crownwheel rotates.

• **Damaged Teeth**

If a crownwheel has obviously damaged teeth examine it closely for work by other repairers. File marks that are brighter than the rest of the wheel are almost certainly an indication that the wheel has been repaired once already and that the tooth pitch (the distance between one tooth tip and the next) will vary around the circumference. Putting this right may easily take more time than making a new wheel. In the event that enough marks are found to arous suspicion use a vernier calliper to check the pitch of the teeth around the circle. There will be some variations as a result of the original method of dividing and cutting the teeth, but these should be limited.

The amount of variation that can be tolerated is difficult to quantify, and your own judgement must be used to decide whether the operation of the escapement outside the area that you *have* to repair, is acceptable. The pitch may be expected to vary by up to one twentieth as a result of the original dividing. In other words, if the pitch in one place measures 5mm (keeping to whole numbers) other teeth may vary from 4.87mm to 5.12mm — a total tolerance of 0.25 mm (0.010in).

The decision to carry out a total replacement or not depends upon the desirability of retaining original work even if the crownwheel is badly mangled, and your ability to reproduce the original style and standard of workmanship. This is an ethical problem that crops up frequently when repairing clocks. If it is not a museum piece the matter can be resolved on commercial grounds — does the replacement lower the value of the clock? But a museum piece is valued for its historical integrity and you will almost certainly be required to keep the old tattered wheel and make it good.

• **Tooth Repair**

Measure the diameter of the wheel and find its circumference by multiplying this by 3.141 (π). Divide this figure by the number of teeth to give the average pitch of the crownwheel, and set your vernier callipers to this measurement. The method of setting the position for the replacement teeth will depend upon whether one tooth is to be replaced or several.

Using the neighbouring teeth and a pair of dividers mark the midpoint between them, (**Fig 2/65**). Now use the vernier to check against the pitch that would result from using

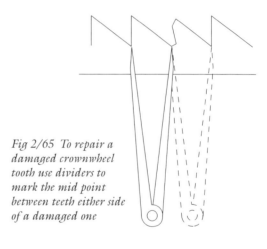

Fig 2/65 To repair a damaged crownwheel tooth use dividers to mark the mid point between teeth either side of a damaged one

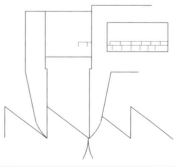

Fig 2/66 Use vernier calipers to compare the mark with the calculated pitch

this mark as the position of the new tooth tip (**Fig 2/66**). If this falls within the tolerance of one twentieth, the mark can be used in the repair. In this case use repair method **A**.

If it does not fall within this tolerance you can be certain that at least one of the teeth that was used in making the mark has been modified and is not correctly placed. Use repair method **B**.

• **Method A**

Using an engineer's square draw a perpendicular line from the base of the wheel to the mark (**Fig 2/67**). Prepare a piece of hard brass to either face a lightly damage tooth or replace a heavily damaged one (**Fig 2/68**).

Hard brass is simply obtained by beating ordinary 70/30 brass sheet or strip with a hammer. If the brass is at all springy and it is not specified as 'half hard' take the precaution of heating it to dull red heat (to soften it) and plunge it in water (to clean off the scale). Beating it until the thickness has been reduced by about one third should make the brass at least as hard as the original — and in all probability much harder.

File or saw a base for the replacement material. A facing for the tooth only needs a shallow saw cut, but the replacement of most of the tooth that results from heavy damage needs more work to ensure that a firm key is obtained (**Fig 2/69**). **Fig 2/70** shows a couple of variations that may be useful. In both cases make the thickness of the new material sufficient to hang over the inside and the out-

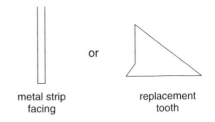

metal strip   replacement
facing   tooth

Fig 2/68 A crownwheel tooth may be repaired with just a facing or a complete tooth replacement

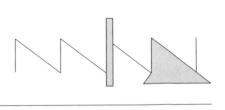

Fig 2/69 A tooth facing is soldered into a slot, while a replaced tooth is keyed in and then soldered

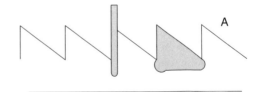

A

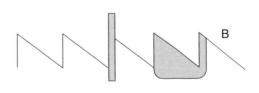

B

Fig 2/70 Variation in tooth repairs. Avoiding sharp corners is a precaution against fatigue failure (A). Even if only one tooth is damaged, facing its neighbour supports the insert (B). Corners may be rounded or square

Fig 2/67 Mark the position of the repair

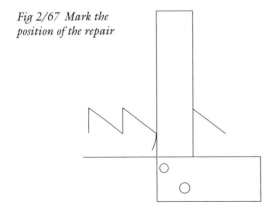

side of the crownwheel. This excess metal will be removed with a file after soldering. Be careful to file only in directions that place no strain on the soldered joint.

Soft solder is used for these joints. It is not easy to ensure that the new metal remains in position while soldering, so support it by any means that do not result in the support also being soldered to the wheel. Aluminium is a useful material to bend into a support because without special techniques it will not bond with the solder. The additional thickness of the new metal will allow scope to file and produce a tooth or facing that does not lean inwards or outwards.

Though hard brass has stresses in it that need to be relieved by heat treatment, the act of soldering is sufficient to do this.

• **Method B**
If a lathe or a dividing engine is available, by mounting the old wheel in a chuck or on a mandrel it is relatively easy to scratch dividing marks around the old wheel to check how great the variation of the tooth pitch is.

However, the dividing method shown on pages 38-39 for making a new crownwheel is just as suitable when checking old wheels. Make a paper strip as long as the circumference of the wheel and divide it into the same number of spaces as the wheel has teeth. Back this with double-sided sticky tape and wrap it around the wheel, aligning the first mark with the front of a tooth that appears to be the least modified. Rub it gently and the fronts of the teeth will make light creases in the paper. Use these creases and the marked divisions to decide which teeth need to be faced or even replaced entirely.

If, after beginning this check, it is decided that the strip could be realigned to demand less work on the teeth, the sticky tape may allow repositioning without distortion. As an alternative, spray adhesive will allow ready repositioning of the paper strip.

Repairs to the Knife Edge
Although at first sight this is a similar repair to the insertion of a pivot it must be remem-

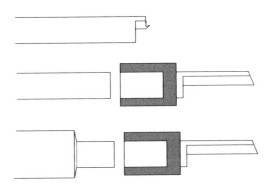

Fig 2/71 A broken knife-edge may be repaired with a sleeve that incorporates both the knife-edge and the mounting for the pendulum rod. If the arbor is larger that the proposed sleeve, reduce the diamer of the arbor by careful filing; this also gives a neater repair

bered that the height of the actual knife-edge extends from the centre line of the verge staff to the outside diameter. The simplest approach is to cut the staff two or three millimetres away from the inboard end of the old knife and then to make a sleeve or muff similar to **Fig 2/71** incorporating the mounting for the pendulum rod. The staff will need filing down on its diameter if it is already larger at the point of pendulum attachment.

Since the knife-edge must be heat treated to make it hard, the filing of the staff must be accurate enough to be a repeatable fit in the hole in the sleeve. By that is mean that when the knife is filed onto the sleeve the piece can be removed for heat treatment and then replaced for locking with acyano-acrylate adhesive (Loctite or similar) and still line up as it did during the filing and testing process.

The filing of this replacement edge is carried out in exactly the same manner as when making a staff complete with its knife edge (pages 30-37).

Replacement Beds
Lay the verge staff on the top of the assembled movement plates in the same manner as described in on page 36 when making a new bed. Since it will tend to lie in the worn-out V it will be necessary to pack the knife edge

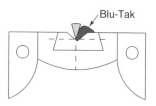

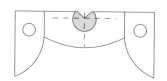

Fig 2/72 Hold the knife-edge in position temporarily while marking the position for a replacement bed. Insert a replacement dovetail (left) or round bed (right) and cut the V to the marks

over to obtain the correct position. Fill the old V with a piece of Blu-Tak and move the staff until it is lying over the centre of the crownwheel. Place a straight edge under the knife to support it and move the pendulum rod to test the clearance of the flags. The Blu-Tak should keep it on its centre and help to maintain its height while a straightedge is used to mark a horizontal line on the brass that represents the desired depth of the new V. Carefully mark the vertical centre line of the knife on the brass too.

The old metal can be removed by making a dovetail and the marks then used as a guide when filing a new V, but a round insert is preferred because it can be renewed easily by a later repairer (**Fig 2/72**). Any drill used to make a seating for this will break through the

slope of the old V and it becomes an impossible task, so this V must be filled in temporarily. File a piece of brass to fill the V and then use a small machine vice to hold it in place (**Fig 2/73**) while a seating is drilled for the nominally-sized plug. As an additional safety measure the packing piece may be soft soldered in place.

Once a satisfactory hole has been achieved the packing piece can be removed (the solder melted free if necessary) and a round plug of brass tinned, fitted and sweated in its place. 'Sweating' simply means heating a pre-tinned piece of metal so that the solder melts and makes a joint.

Now use a triangular file to make the V as desribed on page 36. It will be easier this time because the marks can be used as a guide.

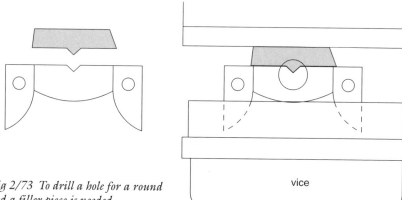

Fig 2/73 To drill a hole for a round bed a filler piece is needed

vice

6 The Crownwheel & Verge Escapement — Faults & Comments

The major fault of the verge escapement is that it is greatly affected by changes in the driving force of the train. This was limited in eighteenth-century watches by fitting a balance spring to the balance wheel, but the variation is only lessened. This escapement was reputed to be an improvement on the simple verge but the author has seen no comparative figures.

The verge escapement has been produced in a deadbeat version (**Fig 2/74**), but its only known use is in John Joseph Merlin's 'band clock'. Since a much better result can be obtained with the Graham deadbeat escapement, there seems to be little advantage to the device, unless, as in Merlin's clock, a vertical escapewheel arbor is necessary.

The cross-beat verge escapement may also be made as a deadbeat escapement, but the linkage, whether geared or fork and pin, is still a weak point and the result unlikely to be worth the effort — except as an interesting and decorative feature. It could of course, be fitted with a balance spring.

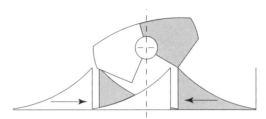

Fig 2/74 The deadbeat verge as used in Merlin's band clock

CHAPTER 3
The Anchor Escapement

1 Description & Operation of the Anchor Escapement

The anchor escapement (**Fig 3/1**) is a very reliable and long-lived type of escapement, capable of operating under the most adverse conditions. It assumes several different forms: the solid types from Britain, France and Germany, and the bent-strip type from Germany and America (**Fig 3/2**). Regardless of their shape, similar geometries can be used to make all variants that have the same span and relationship to the number of teeth on the escapewheel.

Essentially the pallets consist of a curved body that presents two inclined surfaces (impulse faces) to the teeth of an escapewheel working in the same plane. The teeth are in

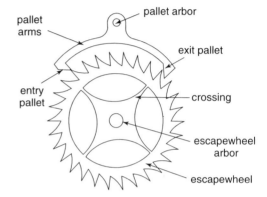

Fig 3/1 The components of the anchor escapement

line with the inclined surfaces and they pass under the pallets as the pallets lift in turn. **Fig 3/3** shows the progression of the pallets through two beats of the pendulum (a complete oscillation). The escapewheel makes a rotation equivalent to half the pitch of the teeth during the time that one of the pallets is in contact with it. At the end of that movement the wheel tooth falls free of the pallet with which it was in contact (the 'drop-off') and another tooth begins to contact the alternative impulse face. So the impulse faces in turn receive a small force and allow the rocking motion of the anchor body to continue.

This rocking motion is transferred from the pendulum via the crutch to the anchor, with the result that one full beat is obtained whenever either of the impulse faces is raised. Since this happens as every half pitch passes through the pallets, the pendulum makes two beats for every tooth on the wheel.

As in the verge this means that when working out the ratios of the train wheels the

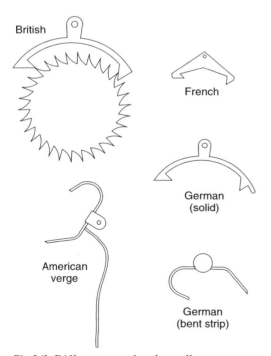

Fig 3/2 Different types of anchor pallets

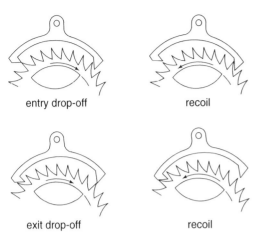

entry drop-off   recoil   impulsing exit pallet

exit drop-off   recoil   impulsing entry pallet   entry drop-off

Fig 3/3 The action of the anchor pallets through a complete oscillation (two beats) of the pendulum

number of teeth on the escapewheel must be multiplied by two.

Recoil

Like the verge the anchor is a recoil escapement. Recoil is the name given to the backwards motion of the movement of the escapewheel after every forward movement. The movement is, obviously, not as great as the forward motion, otherwise the clock would not 'go', however, it is frequently a large fraction of that forward movement. The seconds hand of many longcase, or grandfather clocks shows this effect quite clearly.

Recoil occurs because the impulse face (**Fig 3/4**) that has just swung down to the working position, does not react immediately to the

pressure of the wheel tooth and move upwards, but is carried on by the momentum of the pendulum so that it presses down on the tooth and forces the wheel to turn anticlockwise.

When the momentum of the pendulum is spent, it swings back towards the vertical again and the wheel drives through the escapement pallets. The pressure of the wheel tooth against the impulse plane feeds energy to the pendulum until it slides off the impulse face at the drop-off face.

As one pallet reaches the drop-off position and the wheel tooth leaves it, the other pallet comes into contact with another tooth of the wheel and forces it backwards until the momentum of the pendulum is once more used up and it reaches the end of its swing.

The arc that the pendulum swings through while the pallets are recoiling, and consequently not giving impulse to the pendulum, is called the supplementary arc (**Fig 3/4**). (In an escapement that does not recoil — the deadbeat — the supplementary arc is the difference between the minimum arc needed to operate the escapement and the actual arc of the pendulum or balance wheel.)

Recoil occurs at every beat of the pendulum. The sequence is: drop off, exit pallet recoil, exit pallet impulse, drop off, entry pallet recoil, entry pallet impulse (**Fig 3/3**). Obviously this is true for all forms of anchor escapement regardless of shape and the number of teeth spanned by the pallets.

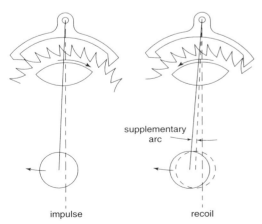

supplementary arc

impulse   recoil

Fig 3/4 Recoil takes place during the pendulum's supplementary arc

Wear

The amount of recoil is directly related to the wear that will occur on the impulse faces. During recoil the driving weight is lifted, or the main spring wound up, a very tiny amount. It should be realised that the gears of a clock movement are best designed and set out so that the gear teeth do not make contact with each other until the line joining the centres of the two gears is reached. This ensures that gear teeth transmit energy on the tooth faces that are moving away from each other instead of coming together. The energy wasted at the gear contact points is much less as a result and is the reason why pinions with a large number of leaves are preferred to those with a low numbers of leaves.

However if the motion of the gear trains is reversed, contact between gear teeth occurs (for this time) before the line of centres and frictional losses are much greater than during forward movement. During recoil the train motion *is* reversed and so the friction is greater. This results in a greater pressure between the pallet and wheel tooth during the supplementary arc, and consequently, greater wear than during the impulse.

In addition to this, when drop off takes place the escapewheel is free of restraint (except friction) and accelerates towards the impulse face. The pendulum is swinging down and accelerating under the influence of gravity. Tooth and impulse face are moving towards each other and the sum of their two velocities when they meet is the impact velocity.

A small pit develops on the impulse face at the point of impact, or first contact of the tooth on the pallet and this is caused mainly by the energy of impact. If this pit is examined under a magnifying glass it will be seen that it has a steep angle on the supplementary arc side (**Fig 3/5**). This steep angle eventually becomes a virtual wall, and the tooth of the wheel tends to lodge here, introducing a shock into the smooth movement of the pallet and pendulum. Removing this pit will make the clock more certain in its running, with no tendency to stop with changes in weather or

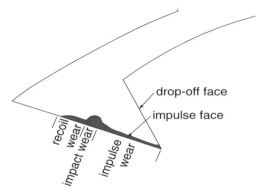

Fig 3/5 Most wear takes place during impact and recoil. Note the relatively sharp edge (exagerated here) to the upper part of the impact pit

local vibration, and produce better timekeeping.

Without going into mathematical detail, it can be stated that the energy of the impact is in direct ratio to the square of the impact velocity. Thus, if the velocity of impact of one escapement is 1ft/sec and that of a similar escapement is 2ft/sec, the energy of impact in the latter case is four times that of the former, and the wear will be very much greater. Hence it is important to keep these velocities as low as possible. Keeping the drop to a working minimum reduces the wear.

If the driving weight or spring is kept to the lowest practical value, two things result. Firstly the speed with which the escapewheel tooth approaches the pallet is kept to a minimum. Secondly the pendulum is not driven higher in its swing than is necessary to clear the escapewheel tooth and so produces a small supplementary arc with less recoil. Both these factors enable wear to be kept to a low level (but may affect timekeeping adversely).

If the anchor is not made accurately (so that the drop on one pallet is greater than on the other), the wear on one pallet is bound to be greater than the minimum. If the effective impulse angles are not the same on each pallet, the pressure of the pallets on the teeth will not be the same, and even if one pallet experiences minimum wear, the other, most definitely, will not. The imbalance therefore becomes greater. This situation can be recognised quite easily because the sound of the tick will be much louder on one beat of the pendulum than on the other.

Hence, reliable though the anchor is, and however tolerant of bad workmanship and thoughtless treatment, it will wear out much faster if it is made inaccurately and it will not give such good time keeping as a well-made one. In addition, the practice of applying a heavier weight or a stronger spring to a reluctant movement, will result in poor time keeping as well as accelerated wear. Weights that are too heavy are often found on longcase clocks, and replacement open springs that are too stiff, (particularly in thirty-hour or one-day American clocks) very frequently lead to heavy wear on the escapement as well as on the gear train.

Table 3/1 gives the weights typical of different types of clock, so that the appropriateness of a given set of weights can be checked before the new escapement is fitted.

Springs are difficult to tabulate, but evidence of 'overdriving' is easy to observe. Look for great wheels that have worn metal pressed out to either side of the teeth (**Fig 3/6**). Normal wear removes metal, it does not usually

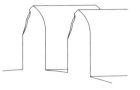

Fig 3/6 Overhanging metal indicates excessive pressure

produce a burr or overhanging edge.

In the USA the pallets are called verges, which is confusing since in Britain the verge escapement is something quite different, as described in Chapter 2.

The anchor escapement is often poorly made in the first place, even more often 're-paired' by bending the pallets down to engage the escapewheel more deeply. Nevertheless it contrives to keep operating until eventually wear makes it fail. It does, in fact suffer more wearing of the working faces than the deadbeat escapement, because of the recoil.

Pits resulting from the impact of the escapewheel on the impulse face will cause an escapement to misbehave. In most cases, by the time that these impact pits are as deep as this the grooves before and after the pits (ie wear produced by recoil and impulse) will cause enough problems to force the clockmaker to restore the pallets. Pitting without bad grooves

British		**German or Austrian**	
30-hour longcase or wall clock	6-8lb	8-day Vienna regulator	
8-day longcase, wall clock or hooded		going train	1-3lb
clock	6-10lb	chiming train	2-5lb
chiming or musical longcase clock,		**German or American**	
chime train	12-16lb	20th century longcase	6-10lb
tavern clock with 24-28in dial	8-12lb		
		Austrian	
British, Dutch or German,		month Vienna regulator	4-10lb
pre-20th century			
8-day longcase clock with strike	8-10lb	**American**	
month longcase clock	12-20lb	30-hour shelf clock	2-3lb
		8-day shelf clock	6-8lb
German			
30-hour cuckoo clock	½-2lb	**French**	
8-day cuckoo clock	3-6lb	8-day Comtoise	6-10lb

Table 3/1 Typical driving weights found on different types of clock

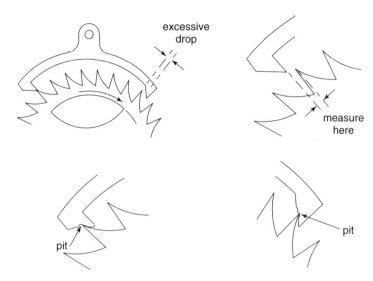

is almost certainly the result of using pallets that have been case hardened.

Case hardening must either be done properly or not at all. Merely dipping a piece of steel into a case hardening compound while red hot, soaking it for five or ten minutes at red heat, and then quenching, is useless for the service that escapement pallets have to perform. A hard surface will be produced, but it will be only 0.005-0.010in (0.12-0.25mm) thick. By the time that this has been polished to a dead smooth impulse surface, there will be very little hard surface left. It will only take a few years' wear to cut right through at the point of first contact.

The pit then grows rapidly in the soft material while the grooves before and after the pit are still borne on the hard surface. The edges of the case hardening, where the pit has exposed them, makes an excellent cutting edge to cut away the tips of the escapewheel teeth. Proper case hardening takes a matter of hours in a properly constituted environment and it is really an industrial process.

Deep grooves in pallet impulse faces increase the amount of drop, round off the drop-off point increasing the drop again and reduce the arc of the pendulum for a given weight or spring. The effect is obvious, the escapewheel can be seen to move a great deal between drop-off and impulse (**Fig 3/7**) and

the clock usually stops.

Less obvious is the effect of ageing on an old and slender suspension support. This is the bar that juts out from the backcock, into which the suspension spring (or its brass block) is fitted and pinned. Clockmakers often made these long with different points of suspension so that the customer was given a choice of positions to suspend the pendulum. Floors were frequently nowhere near level and this allowed the owner to position the pendulum where it would not foul the back of the clock case if it leaned forward or back.

Over the years the support for the pendulum is weakened by the growth of microscopic cracks within the casting and it may very well droop a tiny amount, and move as the pendulum swings. This will cause the escapement to misbehave in the same manner as if it was badly grooved. If a clock is temperamental and yet the pivots are not gummed up and the pallets show little or no wear, take a very close look at the back cock and its suspension points.

The cure for pivot and pivot hole wear is to file and polish the pivot and bush the pivot hole. Resurfacing of the backcock mounting face, or re-tapping of the screw holes is done using a file and hand taps. Any more serious faults of the backcock should be regarded as rebuilding or making anew.

2 Making New & Replacement Pallets

It will help to understand the process of making both solid and bent-strip pallets if the geometry of the anchor escapement is described first as it applies to both types. Methods of manufacture are very obviously different, but the geometry is precisely the same.

Fig 3/8 shows an escapewheel and typical British, French or German solid pallets. The crossing out (the spokes) is not shown because it is necessary to show a circle on the face of the wheel. This circle is concentric with the wheel centre and is about three quarters of its diameter (to be precise 0.707 times its diameter). In most old clocks this circle lies close to the inside rim of the wheel.

The Impulse Faces

In order to produce nearly equal impulses at entrance and exit, the angle of impulse should be the same, and the effective length of the pallet arms too. It is however, impossible to have exactly the same impulse on each pallet of the anchor escapement for two reasons:
• As the incoming wheel tooth slides across the entrance impulse face the length of the lever arm gets shorter, whereas as it slides across the exit impulse face it gets longer.
• As the wheel tooth slides across the entrance impulse face, the angle that its tangent makes with that face (the impulse angle[1]) remains much the same, but on the exit side this angle declines by about 9 degrees.
Fortunately, centuries of anchor escapements have shown that this is not too important.

The system that follows will handle:
• any distance between the pallet and escapewheel arbors that is normal for clocks
• any diameter of wheel and any span (the distance in tooth pitches from one pallet tooth

to the other) down to four and a half pitches on a thirty-tooth wheel
• any number of teeth.
The traditional methods, given in books such as those in footnote 1, are usually limited to 'square' escapements with thirty teeth.

The span could be given in angular degrees, but it is preferrable to state it like this since the span must be in terms of the pitches anyway, and an angle would frequently work out as a decimal fraction. Most clockmakers prefer not to use such inconvenient angular measurements.

Bearing in mind the inherent errors of the anchor escapement (relating to the differences between entry and exit pallets), and keeping within the limits of span that are common, it is sufficient make use of a simple piece of geometry to constuct the impulse faces. This is the fact that all tangents to an inner circle cross the outside diameter of the wheel in a similar

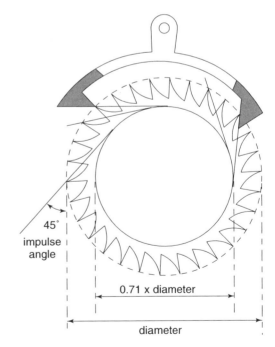

Fig 3/8 An impulse angle of 45° is produced by a tangent from a tooth tip to a circle approximately three-quarters of the escapewheel diameter. This is true for any *position on the escapewheel*

---

1   Note that the impulse angle as defined here is quite different to the term used in older books such as *Britten's Watch & Clock Maker's Handbook, Dictionary and Guide* and *Clock and Watch Escapements* by W. J. Gazeley, where it is used for the arc of the pendulum during impulsing.

fashion, making the same angle to each tooth tip that they touch. **Fig 3/8** explains this more readily.

An inner circle of 0.707 times the diameter of the escapewheel gives 45 degrees between the impulse planes and the tangents. This is the angle customarily used in anchor escapements, as it is neither too steep for the wheel teeth to ride up the pallet surface without transferring enough impulse, nor so shallow that they skip through easily. If the angle is much less than 45 degrees there is a greater tendancy for the tooth tips to contact the pallets 'head-on' with risk of damage to the teeth and greater friction. If the angle is less then there will be excessive friction during recoil. Hence an impulse angle of 45 degrees is the best compromise.

Span of the Pallets

In most cases where a replacement anchor has to be made, the wheel remains, so its diameter is already determined and unless the original pallets are lost, there is a clear idea of what the span of the pallets should be. If the pallets *are* lost then common practice must be taken as a guide. In longcase and bracket clocks this is about one quarter of the circle. French mantel clocks vary from about a quarter of the escapewheel for heavy pendulum bobs, to as little as two and a half teeth for little boudoir clocks, with short, light pendulums and silk suspensions. American clocks with bent strip pallets vary between a quarter and a fifth of the circle generally. German bent-strip pallets range from a quarter to a tenth, while Beha's solid anchor spanned one and a half teeth. The variety is great, so try to study a similar clock.

Anchor pallets with a short span swing through a greater angle than those with a wide span (all other things being equal). If the case of a clock does not allow a wide swing, then the span is clearly nearer to a quarter of the escapewheel circle than a tenth — the latter would produce too wide a swing.

Marking Out a 'Square' Anchor

Once all the elements of the escapement have

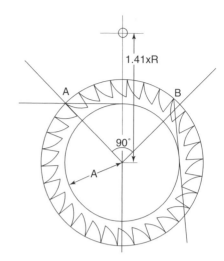

Fig 3/9 The impulse and drop-off faces for a 'square' anchor escapement

been established (centre distance, wheel diameter, span and impulse angle), the impulse faces and the drop-off faces of the pallets are defined by two sets of lines.

Fig 3/9 shows a thirty-tooth escapewheel with a vertical centre line that passes the top tooth one quarter of a pitch to the left. The drop-off faces are radial lines, one is set on the tip of the entry wheel tooth, the other is set exactly midway between two teeth on the exit side. The span between them is seven and a half pitches. The impulse faces are both tangents drawn from the teeth marked A and B to the inner circle.

In **Fig 3/10** the pallets are drawn as triangles by filling in the space between the impulse and the drop-off faces — the entry pallet is on the tip of the tooth. On the exit side the impulse face has just been contacted by a wheel tooth (there are no clearances shown). Once the mechanical details that link these two triangles has been drawn, the escapement is completely defined.

It can be seen that the impulse and drop-off faces were arrived at without any reference to the centre distance or the centre line. They were drawn in because they were a part of the existing escapement and the centre line was positioned to the left of the top tooth because

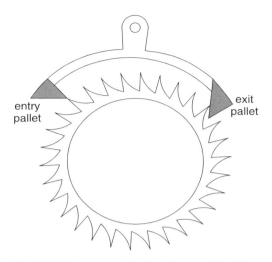

Fig 3/10 The entry and exit pallets are defined by the lines drawn in Fig 3/9

experience has shown that it would give a better balance to the pallets.

However, the impulse and drop-off faces could have been drawn and then the centre line moved until the length of the arms was balanced, and the finished pallets pleasing to the eye. Naturally this can only be done if the pallet arbor hole is drilled after the form of the pallet nibs has been determined.

The entrance pallet is placed on the tip of a tooth, because this means that the exit tooth will be fully sunk into the escapewheel, and the 45 degree impulse angle is set at that position. Remember that on the exit side this angle alters as the pallet swings, getting shallower as the tooth slides along the exit impulse face. On the other hand, if the escapement is set out when the exit pallet is on the top of a tooth, this angle of 45 degrees will occur at the end of the impulse, so that when the tooth first strikes it, the angle will be steeper. It is preferable to have the operating angle of the exit pallet ranging from 45 to about 36 degrees, rather than from 54 down to 45 degrees. This is only a personal preference and there are arguments for the other arrangement, but I do not want to litter this chapter with too many theoretical discussions.

It should be make clear that 45 degrees is

not a magic number, a variation of a few degrees either way is of no great importance unless the arc of the pendulum must be a precise angle. (In any event the actual arc of the pendulum is also determined by the weight or spring power available above that actually required to allow the pallets to escape.) Consequently using a circle that is nearer three-quarters of the outside diameter of the wheel instead of 0.707 will make little difference. The rim of the crossings circle is almost always useful for this tangent circle.

Making Anchor Pallets

The preceding section has been simply a description with drawings to develop the geometry for the pallets, but it has been assumed that the description applies to a drawing that would be used to mark out the pallets.

Such a method with the pallets drawn carefully on stiff paper or thin card and then glued to a carbon-steel blank is often used to make anchor pallets. The author used the same method himself some years ago. However, after making many more anchors, the conclusion was reached that the clockmakers of previous centuries made very little use of card — if any at all. Consequently the method that follows can be carried out in a workshop with dust and filings on the bench, an oily vice and not a clean piece of paper in sight.

Find a piece of scrap metal sheet that is large enough to have the centres of both the pallet and escapewheel arbors marked through from the existing clock plates (**Fig 3/11**). In the case of a new clock, the centres are simply placed there by measurement of course. Drill holes on these centres so that the arbors of the pallet and the escapewheel can pass through and allow the wheel and the metal for the pallet to lie flat on the scrap sheet (**Fig 3/12**). Because of the interference of the collet it may be necessary to place the wheel on the plate so that it appears to be going backwards,[2] this will not matter, but it does reverse the drawings for making the pallets.

If the inside rim of the wheel is close to being three-quarters of the outside diameter,

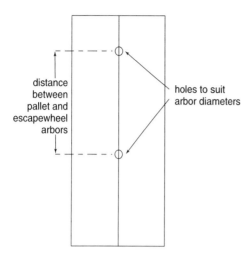

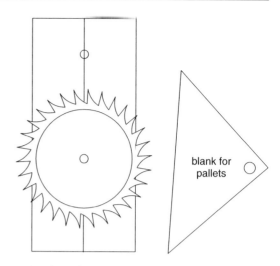

Fig 3/11 Drill two holes the exact distance apart of the escapewheel and pallet arbors

Fig 3/12 The escapewheel must lie flat on the plate and the pallet blank is drilled to take the arbor

this may be used to define the tangents for producing the impulse faces. Escapewheels usually have rim diameters that will serve as tangent circles, but if this is not the case, spin the wheel in the lathe and scribe a circle of three-quarters the outside diameter. If for any reason this is impossible make a brass washer of this diameter that fits on the arbor and lies flat on the wheel.

The span of these pallets are taken as seven and a half tooth spaces. The original span may not always be clear, because the damaged pallet may have been bent, filed or hammered,[3] but the escapement will work well whether it is six, seven or eight spaces and a half. It is always ' — and a half. The only effect will be a change in the arc of swing of the pendulum. Mark the acting teeth (A & B)with a felt-tip pen (**Fig 3/13i**).

Drill the arbor hole in a piece of hardenable steel (high-carbon steel, gauge plate, or flat ground stock) in the soft condition, put the

arbor in position and assemble the wheel, steel and scrap sheet with the wheel lying flat on the steel.

Use a pencil to sketch in the drop-off faces and the impulse faces (**Fig 3/13ii**). The impulse faces are drawn as tangents to the inner circle and are struck from the tips of the acting teeth. The drop-off faces are drawn radially, the entry being on the tip of a tooth and the exit midway between two teeth. This defines the two triangles mentioned earlier.

Now decide whether these triangles look balanced about the pallet arbor centre, if they do not, simply rotate the wheel slightly and make another judgement. (**Fig 3/13iii**). As soon as the anchor looks nicely balanced (and this is largely a cosmetic exercise), scribe round the outside of the steel to locate it on the scrap sheet beneath, and make marks on the same sheet against two of the escapewheel teeth, to locate that as well.

Coat the piece of steel with marking-out

---

2   Apart from when a replacement escapement is being made for a three-wheel thirty-hour clock, where the direction of rotation of the escapewheel is in the opposite direction to that in an eight-day clock.

3   A common reason for having to make new pallets is that a previous 'restorer' has swapped

the old worn pallets for something from his scrap box. Not surprisingly, these rarely work in a satisfactory manner and are best replaced by new ones to the correct principles. At least there is no ethical dilemma in retaining an unoriginal component.

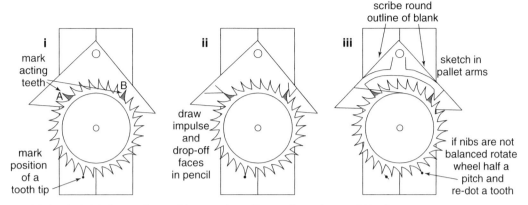

Fig 3/13 The initial stages in marking out the pallets on the carbon-steel blank

blue or a marker pen and then use a steel scriber to mark the pallets more precisely. (A sharp sewing needle held in a pin-chuck makes a very fine scriber.) With the wheel and the blank marked so that they can readily be kept in the same relationship to each other and the sheet beneath, use a short straight edge to scribe the four faces (two impulse and two drop-off) of the pallets onto the steel blank (**Figs 3/14i** and **ii**).

Remove the steel blank from the set-up and saw out the waste metal (**Fig 3/14iii** and **iv**), paying attention to the position of the four faces rather than worrying about the curves in the body of the piece — these can be attended to later. File almost up to the marks on the impulse faces and then replace the blank in the set-up, with the wheel flat on top of it

(**Fig 3/15i**). The length of the drop-off and impulse faces ought to be long enough for the tips to touch the lower curve or the bottom of the escapewheel tooth without the body of the pallets touching the tops of other teeth.

Check that when the entry tooth is just touching the tip of impulse and drop-off faces, the exit tooth is touching the still visible mark of the matching impulse face. This is simple insurance against an error of judgement, do not forget that the marks that locate the wheel and steel blank must still register as they did when you began. Rotate the steel and the wheel as if they were operating in a clock, and check that when the tip of the exit tooth is on the angle made by the impulse and drop-off faces that the entry wheel tooth is touching

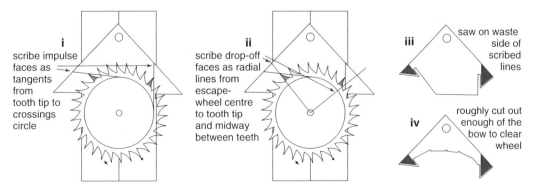

Fig 3/14 Marking accurately and roughing out the pallet blank

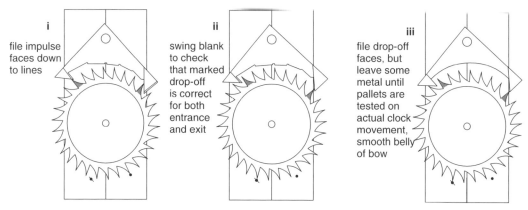

i file impulse faces down to lines

ii swing blank to check that marked drop-off is correct for both entrance and exit

iii file drop-off faces, but leave some metal until pallets are tested on actual clock movement, smooth belly of bow

Fig 3/15 Forming the impulse and drop-off faces

the marked line of the impulse face (**Fig 3/15ii**).

If an error shows up simply mark a new impulse line touching the tip of the tooth that shows the mistake. Once satisfied that there are no gross errors, file down to both the *impulse* faces as marked. Replace in the set-up.

Operate the wheel against the embryo pallets and check that when the impulsing tooth reaches its drop-off point, the other drop-off point is midway between two teeth. You will need to lift the wheel up so that the pallets can be turned and the other condition checked. If either of the drop-off points appears to be out, mark a corrected position for it, but check the pallets again first on both entry and exit conditions.

File down just *short* of the *drop-off* face marks and hollow out the belly of the pallets to produce an approximation of the final form (**Fig 3/15iii**). In practice the drop-off faces automatically come half way between two teeth when the drops are a minimum. If the drop-off faces are not halfway between two teeth then the drops will be found to be excessive.

The escapement will not work yet — it has no clearance. Polish the impulse faces on an emery board using increasingly fine emery paper. The paper does not need to be fastened to the board, simply laid on and held in place with one hand. It is simpler to move the work over the emery than the other way round, and

the surface resulting will stand more chance of being flat and unfaceted. Make sure that the polishing lines follow the same direction that the wheel teeth will rub (**Fig 3/16**), otherwise the impulse faces will act as a microscopic file and over the decades they will abrade the wheel tips.

In all probability polishing the impulse faces will have brought the escapement to the state where it will almost operate. It is now time to put the wheel and anchor into the actual clock movement for checking, instead of the temporary set-up that has been used until now, as the clock arbors may not be parallel.

File both drop-off faces back until, when the tip of one wheel tooth is just dropping-off its pallet, the other has a space the thickness of a sheet of paper between it and the impulse face (**Fig 3/17**). Both entry and exit conditions should give the same result. Now stone the edge of the pallets to show a line as thick as a hair, and then round it off into a smooth radius. It should now be found that the escapement works easily without any hang-ups. Any sticking will require you to examine

Fig 3/16 Polish the impulse faces along the direction of travel of the escapewheel teeth

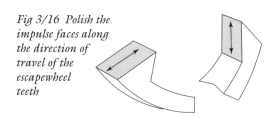

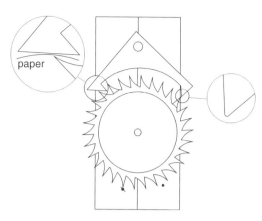

Fig 3/17 Smooth the edges of the pallets; when at drop-off the other pallet should have a clearance of about the thickness of a sheet of paper from the impulse face

the troublesome point and decide which drop-off face to remove a small amount of metal from.

Avoid *altering the impulse faces* and, before removing metal from the drop-off faces, imagine the wheel tooth in the position that will result from filing them. Consider exit and entry positions before taking any action. If an attempt is made at this stage to file both the impulse *and* drop-off faces, a situation can quickly develop where too much is removed and the drops are too large. It is unlikely that the escapement will be ruined at this point, but an anchor may be produced that has much more drop on one beat than on the other. This will be heard when the clock is working, as it will give a loud tick and a soft tick alternately.

Once the escapement works smoothly, take it out of the clock and finish the shape of the body. It can then be hardened and finally polished with 1000 grit emery paper (sometimes called flour paper). Hardening is a matter of heating the triangular nibs in a gas flame until they are a bright red and the body is still black, and then cooling rapidly in oil. It is not necessary to temper the steel, but stress relieving at 150°C is a useful precaution against later cracking. A domestic oven will manage this temperature quite readily.

Mount the pallets directly onto the arbor and lock in position using soft solder or an cyano-acrylate adhesive such as Loctite. Both methods allow a ready option for later removal, but the adhesive allows positioning of the pallets over the escapewheel in the assembled clock without burning your fingers or heating other parts of the clock — a very handy facility. Though makers of longcase clocks usually, but not always, fitted the anchor to its arbor with a collet, this is not really necessary.

The length of time taken to make solid anchors (of longcase size) from high-carbon steel plate, ready for hardening and finishing, is less than two hours. Not the first time that you do it of course — but certainly the third or fourth time. The point of the method shown here is that all the work takes place in a way that relates directly to the situation in the clock, and it can be tested at every stage, quickly and repeatedly. It avoids the need to measure angles closely or adopt difficult marking-out techniques.

Note: the methods described here so far are, for want of a better word, approximations — they work well in most circumstances, but if the escapement is unusual in its proportions or if there are good reasons for establishing a precisely stated pendulum swing, a more accurate geometry must be employed. More accurate manufacture requires precise measurement of angles whether by protractor or by co-ordinates. This is discussed in Section 6 'The Anchor Escapement — Faults & Comments'.

The Shape of British Pallets

Quite apart from the different body shapes that are found with anchor escapements there are a number of difference in the form of the impulse and drop-off surfaces.

Curved impulse faces are seen quite frequently (**Fig 3/18**). The depth of curvature (the radius to be pedantic) varies from a slight curve to quite a deep one. There is no reason given for shallow curves, but one reason (there is another, see pages 69-71) that is often given for a deep curve is to preserve the tooth tip if

Making Anchor Pallets for a Recoil Escapement — Summary

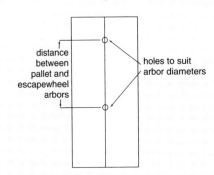

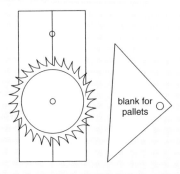

1 Drill two holes in a metal sheet to take the pallet and escapewheel arbors at the centre-centre distance apart.

2 Prepare a blank of high-carbon steel (eg gauge plate) and drill a hole for the arbor. If necessary use a spacing washer so that the wheel lies flat on the blank.

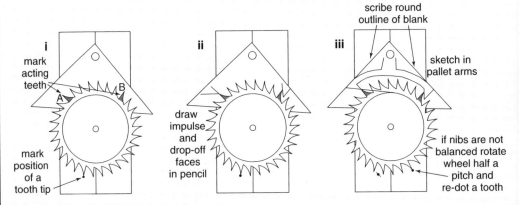

3 Mark the acting teeth A and B (for a square escapement B is seven teeth to the right of A). Centre punch the back plate to mark a tooth tip.

4 Pencil in the impulse and drop-off faces.

5 Sketch in the pallet arms, but if the anchor does not look balanced rotate the wheel half a pitch, redraw and re-dot another tooth. Scribe round the pallet blank to locate it.

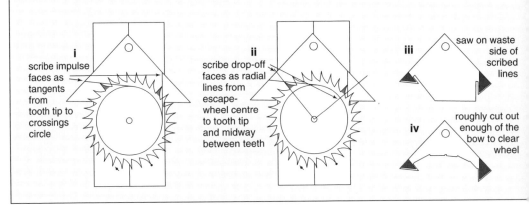

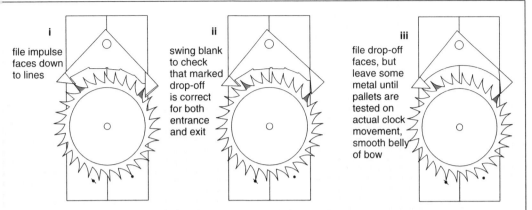

i
file impulse faces down to lines

ii
swing blank to check that marked drop-off is correct for both entrance and exit

iii
file drop-off faces, but leave some metal until pallets are tested on actual clock movement, smooth belly of bow

6 Accurately scribe the impulse faces as tangents from the tips of teeth A and B to the crossings circle (its diameter being about 0.75 that of the escapewheel). If necessary turn a washer to this size (or more accurately 0.71 of the escapewheel diameter).

7 Scribe the drop-off faces as radial lines from the tip of tooth A and mid-way between tooth B and its neighbour.

8 Saw down the waste side of the scribed lines and roughly cut out the bow.

9 Replace with the blank now on top of the wheel. Rotate the blank and wheel to check that the lines are correct. File down to the marked impulse faces.

10 Check again that the drop-off lines are correct. File the drop-off faces, but do not remove all the waste metal until the pallets have been tested in the clock movement.

11 Polish the impulse faces with increasingly fine grades of emery paper, polishing only in the direction that the escapewheel teeth move. In subsequent operations **do not remove any more metal from the impulse faces**

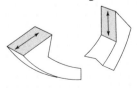

12 Assemble in the actual movement and remove small amounts from the drop-off face until, at the drop-off of each pallet, the clearance between the other pallet and the tooth tip is only the thickness of a piece of paper.

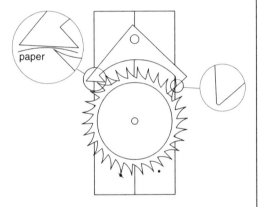

paper

13 Smooth the nib edges to the thickness of a hair. File the bow to the desired shape.

14 Harden the nibs. Do not temper, but stress relieve at 150°C. Polish with 1000 grade emery paper and fix the anchor on its arbor.

the pendulum is swung too robustly. The theory is that the pallet does not crush down onto the tooth tip, but presses firmly onto the curved side of it — the curve of the pallet is

Fig 3/18 British longcase pallets often have curved impulse faces. In this diagram the pallets are so deeply bitten that the exit pallet almost fills the tooth space

Fig 3/19 Flat impulse faces appear to crush the tooth tip slightly

Fig 3/20 A small rake of about 1-2° to the drop-off face avoids the chance of crushing the tooth tip if the pendulum is swung too vigorously

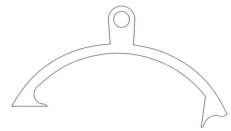

Fig 3/21 Longcase pallets often have a rounded undercut that makes it easy to adjust the drop-off when finishing the pallets and also provides rake to the drop-off face

supposed to match that of the escapewheel tooth.

In the author's opinion this incorrect. In **Fig 3/19** the flat or straight pallets appear to be about to crush down slightly on the tooth tip, but in fact the effect is very slight (**Fig 3/20**). If the drop-off face is raked back slightly, or the over-all length of the impulse face is slightly less than the pitch of the wheel teeth, there is no damaging of the the tip of the teeth.

Practice bears this out. A large proportion of the old clocks that come in for repair have straight pallets and there is no apparent tendency for these to damage the escapewheel to a greater extent than those with curved pallets. Damage to escapewheel teeth is almost always attributable to the wheel slipping under the pallets because of wear or the back cock being removed or slackened while the train is still powered by its weight or spring.

As an aid to adjustment when making the pallets many clockmakers formed the drop-off face as **Fig 3/21**. As can be seen the radial surface has been reduced in length by filing a radius into it. As a result very little metal needs to be removed with a stone when the pallets are hard and the movement still hesitates slightly. It is a practical and an attractive looking solution.

An Alternative 'Square Anchor'

This does not refer to the traditional British square anchor where the distance between the pallet and escapewheel centres is 1.414 times the wheel radius, but one that can be made using an engineer's square.

It is a very simple escapement to make and for the first-time clockmaker it is well worthwhile looking at. The great advantage of the escapement is that it can have its impulse faces made with the aid of a square and very little additional marking out. It is intended for a 32-tooth escapewheel (or any count divisible by four), but it cannot be used for a proper repair to the normal seconds pendulum clock with a 30-tooth wheel, since it makes 3,840 beats to the hour and requires the pendulum to be shortened by about five inches. However it *is* very convenient for making a new clock or building one from the contents of a dealer's scrap box. It could be used for a thirty-hour clock, or indeed any other clock that does not have a seconds hand.

Fig 3/22 shows a blank of flat ground stock, (a bright-finished high-carbon steel)

with a 90 degree cut-out. The position of the corner (B) needs to be marked and the vertical edge needs to be extended upwards by a small distance to allow for the recoil on the exit pallet. This cut-out is filed and the edges polished to the degree that you expect of impulse faces. These faces are now finished — they will not be modified later. The final polishing with flour paper must be done (as noted earlier) by following the line that the wheel teeth will take along the impulse faces.

Lay the escapewheel on top of this cut-out so that the crossing circle just lies over the two filed sides, tooth A lies over the horizontal side and B aligns with the corner mark. Clamp the wheel and steel together and mark C with a centre punch dot (**Fig 3/23**).

In **Fig 3/24** the drop-off faces have been marked on the steel with a scriber. On the left or entry side this is a line that passes through the tip of the escapewheel tooth; on the right or exit side, it passes exactly midway between two teeth. A centre line has been drawn from the centre of the wheel to point C and the hole for the escape pallets is drawn on this line. The distance between this hole centre and that of the wheel is usually measured in terms of the wheel's outside radius (from wheel centre to the tip of the tooth). Here it is shown as $1\frac{1}{3}$ times the wheel radius (eg 31mm from centre to centre for a wheel of

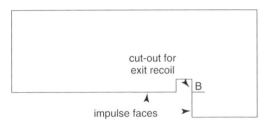

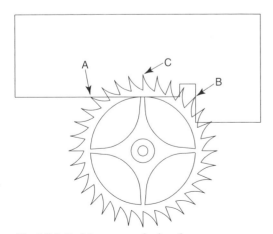

Fig 3/22 Blank for an easy-to-make anchor

Fig 3/23 Position escapewheel as shown

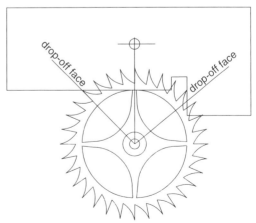

Fig 3/24 Drop-off faces marked

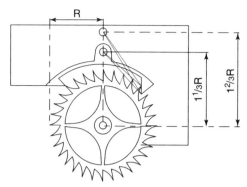

Fig 3/25 The recommended limits of the position of the anchor pivots

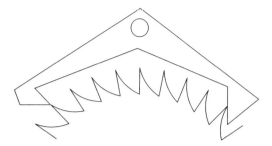

Fig 3/26 An alternative shape for the anchor body

23.3mm radius). This produces a swing of about six degrees of the escapement for a normal pendulum — three degrees either side of the vertical.

An alternative centre for this hole is shown in **Fig 3/25** where the centre distance is more than 1⅔ of the wheel radius, producing about four degrees swing of the pendulum— two degrees either side of the vertical. Though this distance is important it is not critical, however for good time keeping it is not advised to move outside these limits.

The logical developments of the lines drawn in **Fig 3/24** provide the working surfaces of the pallet. The vertical impulse face on the right has been extended upwards.

The actual shape of the body is somewhat arbitrary, arcs are drawn to leave more or less identical masses at either end of the anchor. It is a pleasing shape, but the only necessities are that the body of the pallets cannot crunch down on top of the wheel and that the impulse faces are long enough to ensure that the wheel tooth does not run off during recoil. If the impulse face is twice as long as the distance between the point of first contact and the drop-off, running off will be avoided. **Fig 3/26** shows another shape for the body, the working parts are precisely the same however.

Replaceable Anchor Pallets

Only one pair of faces of the anchor wears — the impulse faces — so it is quite possible to

design a pallet body that accepts inserted wearing surfaces. The one shown in **Fig 3/27** is taken from a mid-nineteenth-century eight-day longcase clock by Conway of Reigate.

It is easily made but no easier than a totally solid anchor, the main advantage is simply to make a future clock repairer's work that much

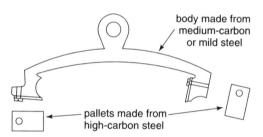

Fig 3/27 Replaceable anchor pallets

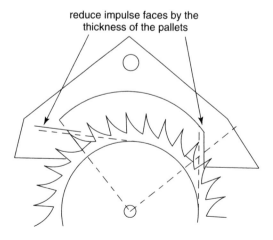

Fig 3/28 Marking out the steel blank when making replaceable pallets

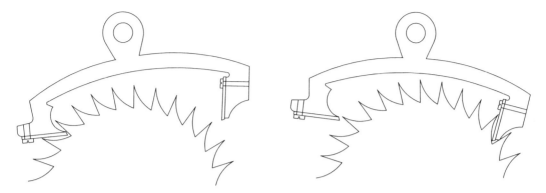

Fig 3/29 The screw heads must be positioned so that they do not touch the teeth even when fully bitten into the escapewheel

simpler. However if the production of a number of clock movements with the same escapement is envisaged, this is a very useful device. The bodies can be made in batches and the impulse faces can be made from varying thicknesses of steel to accommodate any errors in production.

Set the pallet out in the same manner as before (**Fig 3/28**), but allow plenty of metal for drilling and tapping holes for the fastening screws. Clearly the thickness of metal that is to be used for the removable impulse faces

has to decided on and allowed for when making the body.

When placing the screws the diameter of their heads must be taken into account. The drilled and tapped holes must be placed far enough from the tips of the pallets to ensure that the heads do not touch the wheel teeth if the pallet is fully bitten when the pendulum is swung hard over (**Fig 3/29**). If it is not thought out well the anchor body will be much bulkier than the original nineteenth-century pattern shown here.

3 Variants of the Anchor Escapement

The various designs of anchor that have been dealt with so far are the ones in most common use. Despite variations in span, centre distance between pallet and escapewheel arbors, or the means of producing the impulse and drop-off faces, the geometry remains the same. They may all be built using the simple system (shown above), of placing radial drop-off faces and developing tangents to an inner circle for the impulse faces.

Neither the shape of the pallet body, nor its span (down to about one tenth of the wheel circumference), will affect the method of marking and making new pallets described in the preceding paragraphs. However, the extreme case of spans of one tenth of the escapewheel circumference or less, requires a different approach, because the errors that arise

from this method of marking become too large to be acceptable in a practical escapement. This is dealt with in detail on pages 92-94. Apart from this special case there are other variants — some that are rarely encountered, while others are quite commonly found on mass-produced clocks.

Berthoud's Half-Deadbeat Escapement

In an attempt to develop an escapement that had true isochronism (the same time interval for a pendulum making different arcs of swing), a few clockmakers added to the basic geometry. Berthoud is the one most commonly quoted, but the anchor escapement has been modified in a similar way, though possibly not with such scientific intent, by other makers.

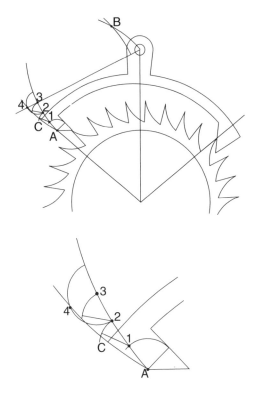

Setting out the entry pallet according to Rees.
The length of the impulse faces reduced so that the pallet width is a little less than half the wheel tooth pitch (to allow for drop). From the start of this reduced impulse face (A) draw an arc centred on the pallet centre. Set out a distance equal to the width of the reduced pallet along the circle three times from A to point 3. Drawn a line from the pallet centre through 3 and a further set out made to point 4. Draw an arc from A through the pallet centre and draw another arc of the same radius from 4. From where the two cross (B) draw the same radius to form the pallet surface from A to C.

Fig 3/30 The method of marking out the entry pallet of Berthoud's 'isochronous' half-deadbeat escapement

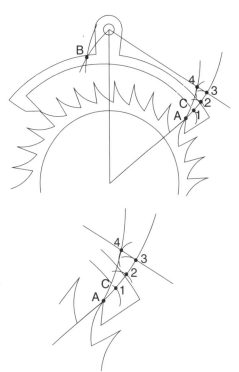

The exit pallet is formed in a similar fashion. The length of the impulse face is reduced so that the pallet width is a little less than half the wheel tooth pitch. An arc is struck from the start of the impulse face at A. The width of the pallet is struck off three times along the arc at 1, 2 and 3. A line is drawn from the pallet centre to 3 and the point 4 is produced by striking the width of the pallet again from 3. B is found by an arc from A passing through the pallet centre and a similar arc from 4. Finally an arc is struck from B to link A and C and form the extension of the impulse face.

Fig 3/31 Marking out the exit pallet of Berthoud's escapement

The recoil of an anchor escapement tends to limit the swing of the pendulum and consequently limit what is known as circular error.[4] This is the variation in time interval for a beat when the arc of swing alters. If a pendulum is isochronous, variations in the swing do not matter (this is the definition of isochronism). Berthoud's intention was to devise a curve on the impulse face that would first of all accept impulse, and then during the supplementary arc, brake the swing of the pendulum in a controlled manner. This is a compromise between the anchor with its recoil, and the deadbeat with no recoil and little restriction on the supplementary arc. It is often called a half-deadbeat. By experiment Berthoud produced a form of pallet (**Figs 3/30-31**) that appeared to meet his requirement and it has been claimed as an isochronous escapement, but this has been challenged.[5]

---

4   The recoil, in fact, gives the anchor escapement one advantage over the deadbeat escapement, in that the anchor is less sensitive to variations in driving force than the deadbeat.
    A. L. Rawlings *The Science of Clocks & Watches* says that if an anchor escapement was 'accurately made with well polished, jewelled pallets [to reduce recoil friction] its performance might be better than the Graham', though no-one seems to have done the comparison and published the results.

5   Saunier in his *Treatise on Modern Horology* (1861), p533, described Berthoud's experiments when he doubled the weight on a clock. With a deadbeat escapement the pendulum arc increased from 8° to 12° and the rate increased (as expected) by 5 seconds an hour. With a recoil escapement, doubling the weight only increased the arc from 8° to 10°, but, because his pendulum bob was rather light, the rate was (surprisingly) reduced by 9 seconds an hour. From this Berthoud deduced that an escapement with moderate recoil would give a rate unaffected by the driving force. Saunier remarks that these 'very positive conclusions … are disfigured by serious errors' and that the same effect would not have been achieved if the pendulum bob had been heavier. He also states (p543) that 'this escapement has rarely been employed'.

The teeth of the escapewheel should just fall onto the 'supplementary' face, just as in the true deadbeat escapement (see Chapter 4).

In the description of this escapement in *Rees's Clocks, Watches and Chronometers 1819-20*, the exit pallet has a slightly concave surface for the extension to the impulse face (**Fig 3/31**), hence it acts more like a dead face. The matter is academic really since there seems little point to using this design for anything but a replacement in an original Berthoud clock.

Pallets like Berthoud's, but with a steeper curve on the supplementary surface, are frequently referred to as 'half-deadbeat. The supplementary part of the impulse face is usually convex on both pallets, probably for ease of filing the curve, and is rather arbitary rather than being mathematically calculated. Presumably a template was made and used on both pallets, or even just checked by eye.

Tic-Tac (Half-Beat) Escapement

The true tic-tac escapement has a very short span of just two or three tooth pitches; note that it is a full, not a half, pitch. It is usually found on French drum clocks with short pendulums swinging through large arcs. This escapement is often made by turning and milling a bar of steel to production tolerances and cutting off slices for each set of pallets (**Fig 3/32**). One surface (the entry) of the pallet is part of a true cylinder and is 'dead', ie it accepts no impulse. Only the exit side is impulsed and this takes place over the full movement of one tooth pitch, hence the span of a whole numbers of pitches. It can often be repaired by soldering on a strip of spring steel in the same manner as in normal anchor pallets. The dead face does not wear as fast as the impulse because of the effects of recoil on the latter.

It is not really a practicable exercise to make new pallets of this type unless the clock is worth very much more than the usual example. The time involved in designing the pallets and then maintaining the machining tolerances is too great.

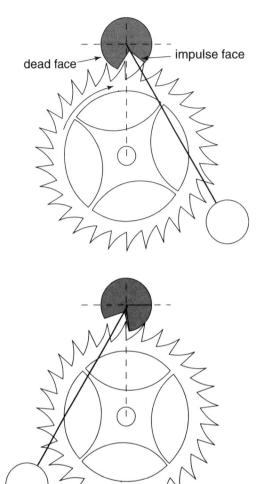

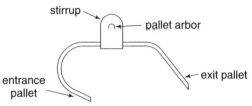

Fig 3/33 The American bent-strip anchor is, rather confusingly, known as a verge

ported on a short post. It is always referred to as a 'verge' — which can be confusing.

The whole system is designed for easy adjustment, removal and replacement. A soft brass wire protrudes from the body of the verge and forms the crutch, and the whole assembly is held in place by a simple bent piece of wire that presses against the outer end of the mounting post.

When a bent-strip verge is grooved badly enough to affect the operation of the escapement, it is worn out. There is no point in doing anything with it except to use it as a guide for providing a replacement. Unlike the German version it is rarely worth trying to make a replacement from raw material, simply find the closest match to the standard verges available and stone it down to suit the movement.

Fig 3/32 The tic-tac escapement is best designed on paper and then machined to size. The pendulum swing shown is 60°, but will decrease if the pallet centre is raised and the diameter of the pallet is increased

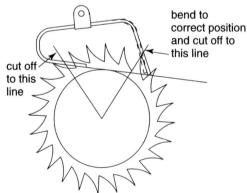

Fig 3/34 Fitting a replacement American verge. The impulse faces are formed by a tangent to the crossings circle. For the entrance pallet it is immaterial if the entance pallet is at the tip of the tooth or fully bitten (as shown here), but the angle of the exit pallet should be set when the entrance pallet is on a tooth tip

As only one side of the pallets is used for the impulse, this has given rise to the term in Britain of 'half-beat', which is sometimes applied to these escapements.

American Bent-Strip Anchors (Verges)

This pallet is formed from a strip of high-carbon steel strip that is bent to shape (as its name suggests), fitted with a stirrup (**Fig 3/33**) which has holes in it for pivoting and sup-

(**Fig 3/34**). It is often necessary to bend the strip as well to adjust the length of the exit and entry arms. Flat (ie unformed) replacements are also available.

The metal of these verges is hard as supplied and it needs to be softened (annealed) by heating to dull-red heat and then allowing the verge to cool off slowly above the hot gasses of the torch. 'Slowly' in this case means taking about two or three minutes and paying more attention to the dropping of the temperature from the visibly red state than the later stages of cooling. Once below the point where all hint of redness has disappeared steel is not greatly affected by the speed of cooling — at least in this context.

It may be necessary to accept a replacement that spans either more or fewer teeth than the original (see page 57 describing the geometry of anchor escapements first). This is acceptable. but bear in mind that doing so will alter the swing of the pendulum. However, this rarely causes any difficulty.

Note that the brass wire that forms the crutch is riveted in different places on the various verges, so check that it will be possible to bend the wire to engage the pendulum without fouling any other part of the clock.

An escapement problem on an American clock is not always one of wear. If the verge does not show definite grooving, test the depth of the pallets. American clocks often carry the verge on a swivelling cock that allows the clockmaker to set it deeper into the escapewheel or withdraw it slightly. There are problems associated with American movements fitted with a verge escapement that can be quite puzzling. These are usually due to the lightness of the pendulum bob and the form of the suspension — they are dealt with in Chapter 10 'Suspensions' and Chapter 11 'Pendulums'.

• **Ingraham Half Deadbeat**

This is also a bent-strip escapement (**Fig 3/35**), though not a common one, and the deadbeat discussed in Chapter 4 is more usual. It can easily be mistaken for a deadbeat (**Fig 3/36**), but there is a much smaller rake on the escapewheel teeth and the dead face is not a true arc centred on the pallet arbor. It has both recoil and deadbeat characteristics. When the American bent-strip deadbeat is made inaccurately it becomes a half deadbeat.

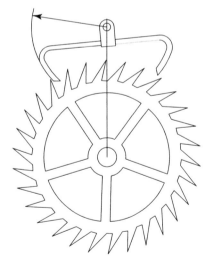

Fig 3/36 *The deadbeat bent-strip escapement. The teeth are raked forward more than the half deadbeat and the pallets are formed very close to a true circle struck from the pallet arbor. To reduce the amount of rake needed the distance between centres is often quite small*

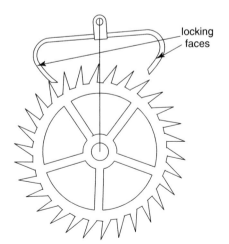

Fig 3/35 *The Ingraham half deadbeat escapement. The locking faces only approximate to arcs centred on the pallet arbor*

German Bent-Strip Anchors

The only difference between German and American bent-strip pallets is that the former is attached directly to an arbor, while the latter is slipped over the post on which it pivots. To confuse matters there are examples of manufacturers in both countries copying their competitors

Apart from some modern clocks, full replacement German bent-strip escapements are not available, because they are mounted directly on an arbor. If it is grooved, take it out of the movement with the intention of making a replacement; if it is not grooved but does not work, examine the arbor.

German arbors are either dovetailed to take the strip, or flatted to allow riveting of the strip to the arbor. In both cases there is a weakness at the middle of the arbor, which can allow it to bend and lift the pallet away from the wheel. In contrast to the American style of bent-strip pallets the German form is not easily substituted by a handyman or rogue dealer, so they can often be relied on to be original to the movement in which they are found.

The most frequent reason for an apparently unworn bent-strip anchor to refuse to work properly is that the weak arbor has bent. The pallets will have either lifted away from the wheel, or an overzealous repairer may have bent it too close. Examine the pallets closely and try to imagine the effect of moving them closer to, or further from, the wheel. If it seems likely to be a successful ploy, bend the arbor accordingly. If this is unsuccessful the bent strip must be made anew.

* Making a Black Forest Bent-Strip Pallet

The geometry of this escapement (**Fig 3/37**), despite appearances, is the same as that of a solid anchor. However instead of filing the impulse faces, the strip is bent so that its surface serves this purpose. As stated earlier the German pallets are either dovetailed into the arbor, or riveted. The dovetail type will be dealt with first.

Cut a strip of high-carbon steel sheet that is a little wider than the dovetail. Alternatively

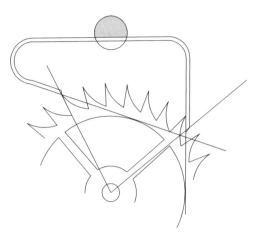

Fig 3/37 The geometry of the bent-strip pallets is the same as for a solid anchor. Drop-off is defined by radials to the tip of one tooth and to the midpoint of a tooth space. Impulse faces make tangents to the inner circle of the escapewheel rim

make use of a piece of old bandsaw blade and reduce its width by cutting off the teeth. In either case the metal should be about 0.030-0.040in (0.7-1.0mm) thick, though the thickness is not very important. It must be stiff enough to maintain its shape, but not so thick that it is impossible to bend. Estimate the total length needed and cut it off.

Make sure that you know which two teeth of the escapewheel are to be the acting teeth. In other words determine the span of the pallets. Two notches are cut, one on either side near the end that will be the exit pallet (**Fig**

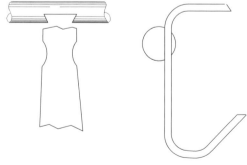

Fig 3/38 The Black Forest bent-strip pallet is held in a slot in the arbor. Two notches allow it to enter the dovetail

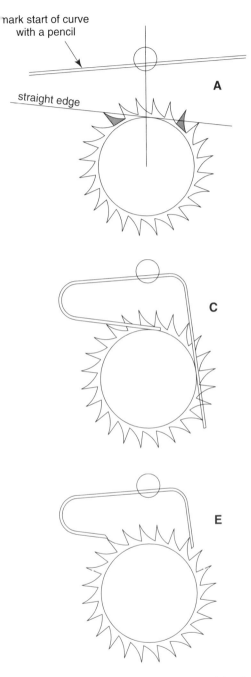

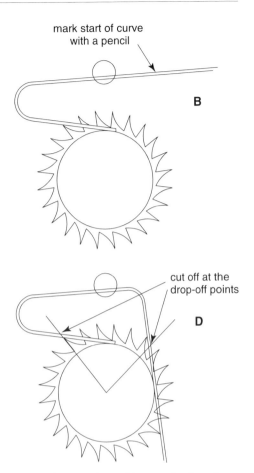

Fig 3/39 The stages in making a pair of new bent-strip pallets

will make the pallets jam fast in the dovetail at the midpoint.

Leave the strip in the dovetail, mount the arbor in the movement with the escapewheel, and using a straight edge sight a tangent from the inner rim of the wheel to the tip of the entry tooth (**Fig 3/39A**). The strip cannot be bent to form a sharp V, so use a pencil to mark the strip where an easy radius would allow the metal to make the tangent indicated by the straight edge (**Fig 3/39B**).

Do not be put off by the imprecise nature of the description, as the technique is to heat the strip to red heat and bend it until the right shape is obtained. Within reason the size of the radius does not matter.

3/38); either match this against the old pallets or make a good guess as to the position of the bend. These notches allow the pallets to be slid into the dovetail when the bend for both entry and exit have been made. Now file a taper towards the middle of the strip that

Heat the steel strip and make the bend for the entry. When the angle is about right let it cool, then remove the arbor from the movement and fit the strip into it again. If the clock has a backcock the next operation will be much simpler, if not try to hold the arbor as near to its proper position as possible.

Offer the bent strip up to the escapewheel, again holding the arbor on its centre distance, check that the bend has given you the tangent required — or nearly so. Mark the bend (about 90 degrees) for the exit pallet, to make a tangent to the inner rim again. Remove the strip, heat and bend it (**Fig 3/39C**). Offer it up and tweak it until you are satisfied that both arms of the pallet make tangents to the inner rim — the exit being made when the entry is considered as being on the top of a tooth. (The pallets are not yet cut to length, so this is a matter of some imagination.)

Mark the drop-off points (**Fig 3/39D**) but leave a ½₂in (0.8mm) or so extra. Cut off the excess and put the pallets into the movement. Check to see whether the angles of the bends are close to what is wanted, adjust them if necessary and then file back the drop-off points until the impulse faces just drop off with the required minimum drop. When this condition is reached they will automatically span exactly 'so many and a half' teeth (**Fig 3/39E**).

This is a process that is easier to teach at the bench than by writing about it, but it is simply a matter of making a good guess, offering the partly bent material up to the wheel and then tidying up the guess. After one or two have been made, the job takes around a quarter of an hour or less.

Rivetted pallets are made in much the same fashion, but because they do not need to enter a dovetail, they can be tried against the side of the wheel with little difficulty. When the angles are obtained, cut the length with at least twice as much spare as in the dovetailed version, remove the arbor from the movement and then drill and rivet the pallets to it. There is always a chance of the pallets

moving while drilling and riveting, which is the reason for the extra metal.

Once riveted, the angles should be tested again, altered if the riveting has not come exactly where it was intended, and then the drop-off points established with a file.

The bent-strip escapement should be hardened and tempered to a very pale amber. The dovetailed type can be heated all over, but the riveted one should be heated at the ends only as he metal must not be brittle in the vicinity of the riveting hole. Polish the impulse surface with emery paper down to 1000 grit, or finish with a fine Arkansas stone. Stone the edges of the cut-off point so that they have a very slight radius.

The Vienna Anchor Escapement

One other variation of the anchor is shown in **Figs 3/40-41**, where only the entry pallet operates like the normal recoil anchor escapement. The exit pallet is more like a simple projection against which the escapewheel presses, impelling it more directly, rather than as against an incline plane. It is found in late eighteenth-century picture-frame clocks — the type of clock that is mounted inside a frame rather like a wide sectioned picture frame, with the dial nestling in a backboard that is often covered in black velvet and decorated with gilt spandrels.

It is an easy escapement to make once the entry impulse angle is established. The exit impulse is shown in the diagram as a radial from the pallet arbor because it is simple to file it to this shape. The exit drop-off is the third face to be finished and then the other drop-off is trimmed until the escapement works and clearance is established. A rudimentary drawing is needed to begin with to ensure that the angle subtended between the drop-off point and the point of first contact on the exit impulse face from the arbor centre, is what is required. Lifting the centres gives a smaller swing, as may be expected. The entrance pallet is made so that it can be twisted to adjust the impulse angle during manufacture.

Fig 3/40 The Vienna anchor escapement as found in late-eighteenth century picture-frame clocks. In this example the pendulum swing is about 20°

Fig 3/41 Decreasing the pallet span by one tooth decreases the spendulum swing by about 11°

4 Repairing Anchor Pallets

When a solid pallet has worn (**Fig 3/42**) it can generally be brought back to effective operation by resurfacing it. This is simply a matter of attaching pieces of spring steel, by soft soldering, to the impulse faces. The same repair could, theoretically, be carried out on bent strip pallets, but in order to accept the new steel, the old pallets must be stoned or filed down, and bent strip pallets are not often thick enough to allow this. It is fairly safe to say that all bent strip pallets should be thrown away when worn — they are cheap enough to buy or easy to make replacements for anyway

— but keep an eye open for the exception to the rule.

Assessing the Repair
Make sure that there is no power on the train, (take the weights off, disconnect the spring barrel ratchet, or dismantle the whole of the train) and try the pallets against the escape-wheel. Rotate the wheel until the tip of one pallet is touching the tip of a wheel tooth, then without allowing the pallets to move, rotate the wheel until it rests against the other impulse face. Either estimate or measure the gap (the 'drop') between the raised pallet's drop-off point and the tip of the tooth that has just left it. Now reverse the test, placing the tip of the other pallet on the tip of a wheel tooth and repeating the exercise (**Fig 3/43**).

There are three things that should be noted:
• the drop (the space between impulse face and wheel tooth)
• whether it is the same in both tests
• is the span 'so many and a half teeth'?
The drop may be measured with feeler gauges

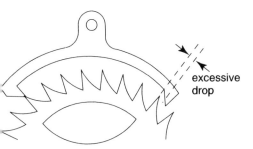

excessive drop

Fig 3/42 Excessive drop must be corrected

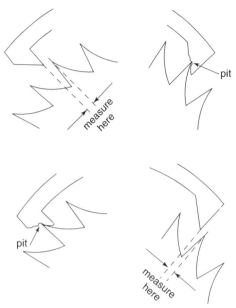

Fig 3/43 The drop caused by wear on the impulse face is best measured at the drop-off point of the other pallet

or an assortment of pieces of metal strip and a micrometer to test them with. Though an exact value for the drop is not necessary it is best to have a similar drop on both pallets. As

it is untidy workmanship to resurface the pallets with different thicknesses of steel, the measured drop should be the approximately same — or made the same.

The amount of drop that is normal is about one tenth of the distance between adjacent escapewheel teeth. If there is less than this and the escapement still clears easily on every tooth of the wheel, then there is a good, practical drop. Any more and the wastage of energy is greater than it should be — bear this in mind when finishing off the resurfaced pallets.

Refacing Worn Pallets

In order to make room for the steel strip that is to be soldered on (and possibly to make the drop even), the pallet must be filed or ground. A file is far more controllable than the grinders that are found in the majority of workshops, and if you decide to file the pallets, they must first be softened. Heat to bright red heat and then plunge into a tin of dry, powdered chalk to cool slowly. Talc or talcum powder makes a readily obtainable alternative, but have a lid ready for the tin, for the powder is so light that it will lift on the convection currents from the hot steel. If you do not want

Tinning & Soldering

Tinning is carried out best with an old fashioned iron, with a copper point of two or three ounces (30-80 grams) on a rod with a wooden handle. It is more manoeuvrable and it can be heated in a gas flame in a shorter time than an electric iron takes to reach solder melting temperature. The point should be cleaned with an old file, dipped in flux when hot and solder melted onto it. If the solder turns blue it is too hot. For most workshop soldering Frysol flux is very good, it is slightly acidic and so should be neutralised after the job is done, with a bicarbonate of soda solution .

Clean the faces that are to be soldered with emery paper and spread flux on both. Hold the component in a pair of old pliers (the heat will damage good ones) on a piece of heat-proof material (similar to asbestos but without its health hazards) and scrub away at the surface to be tinned with the solder-coated point of the iron. If the temperature of the iron is right a film of molten solder will spread over the metal. If there is any difficulty in achieving this apply a little more flux or heat up the soldering iron.

Larger parts are tinned by holding them in a vice, keeping the jaws as far as is practicable from the area to be tinned (they will draw heat away too rapidly if they are close) and use the soldering iron again.

The tinned areas are placed in contact and heated with the iron or a small gas flame to form a perfect soldered joint.

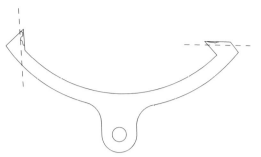

Fig 3/44 The impulse faces should be reduced equally, even if the pitting is more on one pallet than on the other. Do not file the drop-off faces

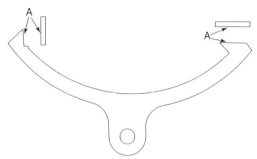

Fig 3/45 The spring steel facings are cut over-size and the four surfaces marked 'A' are tinned with solder

to bother with a chalk box, move the red-hot metal out of the flame over a period of about five minutes, keeping the metal above the flame so that it remains in the hot gasses. Alternatively a diamond-coated file or hone may be used on the pallets while they are still hard; these are available in various grades from coarse to very fine and are very useful for a variety of tasks in clockmaking.

File back both impulse surfaces (**Fig 3/44**) until all the wear is removed and the drop is approximately equal on the entry and the exit pallet. Enough metal must be filed off to accept the thickness of the steel strip *and* the thickness of solder that will hold it in place.

While doing this check that the angle of the impulse face is correct, do not simply assume that what you found on the pallets is correct, the angles may well have been altered by a previous, less skilled repairer, or an incorrect set of pallets substituted for the original ones (this is by no means unknown). To do this position one pallet tip on the tip of the wheel tooth and sight along the impulse face of the other. It should make a tangent to an imaginary circle almost equal to the inner rim of the wheel, ie the crossing-out circle. Test both pallets in this way and if there is a great deal of difference in the results for the two impulse faces go back to section 2 'Making Replacement Pallets' — it is more of a remaking job than simple resurfacing. In any case it is a good idea to re-read about the geometry of making a new escapement at this

point, since it will — or should — illuminate the present problems.

Old mainsprings are a useful source of steel for the new impulse surfaces, brown tempered ones being preferred over blue ones as they are harder. The exact thickness is not important, provided it somewhere about the same as the excess drop, as final adjustment is made by filing back the drop-off faces. The solder film will be about 0.005in thick.

Cut the spring steel to be larger than the impulse surfaces and then tin them and the filed impulse faces of the pallet with solder (**Fig 3/45**). The pallets are tinned while being held upright in a vice, but the jaws must be kept as far away from the pallet faces as possible to avoid drawing the heat away.

Rearrange the pallets in the vice so that one of the steel pieces can be placed on its impulse face without it falling off, and heat up the pallet until the heat transferred to the piece melts the solder and makes the joint. Flux will be necessary again to ensure that the solder flows freely, and it would be as well if a stick of solder is beaten so that its end is thin, before heating up the work. Just a touch more solder may then be added to the joint if needed — thin solder melts quicker and less messily than thick!

The joint is made when a bright fillet of solder shows around it, this will occur before the steel tempers to blue, but do not wave the gas flame over the thin steel facings or they will be over-tempered and turn silvery blue.

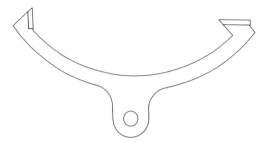

Fig 3/46 *After the slips have been soldered in place*
the drop-off faces are reduced in length to give
satisfactory operation with minimum working drop

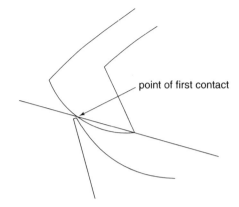

point of first contact

Fig 3/47 *When filing back a curved impulse face*
ensure that a line from the point of first contact
though the drop-off point is approximately a
tangent to the crossings circle

Repeat on the other pallet face. It is as well to solder the exit pallet first, otherwise the heat rising from soldering the exit pallet may undo an already soldered entry pallet.[6]

Fig 3/46 shows how the job should look when the slips are in place, note that the drop-off points overhang the original position.

The edges of the new facings can be filed with a mill file, or saw sharpening file, both of which are hard enough to cut spring steel. Try the escapement in the movement and test as described in the section on making a solid anchor (page 63).

Refacing Curved Impulse Faces
Many old British anchors have curved impulse faces in order to reduce the recoil and give a healthy swing to the pendulum, but it is almost certain that these are not Berthoud's carefully calculated impulse faces. Unless they are quite steep and showing a definite change in curvature at the point of first contact, they are not half-deadbeat pallets. The curve was simply achieved by eye and if it looks as though it is intended to match the curve of the escape-wheel teeth it may be repeated on the new steel slips, but this is usually a matter of choice.

Old main springs are naturally curved and part of a spring that matches the original pallet may be found. File the pallet back in a fash-

ion that ensures that a line taken through the point of first contact and the drop-off point make the required tangent with the inside rim as described earlier (**Fig 3/47**). This is a matter of judgement — just as was the original.

Bending Old Anchors
Many old books dealing with clock repair refer to bending a worn set of pallets so that the impulse faces can be dressed up and the escapement put into operation again. This approach very rarely works satisfactorily.

An examination of the drawings of the pallets will show that bending the pallet body will either bring the points of the pallets (the 'nibs') closer together, or further apart. Whichever of these is the result, the essential span of so many and a half teeth is destroyed, resulting in the drop on one pallet or the other being excessive, and in all probability the impulse angle is modified beyond the acceptable range. The only time when bending a solid anchor is useful is when there is sufficient metal in the piece to enable it to be treated as a blank.

This requires either that the anchor comes from a different escapement altogether, or that the span is altered by a complete tooth pitch. Either way the bent anchor must have metal to be removed on all four faces (impulse and drop-off), to reveal a properly proportioned

---

6   A simple and convenient jig for holding the pallets of longcase clocks while they are being refaced has been described by J. Robey in *Horological Journal* October 1997, pp338-9.

pair of pallets, and it does not happen very often. What does happen often is that the repairer discovers that the pallets in his hand have been bent by a previous repairer, the clock has never worked properly since, and now they will have to be replaced entirely.

Worn Pallets on French Clocks

The pallets on French movements of the type used in nineteenth-century marble clocks, may be adjusted by means of the eccentric bush that is fitted to the front-pallet pivot. (This bush is usually very tight and needs a closely fitting screwdriver in good condition to move it.) The pallets of some of these clocks, but not all, span a relatively small number of teeth, so the impulse faces are more nearly parallel than with a wider span. Hence, after removing the pits on the impulse faces the drop-off

points do not come together to any great extent and the correct drops may be achieved by lowering the pallet arbor by means of the eccentric bush.

Otherwise, adjust the entrance drop by means of the bush and stone back the entrance drop-off edge to give the required drop on the exit pallet. If necessary the pallets can be refaced as already described.

But before doing any of this it is worth attempting to shift the pallet so that the escape-wheel teeth fall on an unworn part of the faces. The pallets of these clocks are often fitted on a long tapered square, so knock off the pallet, reduce the square by the smallest fraction, and knock back on. Do not attempt to knock the pallet further along the taper without first reducing the square, for being glass-hard it is likely to split across the centre hole.

5 Making Escapewheels

The Shape of Escapewheel Teeth

The recoil escapewheel is generally of the form shown in **Fig 3/48** — it always looks to me as though it is rotating backwards.[7] The teeth are not raked and this results in a robust tooth tip and, in view of the increased friction during recoil, this is a distinct advantage. At the same time it must be admitted that several wheels have been seen that were raked and clearly made for deadbeat escapements, yet installed on longcase clocks without showing any great tendency to bend their tooth tips.

As pointed out in the section on the geometry of the anchor (page 57), the rim of the crossing-out lies on a circle that is about three-quarters of the outside diameter. This gives a stout rim, which is also a necessity in a wheel that has to deal with the loading of a recoil escapement.

The depth of the tooth, (and consequently the shape) is important both from the considerations of the strength of the rim and from the necessity of clearing the back of the tooth, (**Fig 3/49**). Generally the tooth shape is a radial line for the trailing face and a concave curve for the leading face. The effect of insufficient curve on the leading face is to cause the point of the pallet to contact the curve at some point of the recoil. This not only tends to cut into the curve, but decreases the radius

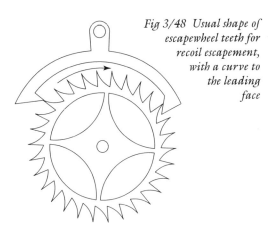

Fig 3/48 Usual shape of escapewheel teeth for recoil escapement, with a curve to the leading face

---

7 Country longcase clocks may even be found with the teeth the other way round, yet still operating satisfactorily. See, for instance, a thirty-hour longacse clock by Giles Coates of Chedworth, Gloucestershire, decribed by J. Robey in *Clocks* Vol 20, No 4 1997, pp41-4.

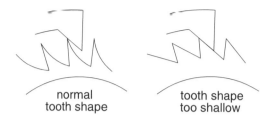

normal
tooth shape

tooth shape
too shallow

Fig 3/49 The face of the tooth must not rub on the pallet during recoil

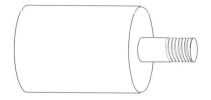

Fig 3/51 A re-useable madrel can be used to hold the escapewheel blank, provided that it is gripped in a collet or a lathe chuck that runs true

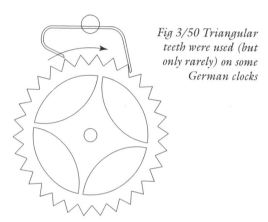

Fig 3/50 Triangular teeth were used (but only rarely) on some German clocks

at which the pressure between the pallet and wheel occurs. Frictional losses will vary from tooth to tooth and as wear progresses the time rate will suffer.

The usual shape is not the only one, for at least one German maker used a triangular-shaped tooth (**Fig 3/50**) with pallets that did not bite deeply into the wheel, but it is not common.

Mounting & Turning the Blank

Although it is possible to make an escapewheel by hand (and is described on pages 84-85) it will take a long time and it is unlikely to be as accurately pitched as a machine-made one. The use of a lathe for drilling, turning the blank and fitting the collet is a necessity however, unless you wish to emulate very early clockmaking techniques.

The type of metal used should be a half-hard free-cutting brass that produces chips when cut, not streams of swarf. If a 70/30 brass is used (even if hard rolled) it will not

machine well and there will be a tendency for the metal to stick to the tool and leave edges that are heavily burred. There are three main methods of mounting for machining and which is choosen will depend upon how frequently you make clock wheels of all descriptions and the accuracy of the available chuck.

• Re-Useable Mandrel

A mandrel (**Fig 3/51**) is a support for the workpiece that requires the blank to be drilled first. It is a bar of metal large enough to support the blank so that it does not vibrate during machining. A turned-down portion is screwed and provided with means of clamping the blank back against a turned face.

The device is intended for using more than once and consequently it must be possible to replace it in the chuck and have it run true, otherwise the blanks that are machined on it may be eccentric to the arbor they run on. If your chuck cannot be relied to hold concentrically and there is no other means of ensuring that the mandrel can be set up to run true whenever it is needed, then a one-off mandrel must be used.

• One-Off Mandrel

A bar of metal is placed in the chuck and faced to produce a true face and a register. The register is simply a short diameter that is turned to fit the bore of the pre-drilled blank, large enough to allow for drilling and tapping for a holding screw (**Fig 3/52**). This means that the bore of the wheel must be larger than when it is to be mounted on a re-usable mandrel, so that the drilling and tapping does not interfere with the register. It is not possible to accurately drill and tap for a holding screw and then locate the wheel absolutely concentric

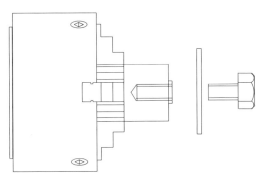

Fig 3/52 A mandrel intended for single use

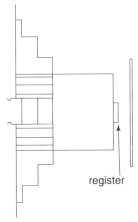

Fig 3/53 The 'wax chuck' with the blank held with shellac is only suitable for turning and marking the divisions of the teeth

register

on the screw, as this calls for precision turning beyond normal clockmaking tolerances.

• **The Wax Chuck**

This device is called a wax chuck because it is similar to a traditional method of holding parts for machining, though other types of adhesive can be used. It consists of a piece of brass held accurately in a three-jaw chuck, a flat face machined on it and the blank then attached to it (**Fig 3/53**). If the chuck is to be used only for turning and dividing, the blank can be held securely by using shellac. If the blank is to have the teeth cut on a machine this will

not be secure enough, and the blank must be held in position with soft solder and located accurately by turning a register.

Locating or centring a wax-held blank is not really a fussy job because the centre hole and the outside diameter will be machined after the wax has set. If a register is used and the blank is soft soldered to the so-called 'wax' chuck, the machine must be capable of accepting a re-chucking of the brass bar (**Fig 3/54**), because it should *not* be heated up to soldering temperature while in the lathe.

If it is suspected that a wheel that has had its teeth cut is not exactly concentric with its bore a wax chuck like that in **Fig 3/55** can be used. This is really a modification of the traditional chuck where a series of shallow

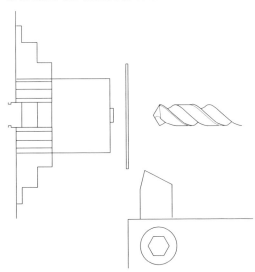

Fig 3/54 Attachment using soft solder is strong enough to hold the blank during cutting the teeth. The register of both this and the wax chuck should be smaller than the final bore so that it can be machined away

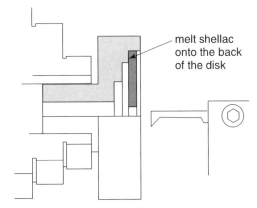

melt shellac onto the back of the disk

Fig 3/55 An escapewheel that has had its teeth cut can be held in a closely fitting stepped mandrel to machine the bore

counterbores are used for rough containment, with the wheel being set true by whirling in the lathe and centering with a stick. Here there is a counterbore that is made to *fit* the outside diameter of the wheel exactly, so that it runs true. The shellac merely holds it in place for boring the hole.

Cutting an Escapewheel by Hand

Cut a strip of paper that can be wrapped around the three-jaw chuck to the exact circumference. Using the method illustrated in Chapter 2 (page 39) for marking out a crownwheel, divide the strip up into the required number of parts. Paste it onto the lathe chuck (**Fig 3/56**).

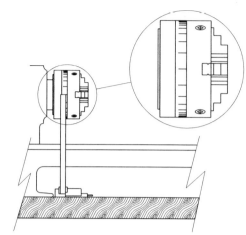

Fig 3/56 A simple set-up for dividing on the lathe

A turning tool is used to mark the blank. To begin with determine the diameter of the root of the teeth and scribe a circle with the point of the tool. Do not use power to rotate the chuck, but turn it by hand to make sure that there is not a 'dig in' to make a disfiguring mark on the face of the wheel. Having drawn the root circle set up a fixed mark against the chuck (a steel rule clamped upright in a vice for instance) and line this against one of the marks on the paper strip. Scribe a radial line with the lathe tool from the root circle to the outside diameter. Proceed until all the radial sides of the teeth have been defined (**Fig 3/57**).

The blank may be taken off its mounting and a saw used to cut into the waste metal, cutting all the radial lines first. When that is done, roughly cut triangles out of the waste leaving plenty of metal for a half round or an oval (crossings) file to cut the curved side of

the tooth — the curve must finish at the top of the radial mark but not go beyond it (**Fig 3/58**). A triangular file with two smooth sides (a barrette file) removes the last of the waste metal against the radial lines. If this system is followed there is less likelihood of the radial face being damaged by filing the curved one. Though it will not make much difference to the operation of the wheel, it will look much better and future repairers will have more confidence in its accuracy.

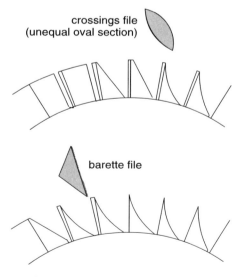

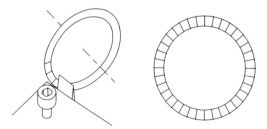

Fig 3/57 Mark the root circle of the teeth and their radial faces

Fig 3/58 File the curved faces with a crossings file and the radial faces with a barrette file

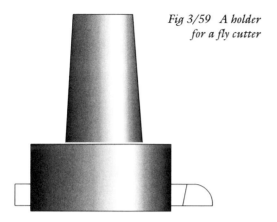

Fig 3/59 A holder for a fly cutter

Machine Cutting of Escapewheels

Escapewheels may be cut on a lathe having a milling attachment, a milling machine or a wheel-cutting engine, but it is not proposed to describe the use of these devices, but rather to discuss the tooling needed.

Commercial escapewheel cutters are multiple-tooth form cutters with relatively shallow teeth, very close to being machine burrs. The teeth are shallow because the cutter needs more of them than is found on a gear-wheel cutter — the length of cut is so much greater that the amount of metal removed by each tooth needs to be quite small. A different cutter is needed for each size of escapewheel tooth.

• Fly Cutter

This tool is also described in Chapter 2 (page 42); it cuts well and is a better means of forming the escapewheel than hand cutting (**Fig 3/59**). The fly cutter is made from high-carbon steel filed to shape, with a relief formed behind the cutting edge to avoid rubbing (**Fig 3/60**), and then hardened. It should be used at a high speed of 2,000 to 5,000 revs per minute. It cuts well but cannot remove all the metal from the tooth space at one pass. After the initial roughing cut advance the cutter so that subsequent finishing cuts are mainly on the straight radial flank of the teeth. How this is done depends on the method of dividing. If, for instance, a dividing head is used make the initial cut with the index a few holes short and the final cuts with the index moved forward by a hole at a time. If the cuts are made as shown in **Fig 3/61**, the teeth should be absolutely straight when finished. The metal is mainly removed by the point of the tool with the long curve barely 'kissing' the curved part of the wheel already produced (**Fig 3/62**). If this is not done the curved side of the cutter will be working throughout the cut and will most probably bend the tip of the tooth.

The tool is set to cut on the centre line of the lathe, so that the face produced is not raked.

Fig 3/61 The escapewheel teeth *should* not *be cut in one pass*

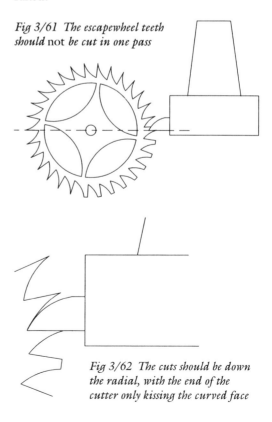

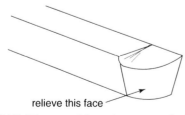

Fig 3/60 The curved face of an escapewheel fly cutter should be relieved so that it does not rub while cutting

relieve this face

Fig 3/62 The cuts should be down the radial, with the end of the cutter only kissing the curved face

6 Repairing Escapewheels

Recoil and deadbeat escapewheels suffer in similar ways. Either the teeth are bent over at the tips as a result of the wheel running free under the pallets, or one or two drop out (in part or completely) as a result of age, corrosion, grain growth, or bad repair. Bent teeth can frequently be bent back. There is similarity between the description of wheel repair given here and that given in Chapter 2 for the verge escapement, because some of the principles and techniques are similar. Hence there is some repetition, but this is more convenient for the reader than having to refer back.

The decision to carry out a repair to an escapewheel or its total replacement depends upon the desirability of retaining original work, even when badly mangled, and your ability to reproduce the original style and standard of workmanship. This is a problem that crops up frequently when repairing clocks. If it is not a museum piece then the matter can be resolved on commercial grounds. Does the replacement lower the value of the clock? But a museum piece is valued for its historical integrity and a restorer will almost certainly be required to keep the old damaged wheel and make it good.

Bent Teeth

Escapewheel teeth, being relatively sharply pointed, are quite often bent over at the tips.

Fig 3/63 The flat side of the escapewheel teeth may be radial or raked

This is more likely to have been the result of slipping under the pallets than the old accusation of over-swinging the pendulum when starting the clock. It is a condition that can be corrected with the careful use of smooth-jawed pliers, but the result needs close inspection afterwards. As with damaged teeth, there is no point in carrying out this operation if there is evidence that the wheel has been heavily modified by a previous repairer.

The flat side of the tooth is either a true radial from the centre of the wheel or is raked and makes a tangent to a small circle that is concentric with the wheel. If the teeth are raked make a judgement about the size of the rake circle (**Fig 3/63**). This can be done by lining up a straight edge with an undamaged tooth or by eye — it is not critical to half a millimetre on the radius of the circle.

Grasp the tooth with the pliers and align the jaw that touches the flat side of the tooth, so that it makes a tangent to the rake circle. Squeeze the other jaw onto the curved side and, maintaining the pressure, draw the pliers off the tooth still keeping the first jaw on the tangent. Carry the operation out smoothly and do not feel that the correction has to be achieved in one go. Two or three attempts will do no harm, but at the end there must be a flat side that is similar to the other teeth of the wheel.

Use a magnifying glass to ensure that the corrected tip is not cracked, because if it is, the tooth must be replaced regardless of how much time has been invested in it. A cracked tip will fall off well inside the guarantee time.

Damaged Teeth

If an escapewheel has obviously damaged teeth examine it closely for work by other repairers. File marks that are brighter than the rest of the wheel are almost certainly an indication that the wheel has been repaired once already and that the tooth pitch (the distance between one tooth tip and the next) will vary around the circumference. Putting this right may easily take more time than making a new wheel.

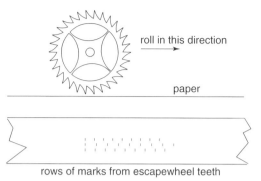

rows of marks from escapewheel teeth

Fig 3/64 Testing the escapewheel teeth for variations in pitch

In the event of finding enough marks to arouse suspicious use a vernier calliper to check the pitch of the teeth around the circle. There will be some variations as a result of the original method of dividing and cutting the teeth, but these should be limited.

A simple test to check the pitch of the teeth is to lay a piece of clean white paper on a hard surface and roll the periphery of the wheel over it in a straight line to leave a series of marks. If one tooth tip is lined up at the side of the first mark and the wheel rolled over the paper again any differences in pitch between one tooth and another will become evident. A third run will make the differences even more obvious (**Fig 3/64**).

The variation that can be tolerated is difficult to quantify and your own judgement must be used to decide whether the operation of

the escapement outside the area that you have to repair, is acceptable. The pitch may be expected to vary by up to one twentieth as a result of the original dividing. In other words if the pitch in one place measures 5mm (keeping to whole numbers) other teeth may produce as large a variation as 4.9mm to 5.1mm — a total tolerance of 0.2mm (0.01in).

The variations must not be regular, but random about a mean. If the rolling test shows the pitches gradually increasing and then decreasing in size around the wheel, then the wheel is eccentric (**Fig 3/65**). It has been turned to make it true leaving the minimum pitch diametrically opposite the maximum. Do not bother with such a wheel — it is pure grief and a sign that no-one has had the clock working properly since at least the last repair.

• **Effect of Eccentricity**

Escapewheels that have suffered damage, or have been modified, frequently have teeth of differing heights. This can be corrected by mounting the arbor in a lathe, spinning at high speed and just touching the tips with a very sharp pointed tool. This is a very satisfactory solution as long as certain things are borne in mind:

• The diameter of the wheel will become smaller and therefore the pallets will not match completely. This will not matter if the reduction of diameter has been no more than a few thousands of an inch or if the pallets are to be resurfaced anyway, allowing the adjustment of the drop-off points.

• Concentricity must be maintained. This refers to the centre of the wheel that was established before the teeth were cut. It is obvious that the existing wheel and arbor must be set up to run true before any metal is removed from the teeth, but it is important to know that a previous repairer has not remounted the wheel on a different centre. **Fig 3/65** shows how the pitch of the teeth is modified by machining the wheel to a new centre. The pitch is no longer constant around the periphery of the wheel and this puts the wheel in the category of those parts that are no longer recoverable by repair work. Throw it away, or if

Fig 3/65 A wheel that has been machined eccentrically will have unequal tooth pitch at A and B

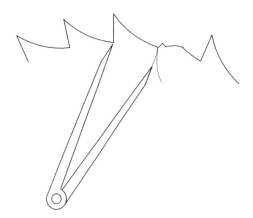

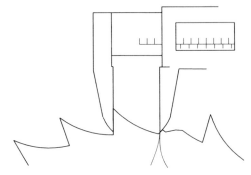

Fig 3/67 Check the mark with the position calculated from the measured diameter and number of teeth

Fig 3/66 Use dividers to find the position of the damaged escapewheel tooth

it is *very* important to retain the original component, centre the wheel with regard to the root circle of the teeth, bore out for a new collet and then mount and turn the wheel. The tips will need to be thinned by filing the curved side of the tooth and the pallets will definitely need resurfacing

Escapewheel Repair

First check the wheel by tracking on paper as above. Measure the wheel diameter wheel and find its circumference by multiplying this by 3.142 (π). Divide this figure by the number of teeth to give the average pitch of the wheel, and set vernier callipers to this measurement. The method of setting the position for the replacement teeth will depend upon whether one tooth is to be replaced or several.

Using the neighbouring teeth and a pair of dividers mark the midpoint between them (**Fig 3/66**). Now use the vernier to check against the pitch that would result from using this mark as the position of the new tooth tip (**Fig 3/67**). If this falls within the tolerance of one twentieth of the pitch, then the mark can be used for the repair. If it falls outside this tolerance then it is certain that at least one of the teeth that was used in making the mark has been modified and is not correctly placed. Run a rolling test and if it fails make a complete replacement wheel.

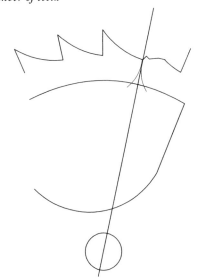

Fig 3/68 Scribe the radial for the damaged tooth

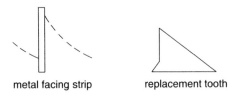

metal facing strip   replacement tooth

Fig 3/69 The damaged tooth may be faced or replaced entirely

Draw a line from the centre of the wheel through the mark and scribe a good, clear line on the rim of the wheel (**Fig 3/68**). Do not worry about producing a rake at this time.

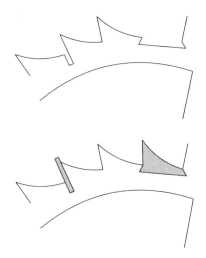

Fig 3/70 Cut slots for facings or new teeth. A dove-tail makes a strong-looking repair, though there is little difference to the actual strength of the joint

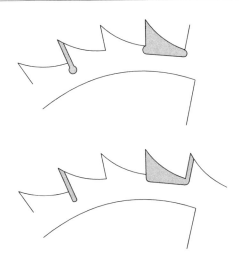

Fig 3/71 Radii or a drilled hole help to prevent fatigue cracks forming in the sharp corners of the cut out

Prepare a piece of hard brass to either face a lightly damaged tooth or entirely replace a heavily damaged one (**Fig 3/69**). Though hard brass has stresses in it that need to be relieved by heat treatment, the act of solder-ing is sufficient to do this.

File or saw a base for the replacement ma-terial. A facing for the tooth only needs a shal-low saw cut, as can be seen from **Fig 3/70**, but replacement of most of a tooth due to heavy damage needs more work to ensure that a firm key is obtained. **Fig 3/71** shows a number of variations that may be found use-ful. In both cases make the thickness of the new material greater than that of the wheel.

The excess metal will be removed with a file after soldering has taken place. Be careful to file in directions that place no strain on the soldered joint.

Soft solder is used for these joints, tinning both parts of the joint first and then just touch-ing the hot metal with a thin piece of solder if more is required. It will be found that it is not easy to ensure that the new piece of brass re-mains in position while soldering. Support it by any means that do not result in the sup-port being soldered to the wheel. Also use a material of low thermal conductivity to sup-port the wheel so that the joint can be made without the need for large quantities of heat.

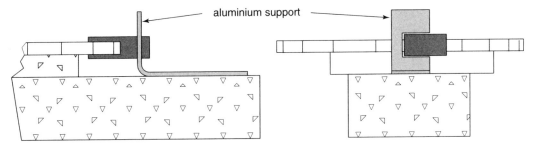

aluminium support

Fig 3/72 A strip of aluminium makes a useful support while soldering the new tooth

Aluminium is a useful material to use as a support (**Fig 3/72**), as it bends easily and without special techniques it will not bond with the solder, though it will tend to draw the heat away. The additional thickness of the new metal will allow scope to file and produce a tooth or facing that does not lean inwards or outwards.

When the tooth is securely soldered in place and has been reduced to the thickness of the rest of the escapewheel, use a flat needle file to accurately align the flat face with the mark on the rim and then apply any rake that is needed to match the other teeth. Finally remove all burrs and smooth off the tip of the tooth.

7 The Anchor Escapement — Faults & Comments

When very well made and driven by a smoothly-working gear train, a clock with an anchor escapement can keep time to within about 10-15 seconds a week. It is quite possible that these results could be bettered if the same gear trains that are used in regulators were used with an anchor escapement, but it is more susceptible to the effects of changes in friction and temperature than a deadbeat escapement. As will be seen in the next chapter, a deadbeat escapement driven by a 'jewelled' movement can achieve results of 3-5 seconds per month. Whether the half-beat escapement really achieves a result halfway between these two, I have no way of knowing, but it is doubtful.

The system of defining the anchor that has been discussed here has the advantage of a more obvious logic than others that have been published and copes with a wide range of circumstances — down to very short span of four and a half teeth.

It also has the advantage of not relying on the accurate placing of dots and scribed lines, but instead uses rough pencil marks for initial decisions on form, and a straight edge and a piece of scrap brass for the accurate establishment of the working faces and drop-off points. If the number of tolerance errors involved in placing and using dots and scribed lines are counted and compared with the direct alignment of a straight edge on the work itself the advantage of the latter is readily seen.

The task takes about 1¼-1½ hours to produce a working escapement, including the drilling of the scrap brass; it needs no special tools to be made, and it may have been the method used by most of the working clockmakers — as opposed to academic writers — of the nineteenth century, though no contemporary accounts by actual clockmakers seem to have survived.

To recap, the basis of the marking out is that if a circle of diameter 0.707 times the escapewheel diameter is established on the wheel's centre, the tangents from *any* tooth tip to this circle make an angle of 45 degrees to the tangent of the outer circle at that tooth (**Fig 3/73**). The teeth chosen for the acting teeth are in the positions to give the preferred span of the pallets.

Though 0.707 is the theoretical choice, since it is the sine (and cosine) of 45 degrees, using a ratio of 0.75 results in a deviation from this of less than four degrees. In practice most recoil escapewheels in British clocks have the

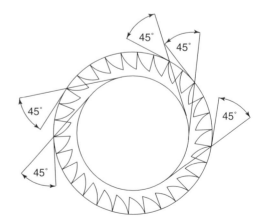

Fig 3/73 The tangent from any *tooth tip to a circle 0.707 times the escapewheel diameter is at 45° to the tangent to the outside diameter*

outer arc of the crossing circle at a radius of between 0.707 and 0.75 of the wheel radius. Hence if a straightedge is placed on the tip of a tooth to a tangent to the crossing-out rim the impulse faces of the pallets are defined — the drop-offs, of course, are placed at a span of 'so many and a half' teeth.

Entry & Exit Errors

The geometric errors of the recoil anchor pallets differ according to whether the entry or the exit pallets are considered (**Fig 3/74**). On the entry pallet the angle between the impulse face and the tangent at the tip of the tooth remains fairly constant (a change of about 0.5 degrees) as the tooth moves along the impulse face. This is because as the pallet rises and the impulse face tilts, the tooth rotates through a small angle (about half the pitch) and its changing angle compensates for this tilt.

On the exit side the reverse is true. The pallet rises, tilting the impulse face down with respect to the acting tooth, and the rotation of the wheel aggravates the change. Quite commonly the impulse angle at the drop off is about 9 degrees smaller than the angle at the first contact of tooth on pallet.

Now the clockmaker can make a decision as to whether the impulse angle is set for the position when the tooth first hits the pallet on the exit side, or when it drops off, or halfway through the working movement on the exit. It is easy, using the straight edge method of defining the pallets described in Section 2 of this chapter, to make the choice. The result will be that the exit pallet works through an impulse angle of 45-36 degrees in the first instance, 54-45 in the second, or the halfway situation of 49.5-40.5 degrees may be chosen. The author prefers the 45-36 degree situation as there is less crushing of the tooth tip on first impact, yet more impulse just before drop-off.

In all forms of the anchor pallet, whether

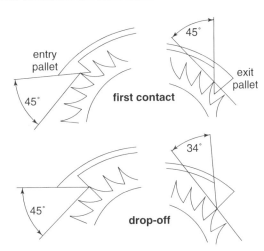

Fig 3/74 The change in angle of the entrance face as the tooth moves along the impulse plane is almost compensated by the tooth rotation, to give a virtually constant impulse angle. At the exit face these two effects are additive and the impulse angle decreases by about 9° during impulse

recoil or deadbeat, the torque at the pallet arbor varies cyclically between entry and exit as a result of these unavoidable changes in impulse angle. Also during impulse on the entry pallet the lever arm is shortening, while during exit it is lengthening.

On the other hand, in escapements where entry and exit impulse planes are on the same side of the escapewheel, the impulse faces can be adjusted to give almost identical torques (the Gallileo escapement is a recoil example). Escapements that impulse once every two beats of the pendulum (eg the grasshopper and other detent systems) and gravity escapements have no difficulties of this sort.

This method also allows the buyer of a clock to check the escapement by simply sighting along the line of the impulse face to see whether it makes a tangent with the crossing out rim at first contact (the usual clockmaker's choice).

8 The Geometry of Small Pallet Spans

The systems of marking out shown so far are approximations that work well in most cases. However the aim of these methods is to obtain an equality of angular movement between the entry and the exit pallets, and when the span is shortened to an extreme the shortcomings of any approximate system become only too obvious. The usual result is excessive drop on the exit side — which means that the amount of energy being passed to the pendulum is severely restricted — as a consequence, the clock will not go, or is very prone to stop if it can be persuaded to perform.

Fig 3/75 shows a thirty-tooth wheel with pallets spanning two and a half teeth. This is the type of situation where the marking system described earlier fails to produce a good escapement. The left-hand drawing has a pallet arbor that is mounted higher than the one on the right. Both impulse faces make a tangent to the inner rim of the crossing out. As can be seen there is a very large drop on the entry pallet. No common circle can be derived for tangents that define correct impulse faces, whether the circles are based on the pallet arbor (as done by earlier writers such as Britten, see page 94), or the wheel arbor centres.

Even the example on the right, with its pallet centre mounted lower, is not very good, though it might well work with a light pendulum. The difference in the drop for entrance and exit is still too large. In both cases quite a small amount of wear will definitely stop the clock working. A small amount of wear on the arbor pivots exacerbates this.

In **Fig 3/76** the entrance and exit impulse faces are developed from the required swing of the pendulum and pallets. A line is drawn from the tips of the acting teeth for both faces at drop-off and at first contact, to the pallet centre — there are, quite logically, four lines, although the two for the exit are very close together. In greater detail the method of obtaining these lines is:

The escapewheel is placed so that either the entry or exit pallet is impulsing. (In **Fig 3/76A** the dotted escapewheel is impulsing on exit and at entry drop-off the centre line coincides with a tooth tip.) Lines are drawn from the centre of the pallet arbor to the tip of the acting teeth at the drop off on one side and at first contact on the other. *Note that the centre line can be placed in line with a tooth tip or a midpoint — there is no need to place it a quarter of a pitch to left or right according to whether it is an odd or even numbered span.*

A semi-arc of 6 degrees has been selected for the pendulum and so the pallets are swung

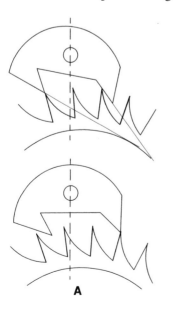

A

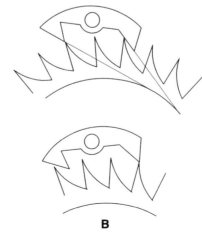

B

Fig 3/75 If short-span pallets are drawn by the normal method (tangents to the inside rim of the escapewheel) there will be correct drop on the exit pallet, but excessive drop on the entrance pallet (A). A lower centre (B) is better, but the drop is still not correct

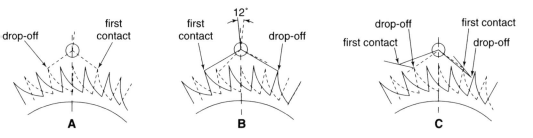

Fig 3/76 The impulse faces for short-span pallets are determined by the first contact points and the drop-off points for the desired pendulum swing (semi-arch of 6° in this case). The working surfaces produced must be extended to the left of the point of first contact to allow for recoil. Note that the lines shown are not the pallet arms, but the distance to the points of drop-off and first contact

anticlockwise through twice this angle (**Fig 3/76B**) to produce the opposite conditions for the escapement, ie the entry pallet now impulsing.

Lines are again drawn from the centre of the pallet arbor to the acting tooth at entry (giving the point of first contact), and from the centre to the exiting tooth to define the drop-off (full-line wheel).

If the ends of these lines on the entry side are joined, and the same is done on the exit, then the impulse faces that produce these conditions is defined. It must be noted that these two surfaces are only the faces that are contacted during the working arc, they must be extended to the left of the point of first contact to give a surface for recoil. The form of the pallets that is developed from these two faces (including recoil) is shown in **Fig 3/77**.

Note that simply marking the drop-off points on each arm and then rotating them through 12 degrees would not produce the same result. Generation of the impulse faces, as has been done here, is the only method

which will always produce a correctly shaped pair of pallets. All other systems are simplifications aimed at making the design of pallets of normal span relatively easy, and are not suitable for short-spans. The error caused by using these methods for short-span pallets is shown in **Fig 3/81**.

Since short-span pallets are almost always small it is not easy to produce the required angles with the equipment available in the normal workshop. It is simpler to develop the shape in large scale on drawing paper and then define circles on the pallet arbor centre whose tangents correspond with the impulse faces (**Fig 3/78**). Four circles are shown: two of them are based on the wheel centre and two

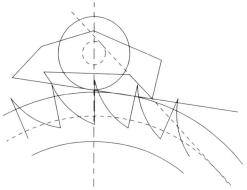

Fig 3/78 Using a large-scale drawing to find circles whose tangents define the impulse faces. These circles my be centred on the escapewheel arbor ot the pallet arbor. The circles for the exit pallet are shown dotted

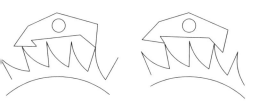

Fig 3/77 Short-span pallets as developed by the method shown in Fig 3/76

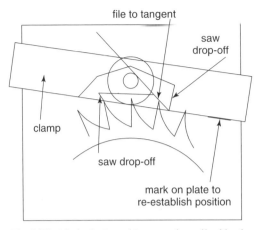

Fig 3/79 Method of marking out the pallet blank for a short-span pallet

on the pallet arbor centre. Either pair will do for establishing the impulse faces.

It must not be forgotten that these circles are developed when the pallet is fixed relative to the wheel and consequently both tangents must also be drawn without moving the pallets. Disks turned to the diameter of these circles and placed on the arbor will help form the proper impulse faces. either by hand or by machining. Because the anchor is so small it is best to make it from a piece of bar that can be clamped to a plate, as in the earlier methods described for pallet making, thus allowing the easy attachment of a strip of brass to follow the tangent (**Fig 3/79**). The lower edge of the bar forms the entrance impulse face.

9　Other Methods of Marking Out Anchor Escapements

Britten

The system for marking out ordinary recoil anchors given in *Britten's Watch and Clock Maker's Handbook Dictionary and Guide* relies on the generation of the impulse faces by defining the swing of the pendulum, then two lines (BE and BF in **Fig 3/80**) including this angle are drawn from the centre of the pallet arbor. The point of first contact and the drop-off points are then defined as the intersection of these lines with the radials AC and AD to the acting teeth and the midpoints.

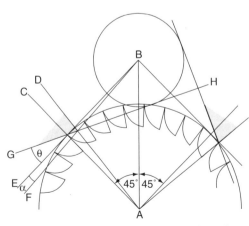

Fig 3/80 Britten's method of drawing the pallets for a square recoil escapement

The line GH passing through opposite intersections of these four lines defines the impulse face. A circle centred on the pallet arbor B is drawn to touch GH and a tangent to this circle from the tip of a tooth on the exit side produces the exit impulse face.

Britten specifies the impulsing arc (α) of the pendulum and this results in impulse angles (θ) that produce this arc. (In comparison with the simpler method recomended in this book, where the impulse angle is defined, giving an unspecified pendulum arc.) Britten's impulsing arc of 4 degrees produces an impulse angle of only 33 degrees, while 6 degrees arc is necessary to give the usually recommended impulse angle of 45 degrees.

Its practical disadvantage lies in the difficulty in extending the line joining opposite corners of the very small quadrilateral formed by the intersection of triangles ACD and BEF. A very small inaccuracy in joining these points can result in a large difference in impulse circle diameter.

Another point to consider is that though this method does give an equal swing for both the entry and exit pallets it *is* an approximation and will produce unacceptable errors when applied to small spans. The problem is that the drop-off points are defined a

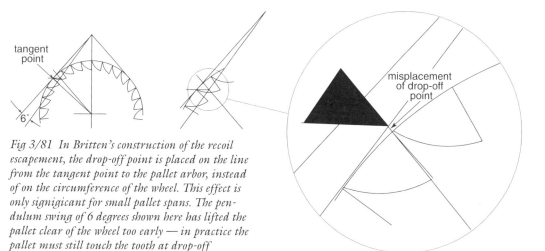

Fig 3/81 In Britten's construction of the recoil escapement, the drop-off point is placed on the line from the tangent point to the pallet arbor, instead of on the circumference of the wheel. This effect is only signigicant for small pallet spans. The pendulum swing of 6 degrees shown here has lifted the pallet clear of the wheel too early — in practice the pallet must still touch the tooth at drop-off

lying on a line projected from the centre of the pallet arbor and not on the periphery of the escapewheel (**Fig 3/81**). Although this may be almost true for spans equivalent to a quarter of the escapewheel circumference it is not always so and will be affected by the width of span, the height of the pallet centre and whether the tangent from the pallet centre leads or trails the acting teeth. A glance at **Fig 3/76** and the exit side of the short-span pallets shows just how large an error can result. The included angle between lines from each end of the impulse face to the pallet centres is quite clearly not the same as on the entry side, yet both are correctly placed.

Britten places a great deal of emphasis on the need to place pallet centres at the intersection of tangents struck from the working teeth of the escapewheel (the teeth that the entry and exit pallets contact). In point of fact this is not a particularly important matter for the working of the escapement — and it only eliminates one element from the errors of the marking system.

It does produce the deepest 'bite' of the pallet into the tooth space for a given pendulum arc. But in the case of spans that exceed one tenth of the circumference of the wheel, the position of the pallet centres can wander well away from Britten's optimum position

without making any practical difference to the working of the escapement if the impulse faces are generated from the true drop-off points and first contact.

While tangential contact results in the most

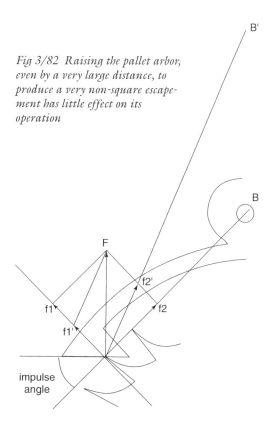

Fig 3/82 Raising the pallet arbor, even by a very large distance, to produce a very non-square escapement has little effect on its operation

efficient escapement, **Fig 3/82** shows that even when exaggerated the effect is not very significant. Raising the pallet arbor from B to B' reduces the impulsing force from f1 to f1' and only increases the force f2 on the pallet pivot very slightly. This diagram is for a constant impulse angle, and, if necessary, the reduction of impulse may be countered by a variation in the impulse angle.

Lord Grimthorpe in the *Encyclopaedia Britannica* of 1874 claimed that the habit of French clock makers of ignoring the tangential rule would result in an escapement that would wear out very quickly. History has shown that this opinion has not proved correct and this example should make all authors very cautious in their pronouncements.

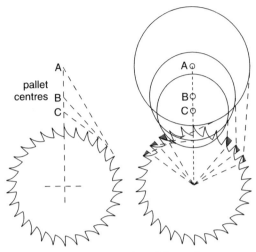

Fig 3/83 Rees's construction of the anchor escapement for three different pallet spans

Rees

Rees's Clocks, Watches and Chronometers (published in 1970) is an extract from Abraham Rees's *Cyclopaedia* of 1819-20. It contains a large section on escapements, is an excellent reference for the history of technology and is probably the primary source for a number of the methods that have been published since.

As in Britten's method, Rees puts emphasis on placing the centre for the pallets at the intersection of the vertical centre line and tangents from the acting teeth (the teeth, at entry and exit, that actually make contact with the impulse faces). **Fig 3/83** shows his construction for three different pallet spans. On the vertical centre line are the three pallet centres, each one defined by a tangent from three different acting teeth on the exit side. As the span is extended from 7½ teeth to 8½ teeth to 9½ teeth these centres rise above each other.

The geometrical construction is basically similar to that of Britten, but instead of defining the impulse circles as already described, an arbitary value for their radii of half the distance between the circle centre and the escapewheel centre is chosen. Consequently the circles become larger as the pallet span in-

creases and the centres rise along the centre line.

The impulse faces are formed by taking tangents from the acting teeth to the relevant circle: the 7½ span to the smallest circle, the 8½ to the medium-sized one and so on. These tangents are extended to intersect the radial drop-off faces and for clarity the triangle implied is shown shaded. Note that the triangles become smaller as a result of the length of the drop-off face shrinking as the spans increase.

The diameter of the circle used in Rees's book results in a pendulum semi-arc of about 3 degrees and a small impulse angle of only about 26 degrees.

If the drop-off becomes smaller as the span increases, then the arc of the action (and that of the pendulum) becomes smaller too and this effect is exaggerated by the pallet arms lengthening also. It is not a method that will give a good result unless it is limited to a small range of pallet spans, in fact 6½ to 7½ teeth.

The altenative system of using a single tangent circle (the rim of the crossing circle), maintains an adequate length of drop-off face (bite) for a wide range of spans, as has been shown (page 57).

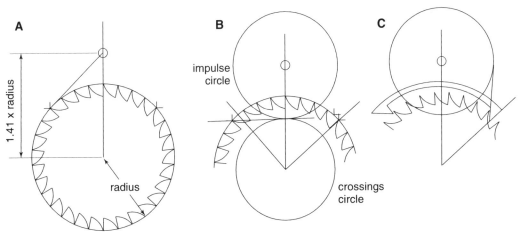

Fig 3/84 Gazeley's method of marking out a 'square' recoil anchor escapement. The impulse circle is defined by the impulse face of the entry pallet, and provides the tangent for the exit impulse face

Gazeley

Clock and Watch Escapements and *Watch & Clock Making & Repairing* by W. J. Gazeley shows a marking-out method which he calls 'making recoil pallets to depth'. Probably this was originally an empirical workshop system for the specific pallet span of 7½ teeth and a thirty-tooth escapewheel (a quarter of the circumference), with the pallet arbor centre defined by tangents from the acting teeth. When the span has this relationship to the number of teeth in the wheel the method produces impulse faces that make tangents to the crossing rim (ie impulse angles of about 45 degrees) — but not at others and there is no real geometrical basis for the method. It is a very limited syatem, but is quite a quick one.

A thirty-tooth escapewheel is placed so that one tooth tip lies on the vertical centre line and then the acting teeth are marked for impulsing at entry, ie the left-hand mark is the point of first contact and the right-hand one is the drop-off (**Fig 3/84A**). The wheel is now rotated half the tooth pitch — turning through an arc of 6 degrees — and the exit point of first contact is marked. In **Fig 3/84B** the wheel has not been rotated — it is actually simpler to make the second mark halfway between the existing one and the preceding tooth tip.

A line is drawn from the first point on the entry to a point midway between the two marks on the exit side. This line represents the impulse angle for the entry pallet and a circle based on the pallet centre is drawn to just touch it.

After defining the entry pallet the body of the anchor is raised to give drop-off there (at this point **Fig 3/84C** shows the wheel to have made a half-pitch rotation) and the exit impulse face is produced by making a tangent from the right-hand acting tooth to the circle. Unfortunately the drawing in both of Gazeley's books shows both pallet nibs fully bitten — which is rather confusing.

In practice this method works well if translated for the use of a straight edge, and a brass plate to mount the escapewheel and pallet body. The precision of the line that is drawn to the midpoint on the exit side does not need to be great unless the wheel is very small (less than about 20mm) and the circle on the pallet centre can be clearly marked on the brass plate. But it is essentially a special case and only works well when the impulse circle produced touches the crossing out rim (approximately 0.75 of the wheel diameter) and it does not, of course, make any claims to handling short-span pallets.

Gazeley's method has been widely used by

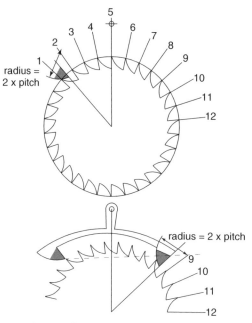

Fig 3/85 Gordon's method of marking out the recoil anchor escapement

other writers who have often reproduced his drawing with the same error — and without commenting on it.

Gordon

Clock making Past & Present (second edition 1949) by G. F. C. Gordon describes a practical method of marking out recoil pallets (**Fig 3/85**). This method sets the distance between centres as 1.4 times the radius of the escape-wheel but in fact, because no geometric reference is made to the position of the pallet centre, there is no reason why it should be limited to this. Essentially it places a stated form, a specific radius, at the entry and exit and establishes the drop-offs in their proper place.

A piece of brass plate is marked and drilled to accept the pallet and escapewheel arbors in a similar fashion to that described in **Figs 3/11-15** (pages 60-62).

The teeth of the wheel are numbered from 1 to 12 and number 5 is placed on the vertical centre line. The assumption is clearly made that the span is 7½ teeth. For 8½ teeth span

the centre line would be set midway between teeth 5 and 6. In effect, the rule is that for odd-numbered spans the centre line falls on a tooth and for even numbers it falls between two teeth. In both cases tooth number 1 is placed at half the nominal span (7 and 8 in this case) plus half a tooth pitch to the left of the vertical. The drawing will make this complex-sounding rule plain.

Fig 3/85 shows tooth number 1 making the first contact on the entry pallet and the curve for the impulse face is defined as a radius equal to two pitches. This radius is drawn from a centre vertically above the tip of tooth 1. The drop-off is drawn in the usual way on the radial at the midpoint of 1 and 2.

This curve, marked onto the pallet blank, is filed to shape and the blank replaced on its centre with the filed pallet nib set on the outside diameter of the wheel and the wheel itself rotated to bring a tooth tip beneath it — at drop-off.

The exit pallet impulse face is constructed in a similar fashion using a radius of two pitches with its centre on a line joining the tips of tooth 1 and tooth 8. The drop-off is drawn on the radial midway between teeth 8 and 9. This is also filed to shape and then, with both pallets formed, the clearance is made as usual by filing back the drop-off faces.

It is a simple system, with no need to draw tangents to external circles, but it still relies on making marks on the steel with dividers for the sole purpose of providing a curved impulse face. The impulse angle at drop-off is approximately 45 degrees. The curve reduces the recoil, but it is not a calculated effect such as with the Berthoud or the half-deadbeat escapements.

Another method is given in *Clock Cleaning and Repair* (1917), written by an anonymous 'G', who was described as 'a clever and practical horologist', and edited by Bernard Jones. The exit pallet is placed at the drop-off point and the impulse face drawn 'vertical and a trifle curved. Draw in the impulse face of [the entrance] pallet, letting it be horizontal and also slightly curved. Its point should penetrate the escape wheel exactly mid-way between two teeth, and its face should just touch the tooth point before it. The backs of the pallets should be straight lines pointing to the escape wheel centre.' Though this no doubt worked after a fashion, the reader by now should be aware of the deficiencies of this method, but most makers of longcase clocks probably used a very similar empirical method.

CHAPTER 4

The Graham Deadbeat

1 Description of the Deadbeat Escapement

George Graham is credited with the development of the deadbeat escapement (**Fig 4/1**) in about 1720. When linked with other developments in clockmaking it produced clocks capable of measuring time to within a minute or better over a period of twelve months. Since then this escapement has remained popular for good timekeepers (it forms the basis of the lever escapement widely used in mechanical watches and small portable clocks), and particularly for longcase and wall clocks.

It is a robust escapement and need not be difficult to manufacture, since all its elements can be calculated and measured accurately. However, *repairing* a Graham escapement is not a manufacturing job, it is a one-off. What is more, the elements that can be measured

Fig 4/1 The Graham deadbeat escapement

during the manufacturing process are difficult to establish when remaking the pallets or escapewheel.

Advantages of the Deadbeat Escapement

As shown in the previous chapter, a recoil escapement forces the train of a clock to reverse its action, and for a very short period of time the movement is actually wound up by the pendulum forcing the pallets against the escapewheel. Graham recognised that a large part of the variation in driving force and frictional losses could be reduced by removing the recoil. The pressure on the impulse faces is greater during recoil because the pressure of the wheel teeth is being overcome by the pallets. What is more the train is being driven in a way that results in pinions driving wheels when the point of contact between the teeth occurs before the line of centres. The working surfaces of the teeth are grinding together rather than rolling away from each other. The frictional losses at the pallet faces and tooth contacts vary more greatly than during the 'forward' movement of the train. Also changes in the lubricant and the entrapment of grit result in greater wear and any change in the driving forces will affect the swinging pallet during both the working arc and the supplementary arc (ie the swing that continues after drop-off has taken place).

Recoil was eliminated by presenting a 'dead' face to the escapewheel during the supplementary arc (**Fig 4/2**). This face is dead because it is makes a true arc to the centre of the pallet arbor and, as it swings past the tooth tip, neither allows nor forces movement in any direction. The escapewheel remains still until an

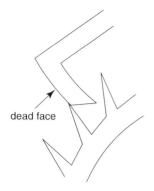

Fig 4/2 The escapewheel tooth falls onto a dead face, so during the pendulum's supplementary arc there is no recoil

dead face

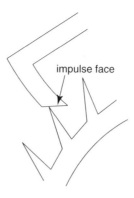

Fig 4/3 The impulse face of the deadbeat escapement

impulse face

impulse face is exposed again (**Fig 4/3**).

The reliability of the timekeeping of a clock fitted with a deadbeat escapement is significantly greater than that of a recoil escapement. A very obvious difference in the operation of the escapement is the fact that a clock fitted with it will run with a weight or a spring of approximately half the power needed than with a recoil escapement. Variations in the power delivered by the driving spring or weight have a smaller effect on the time keeping of the escapement, as do any alteration in lubrication characteristics due to age or temperature of the lubricant.

Graham's escapement (and the improvements on it that followed) was quickly adopted for all accurate timekeepers, and until the invention of escapements that were detached

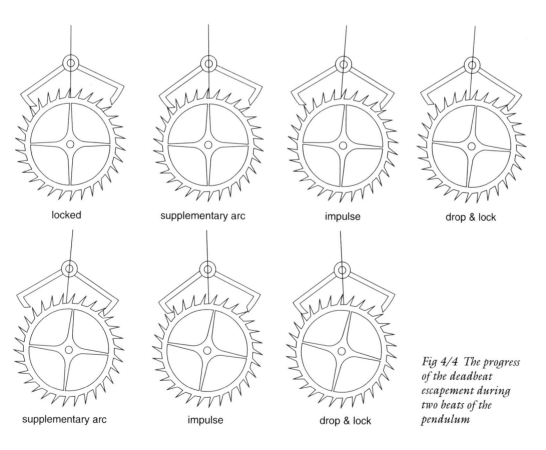

locked   supplementary arc   impulse   drop & lock

supplementary arc   impulse   drop & lock

Fig 4/4 The progress of the deadbeat escapement during two beats of the pendulum

from the oscillator (ie the pendulum or balance wheel), it reigned supreme. In its guise as a lever escapement, it is still the most frequently used escapement for mechanical watches.

Operation of the Deadbeat Escapement
In **Fig 4/4** the progression of the escapewheel during two beats of the pendulum may be seen. The features of its operation that distinguish it from the recoil escapements are:
• The virtual lack of movement of the escapewheel during the supplementary arc.
• Positive locking of the escapewheel immediately after drop-off.

The first has already been demonstrated — the face that the waiting escapewheel tooth rests upon is a true arc and has a constant radius based on the centre of the pallet arbor. The second feature is seen in **Figs 4/1** and **4/2**. When one tooth drops off a pallet, the other one immediately falls onto the dead face and is prevented from touching the impulse face until the supplementary arc has been completed.

It may be thought that the second feature is simply a restatement of the first, but it is definitely a separate matter. If that part of the pallet onto which the wheel tooth falls becomes worn so that it curves into the impulse face (**Fig 4/5**), the escapement will no longer be deadbeat — it will give recoil instead. Such a clock will not keep its pendulum going unless at least twice as much power is fed to the

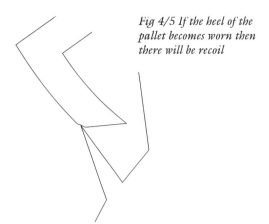

Fig 4/5 If the heel of the pallet becomes worn then there will be recoil

movement (and the crutch will vibrate strongly when the pendulum is disengaged). Even then the escapement will perform worse than a properly designed recoil escapement.

Modified Deadbeat Escapements
Although a deadbeat escapement will not operate properly without locking, the dead faces do not necessarily have to be absolutely perfect arcs centred on the pallet arbor. In many small movements they are in fact flat surfaces approximating to a curve. According to the angle at which these flat surfaces are presented to the escapewheel there will be a slight recoil as the tooth makes its first contact or, more commonly, when the pallet moves in the opposite direction. The last has the complementary effect of drawing the pallets towards the wheel centre, and is referred to as 'draw'.

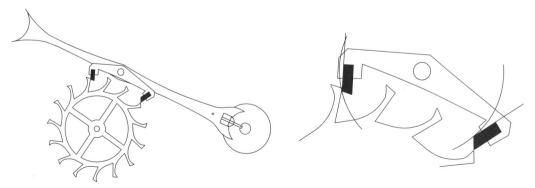

Fig 4/6 A deadbeat lever ecapement with a club-foot escapewheel. The arcs (right) show the position f true dead faces, but the actual faces are flat. Hence the pallets are drawn towards them. This is known as 'draw'

• Draw

There are two well known instances of draw in deadbeat escapements. One is the lever escapement used in watches and often in platform escapements (seen on top of the movement of a carriage clock and immediately under the glass), and the other in 400-day clocks. In the lever escapement this tendency to draw the pallet into the tooth space (**Fig 4/6**) prevents the fork at the other end from interfering with the free movement of the balance wheel. In conjunction with the 'banking pins', the draw holds the fork ready to accept the impulse pin when the wheel swings back towards it. Platform escapements are discussed in Chapter 6, with a complete description of the terms used here.

The escapement pallets of a 400-day (or 'anniversary') clock are drawn into the wheel for a similar reason. Because the rotating pendulum is moving quite slowly it is necessary to keep a certain amount of pressure against the fork (clamped on the suspension spring) as the supplementary arc is made. This too is discussed later, in Chapter 7.

• Half-Deadbeat Escapement

A form of bent-strip escapement called the half-deadbeat is used in some American clocks (Ingraham and Gilbert are two makers who employed this pallet). The term refers to the fact that the pallets produce a slight amount of recoil on either the inward motion of the pallets or the outward (**Fig 4/7**). Some Brit-

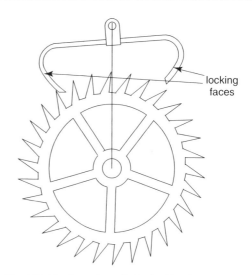

Fig 4/7 The Ingraham 'half-deadbeat' escapement. The locking faces only approximate to radii struck from the arbor centre

ish escapements have a form like an exaggerated Berthoud pallet (see **Fig 3/30**, Chapter 3) where a steep angle or curve takes the place of a true dead face. It was also used, in conjunction with short-span pallets, in boudoir and swinging cherub clocks to give a large swing. In effect the term means 'not quite deadbeat', but it must not be confused with the other use of 'half-deadbeat'. The latter refers to an escapement where impulsing takes place only on one side (usually the exit) and the other side is a complete dead face with no impulse face. This impulses once in every two

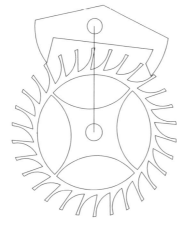
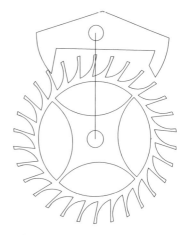

Fig 4/8 The other type of half-deadbeat escapement only produces an impulse on the exit pallet

beats of the pendulum and the exit pallet may be either a deadbeat or recoil (**Fig 4/8**). This type of escapement is sometimes used on French boudoir clocks or swinging cherub clocks, with a short pallet span and a wide pendulum swing.

2 Making a New or Replacement Deadbeat Escapement

Marking Out Deadbeat Escapement

This method of making new pallets employs a geometry that is, like that for the recoil anchor, an approximation. It aims to make the production of pallets easy and it is accurate enough for normal spans of escapewheel teeth. If a precise definition of the pallets is required it has to be carried out by generating the working surfaces in a similar fashion to the recoil escapement. This is dealt with in the section describing the second method of defining the impulse faces. (pages 113-115).

Fig 4/9 illustrates the normal shape of pallets for a Graham deadbeat escapement. This can be made as a solid anchor or as a body with adjustable pallets, commonly called a Vulliamy-style escapement (**Fig 4/10**). There are obvious advantages to the latter: it is easy to make with machine tools and it is easy to resurface the impulse faces when they are worn or alter the impulse angle if a mistake is made.

Vulliamy-style pallets are usually associated with a means of adjusting the distance between wheel and pallet arbor centres, which increases the manufacturing tolerances and the possibility of correcting errors.

In the following description it is assumed that the escapewheel and the centre distance between the arbors is correct and it is only necessary to make new pallets to suit the movement.

A piece of brass is marked with a centre line and two holes are drilled through from the existing front plate of the clock (**Fig 4/11**). These holes should be enlarged to a size that allows both pallet and escapewheel arbors to pass through, so that the wheel and the high-carbon steel blank for the pallets lie flat on the brass. In the early stages the wheel will rest on the steel, but the final adjustments to the pallets requires both to lie flat so that they can be tested one against the other.

The collet of the escapewheel may prevent it lying flat when placed as shown here, and set for clockwise rotation. This is not important, simply reverse the wheel so that it rotates counter clockwise — and remember to reverse all the drawings that follow.

If a lathe is available, put the pallet blank (drilled for its arbor) on a stub in the chuck and turn a boss on it. This does not need to be very tall, just sufficient for a vernier calliper to register on it for a later operation. (This boss is not absolutely essential, as the callipers could be made against the halved rod to be described next, provided that the rod was a very close fit in its hole. An advantage of the boss is that it later acts as a collet when fixing the pallet body to its arbor; it is more important that deadbeat pallets are at right-angles to the arbor than anchor pallets.)

In addition make a short rod the same diameter as the pallet arbor, with a flat filed on one end to 'halve' it (**Fig 4/11**). The flat

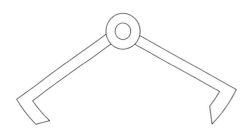

Fig 4/9 Solid Graham-type deadbeat pallets

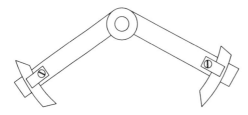

Fig 4/10 Vulliamy-style deadbeat pallets with adjustable and replacable nibs

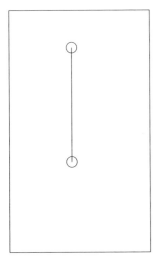
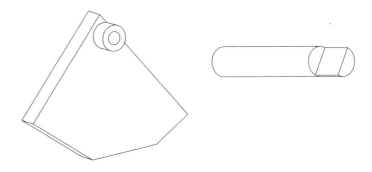

Fig 4/11 The items needed to make the pallet for a deadbeat escapement: a brass plate with the arbor centres drilled (left), a carbon-steel pallet blank with a turned boss (centre), and a steel rod halved at one end and with a small centre dot at the other

passes through the centre of the rod — again the reason for this will become clear later on. Turn the rod round in the chuck and, after making sure that it is running true, make a tiny centre dot in the other end, with a small centre drill.

Coat the steel blank with marking-out fluid or copper plate it with a solution of copper sulphate in water (the copper will turn black and provide a better background for marking if it is heated). This ensures that marks scribed on it show clearly. A large felt marker pen is a convenient way of producing a background for scribing the marks on to, but it should contain a spirit based ink otherwise it takes ages to dry.

Mount the steel blank on its rod and pass the rod through the brass plate — it should twist readily in the hole, but without shake. Any tightness should be adjusted by polishing the rod with emery paper.

Also pass the arbor of the escapewheel through the plate, so that it rests on the face of the steel blank. Move the blank about until enough shows on both sides of the wheel to allow the making of a pallet that embraces the wheel evenly, and mark a centre line on the blank between pallet arbor and wheel arbor. It is necessary to remove the escapewheel to do this, and to ensure that the blank does not

moved, scratch its outline onto the brass plate. Now replace the wheel (**Fig 4/12A**).

To determine the acting teeth used in the marking of the pallet, take a straight edge and scribe two lines from the centre of the pallet arbor to make tangents to the wheel, (**Fig 4/12B**). The halving of the rod will enable this to be done fairly easily — simply twist the rod until the straight edge lies along the flat, just kissing the outside of the wheel. Scratch a mark against the tips of the teeth at entry and exit that are closest to the tangents to the wheel. Now twist the wheel until the marked teeth are equidistant from the pallet arbor centre.

If the number of spaces between these two teeth is even, the centre line marked on the brass plate will touch the tip of a tooth (**Fig 4/12B**). If it is an odd number the centre line will cross the middle of a tooth space. Use these criteria to position the wheel with the acting teeth equidistant from the centre line.

If you are uncertain of maintaining the relative position of wheel and centre line, drill and tap a hole in the plate at the approximate position of X, and strap the wheel down against the steel blank and plate. The strap is not shown as it would obscure the drawing.

The following text explains the reasons for the various operations in making the pallets,

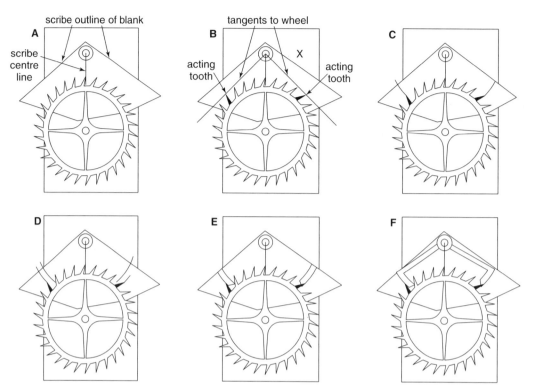

Fig 4/12 Marking out a Graham deadbeat escapement

but as this makes confusing reading while at the bench a summary of the tasks is given on pages 112-113.

Remove the rod and turn it around so that the centre dot can be used; it should not protrude from the blank. Use dividers, with one point resting in the centre dot, to draw arcs of equal radius just touching the tips of the acting teeth (**Fig 4/12C**).

The escapement dealt with here is large enough to be accurately made using a scriber to mark the working surfaces, and under these circumstances it is unimportant whether the arcs just drawn mark the inside or the outside curves of the pallets. They are shown as the outside faces in these diagrams.

The outside curves have now been drawn, and it is necessary to define the inside curves. These lie on a radius that passes midway between two tooth tips: the teeth already used and the adjacent ones that lie nearer to the centre line (**Fig 4/12D**). The best way to pro-

duce this arc is to measure the pitch of the teeth (the distance between adjacent tooth tips) with a vernier calliper, divide it by two and subtract this amount from the span of the dividers that was used to draw the first arcs. This second arc will be exactly half the pitch shorter than the first. Matching the divider points against the jaws of the vernier callipers will produce accurate measurements.

(It may be more convenient and accurate to calculate the pitch by multiplying the diameter by 3.142 [π] and dividing by the number of teeth. The error between the pitch cord and the arc may be ignored.)

In **Fig 4/12E** a rough guess has been made at the lengths of pallets, which still leaves them longer than they will be in the finished job. Quite clearly the escapewheel could not operate with pallets this long, but it gives the opportunity to swing the pallet blank on its centre so that the overall form can be marked out (**Fig 4/12F**). The actual shape of the iece — apart from the working surfaces — is matter of taste, the shape of the original pallets and the need to produce a sufficiently robust device. There is no point in linking the working faces with arms that are so weak that he body deforms easily. Consequently the body is shaped to provide sturdy arms that will not clash on the wheel teeth.

The pallets shown are longer than necessary so that it will be easy to mark the impulse faces and the lock. At the moment however, he outer and inner radii are geometric dimensions that could not possibly work — because practical escapements demand clearance of the working surfaces, which must be applied before the impulse faces are defined.

Clearance is the free angular motion of the escapewheel as a tooth drops off one pallet and another tooth falls onto the other pallet (**Fig 4/13**). This is referred to as 'drop' — it produces the 'tick', and since its loudness is dependent on the distance that the escapewheel rotates freely, a clock with uneven loudness to the tic reveals a variation in the drop from one tooth to the next. Free movement of the wheel uses energy that is not passed to the pendulum, so when the drops are unequal one of them must be greater than is strictly necessary and energy is being wasted. In addition the pallet making the loudest tick is also unneccessarily suffering more wear.

In view of this a clockmaker attempts to produce an even amount of drop onto both

Fig 4/13 The drop should be 5-10% of the tooth pitch, but the smaller figure is only possible for an accurately made escapement

pallets. The answer to the question 'how much?' is quite simply 'just enough — and a little bit for easy working'. A rule of thumb that can be applied is to allow 5-10 per cent of the pitch of the escapewheel teeth for drop (pitch being the distance between the tips of adjacent teeth). Small drops can only be used if the escapement is made very precisely and the wheel has very pointed teeth, the larger amount is common in well made, but not superb clocks.

The reason for the shape of the teeth affecting the drop is very simple. When one pallet is fully locked there must be sufficient space between the other pallet and the point of its acting tooth for the descending pallet to clear the back of the tooth as the locked pallet rises. A 'flat' at the top of the escapewheel tooth occupies an angle of rotation during which no impulse can be given to the pallets. No further rotation of the wheel can occur of course, until unlocking is complete.

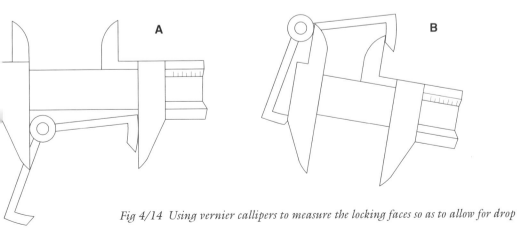

Fig 4/14 Using vernier callipers to measure the locking faces so as to allow for drop

The drop is shared between both pallets
and consequently only half this amount is removed from the outer radius — and added to
the inner radius. In **Fig 4/14A** vernier callipers are being used to measure the distance
between the boss and the outside radius. If
the pitch is (for instance) 0.2in the total clearance is a tenth of this, 0.02in, and the amount
of metal removed from the outer curve will
be 0.01 inches. In **Fig 4/14B** the inside jaws
of the vernier are being used to gauge the removal of metal and extend the radius by 0.01
inches. Now it is clear why a boss was turned
onto the blank at the beginning of this exercise.

In **Fig 4/15** (the pallet shown is not completed yet) the lock of the pallets is shown on
the entry pallet. At this point it is simply a
mark — capable of being changed if its position results in asymmetry of the pallet body
— necessary for the first step in developing
the impulse face. For the pallets to work properly each pallet in turn must lock the escapewheel at the time when the other pallet has
just dropped off a wheel tooth. **Fig 4/16** re-
iterates the operation of the escapement so
that the necessities can be appreciated before
developing the impulse faces. The pallets are
still oversized and the heels are simply left as
marks, so that what follows describes what
would occur if they were cut back to the marks.

The wheel is rotating clockwise and a tooth
is resting on the left-hand (entry) pallet. The
other (exit) pallet is raised and drop-off takes
place at the point marked with a cross. As can
be seen, the exiting tooth is free of the pallet
and has moved a small distance beyond it, but
the entry tooth can proceed no further until
the swing of the pendulum back towards the
centre raises the entry pallet. It is 'locked' (by
the mark only at the moment) and the lock is
the small amount of overlap shown in **Fig
4/16**. The curved surface on the outside of
the entry pallet and the inside of the exit are
the locking faces. The inside curve of the entry and the outside of the exit pallet are the
drop-off faces (**Fig4/17**).

As stated above, lock is defined as the

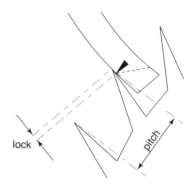

*Fig 4/15 The lock on the dead face should be 5-10%
of the pitch from the heel, ie the junction of the
impulse face and the dead face*

Fig 4/16 The entrance and exit drop-off points

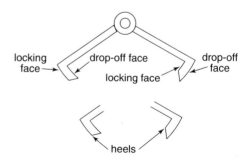

Fig 4/17 The locking and drop-off faces

mount of overlap of one escapewheel tooth
nd the pallet it engages, *when the other pallet
* *just touching a circle representing the outside
iameter of the wheel.* Lock can be measured
s an angle or a linear dimension.

Nothing happens instantaneously in a clock,
nd as a consequence, when the clock is actu-
lly working, lock occurs when the other pal-
t has lifted a tiny bit further than the bare
utside diameter of the wheel, but if the gear
ain is free and has low inertia, this divergence
om the theoretical is small enough to be ig-
ored. If the train is very sluggish then it *is*
ossible to have the one pallet begin its decent into the tooth space before the other
as been contacted by the locking tooth. This
not a happy situation and demonstrates the
ecessity of having lightly-made wheels with
w inertia and good bearings. It is also a de-
cription of the behaviour of a clock with sticky
brication; the clock will stop not simply be-
ause of friction but because of the resulting
nodification to the operating geometry of the
scapement.

Measuring Lock

he amount of lock is clearly important; if it
too great the escapement will need more
rop for the pallets to clear the back of the
scapewheel teeth, if there is too little, a slight
mount of wear on the edge or heel of the
allet (**Fig 4/5**) will allow the escapewheel
fall onto a surface that is inclined and re-
ult in the escapement recoiling. This will al-
nost certainly stop the clock, because a sys-
m in recoil needs more energy to operate.
Lock can be expressed as an angular move-

ment of the pallets, but it is difficult to measure small angles accurately, and another rule
of thumb is easier to apply. It is the same as
that for drop: 5-10 per cent of the pitch of
the escapewheel (only a precisely made clock
would operate successfully with the smaller
value). Making a measurement of the lock is
not easy; possibly the simplest method is to
use the depth probe that is incorporated in
most modern vernier callipers, and then to
scribe a mark on the face of the wheel tooth
on the entry side (**Fig 4/18**).

When the wheel is placed over the pallet
again (**Fig 4/19**) the lock is transferred to
the rough pallet to mark the heel of the impulse plane when its partner's drop-off point
is on the very tip of its escapewheel tooth.
Check that the inked or coppered surface is
still good enough to show the mark clearly;
after much handling it will probably need re-
newing. Arranging the mark so that the entry
and exit pallets look similar in size when the
impulse faces have been cut is a matter of
judgement. It is not a critical matter, unless
the discrepancy is so great that the arms of
the pallet body are in danger of touching the
escapewheel teeth on one side or the other.
Rough marking of both pallets with a fine fibre tip pen will help — the ink will show faintly
even on the blackened surface — and the exact mark for the heel should be scribed so that
the bright mark show clearly.

Fig 4/18 Measure the
amount of lock with the
depth probe of a vernier
calliper

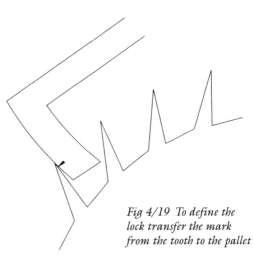

Fig 4/19 To define the
lock transfer the mark
from the tooth to the pallet

The new mark on the pallet, and that on the face of the escapewheel tooth, must be checked using a magnifying glass to obtain the closest possible match when the exit pallet is in the imagined drop-off position.

The locking of the exit pallet cannot be determined accurately until this first impulse face (entry) has been made. There are at least three methods of defining the angles of the impulse faces of the pallets.

Determining the Impulse Angles
• Approximation Method

This is accurate enough for large clocks such as longcase, semi-regulator or dial clocks, and though there is an error of around 5 per cent in the angle of the exit pallet this will normally make little or no difference. For precision regulator clocks, controlling the pendulum swing is a more important consideration than specifying the impulse angle, and for these clocks the more accurate method (and the alternative of grinding the faces) given on pages 111, 114-117 is recommended.

The impulse angle (measured between the impulse plane and the tangent) of the entry pallet is usually 35 degrees, and as long as the distance between pallet and wheel centres is kept within the normal range of 1.25 to 1.5 times the escapewheel radius, the movement will run easily on an 8lb weight — probably much less. That is assuming that the gear teeth and pivot sizes are not larger than normal for a semi-regulator. Say 0.7 module for the gears and 1.5mm diameter for the escapement pivots.

The impulse angle is determined by exactly the same geometry as that used for the anchor escapement (**Fig 3/9**, page 58), though the impulse angles are smaller and the tangents are drawn to a larger circle. Mount the escapewheel on the brass sheet again (**Fig 4/20**). The pallets are in position beneath it and the radii have already been defined. A disk of brass with an outside diameter of 0.82 times the wheel diameter is placed on the wheel arbor, to give an impulse angle at entry of 35 degrees (cos 35° = 0.82). On the drawing this

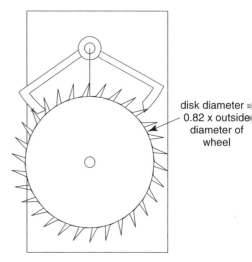

disk diameter = 0.82 x outside diameter of wheel

Fig 4/20 A disk 0.82 time the escapewheel diameter gives an entry pallet impulse angle of 35°

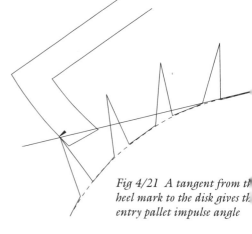

Fig 4/21 A tangent from th heel mark to the disk gives th entry pallet impulse angle

diameter corresponds approximately with th root of the wheel teeth — as it does on man old clocks.

The entry pallet is raised until the mark o its face (the heel marked from the locking mar on the wheel tooth) is level with the top c the wheel tooth (**Fig 4/21**) and it is strappe in place. Using a straightedge draw a line fron the tip of the wheel tooth through the hee mark, to make a tangent to the disk. This lin defines the impulse face and where it crosse the inner radius also defines the drop-off poin

Now take the marked escapement throug

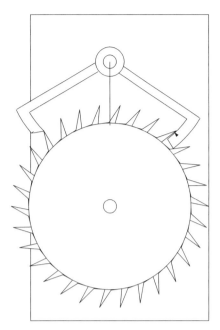

Fig 4/22 To determine the position of lock on the exit pallet a tooth should have just dropped off the entry pallet

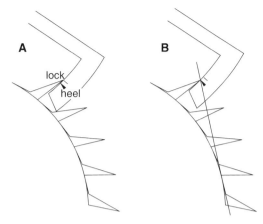

Fig 4/23 The depth of locking is marked (A, shown exaggerated), the tooth tip is moved to the heel mark and a tangent from the heel to the disk defines the exit pallet impulse face (B)

the actions of entry lock, impulse and drop-off, observing it closely to make sure that there is enough metal left for both filing an impulse face and obtaining the right amount of lock. When this is certain the entry pallet is filed and finished with fine emery paper on a metal backing. The impulse face is given a final polish and then the pallets are set back on the marking jig.

It is much easier to define the exit pallets while working the escapement against the finished entry impulse face rather than merely against marks on the pallet surface. The wheel is now rotated until the drop-off point of the entry pallet rests on the top of the tooth. It is again fastened down with a small strap and the escapewheel moved forward the small amount that is needed for it to rest against the locking face of the exit pallet (**Fig 4/22**).

The depth of the locking is marked. When the exit heel has been defined, the strap is released, the wheel eased back a little so that the pallet can be raised until the heel mark is at the top of the tooth and a tangential line

from the top of the tooth to the disk is marked with a straightedge in the same manner as the entry pallet (**Fig 4/23**). This is the final mark and it defines the exit impulse face and the drop-off point. It is filed and polished and the result is tested against the wheel at frequent intervals.

This is a workshop method and, since many escapewheels have a depth of tooth that places their roots on the 0.82 diameter of the wheel, it is quite probably the method that was used for the common deadbeat escapement, the craftsman laying his straight edge to the root circle rather than making a separate disk.

• **More Precise Method**

For accurate regulator clocks the angle through which the pallets swing to release the wheel should be precisely equal on entry and exit and, more importantly, small. If the heels of the pallets and the drop off points are defined so that the angle that these two make with the centre of the pallet arbor is the same on both sides, these aims will be achieved. The following marking system ensures that each pair of heel and drop off points has the same relationship to the wheel centre. It is essentially the same marking system as before, but the tangent circles are governed by different disks for each pallet, specifically dimensioned

Making an Ordinary Deadbeat Escapement — Summary

1 Scribe a centre line on a metal plate and drill two holes to accept the pallet and escapewheel arbors at their correct centres.

2 Turn a boss on a high-carbon steel plate large enough to make the pallets from. Make a rod, halved at one end and a very small centre dot at the other.

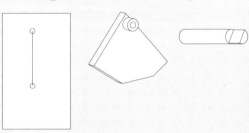

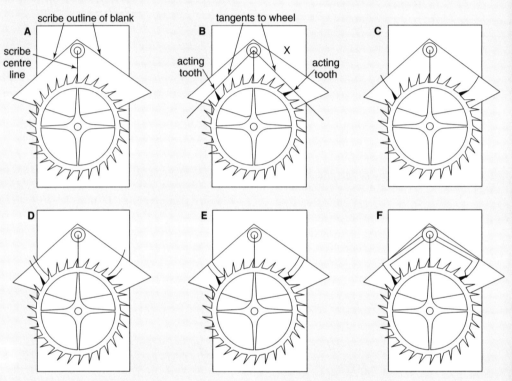

3 Mount the wheel, blank and arbors on the drilled plate. Mark the parts so that they can be realigned on the plate.

4 For an even number of teeth line up a tooth tip with the centre line (**A**). For an odd number the line should pass through the middle of a tooth space.

5 Draw tangential lines from the centre of the rod (using its flat and a straightedge) to both sides of the wheel. The acting teeth are those nearest to the tangent points (**B**).

6 Use the other end of the rod to provide a centre and draw arcs from the tips of the acting teeth using a pair of dividers (**C**).

7 Shorten the radius of the dividers to produce arcs at the mid-point of the adjacent tooth spaces (**D**).

8 Mark the length of the pallets to leave plenty of metal for the rest of the marking out (**E**) and outline the body of the pallets (**F**).

9 Cut out and file the pallet body.

10 Decide upon the drop to be used (5-10% of tooth pitch), measure the locking (dead) faces and alter the radii of the inner and outer curves accordingly.

11 File or machine these curves to the finished dimensions, checking with vernier callipers (use the boss turned on the pallet body for locating one jaw of the vernier). Polish.

12 Determine the lock for the entry pallet (5-10% of tooth pitch) and mark the heel of the pallet. Make sure that there is enough metal on the other pallet for it to lock in its turn and leave both pallets fairly equal in length.

13 Lift the heel mark of the entry pallet to the acting toothtip and clamp it in position.

14 Make a tangent from the tip of this tooth to either the base circle of the teeth or a prepared disc and scribe this tangent across the entry pallet to define its impulse face.

15 File and polish the impulse face.

16 Reassemble the wheel and pallets, partly rotating the wheel so that the exiting tooth lies against the inside curve of the exit pallet.

17 Position the entry pallet in the drop-off state and mark the required lock on the exit pallet.

18 Lift the exit pallet until the heel is at the tip of the escapewheel tooth.

19 Using a straightedge scribe a tangent from the tooth tip to the tooth base circle or the prepared disk, to define the impulse face.

20 Carefully file a surface parallel to this line using a fine file when getting close to the line.

21 Test the pallets against the wheel by mounting both in the clock plates and con-

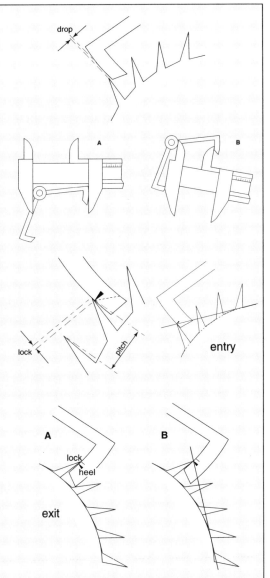

tinue filing the impulse face until the pallet operates on a full rotation of the wheel. Polish the surface with reducing grades of emery paper until the pallet work easily.

22 Heat both pallets to red heat, quench in oil or water and then polish. Stress relieve the pallets by warming in a flame until the pallet tips are a *very* faint amber colour. Repolish all working surfaces.

for the escapement's span, number of teeth and arc of pendulum. For small impulsing arcs, as required for a precision regulator, the two disks to define the entry and exit pallets are virtually the same diameter. The inner and outer radii of the pallets and the clearances are produced as previously described so that the drop is already defined and the same figures are referred to.

Disks that will fit on the wheel arbor are prepared according to **Table 2**. The disk diameter is calculated to produce the correct tangents for the impulse faces, by using a straightedge (**Figs 4/20-21**).

The lock and the heel of the pallet are marked in the same manner as before. Beginning with the entry side, the heel is placed on the top of the wheel tooth and clamped in position. With a straightedge draw a line from the tooth tip to form a tangent to the disk. Where the line crosses the inner radius of the entry pallet defines the drop-off point (**Fig 4/21**).

The impulse face is filed to match this line, and then finished with a fine file and emery paper on a block. All burrs are removed from the edges.

The entry drop-off is now placed on the top of a wheel tooth (**Fig 4/22**) and the heel of the exit pallet marked for lock. The exit heel is lifted to the top of a wheel tooth and clamped. Again the straightedge is used to make a tangent from the pallet centre to the disk to define the impulse face and the drop-off point (**Fig 4/23**). The heel and drop-off are filed and finished as before. This method gives precisely equal angles to the operation of the escapement.

Note that it is safest to finish the second pallet face by trying the escapement in the clock plates. This allows for any error in the parallelism of the clock arbors, or damage done to the plates over the years. The tangent circle will not be altered, but it may be necessary to alter the heel mark to obtain the correct lock.

The table shows the diameter of disks needed to obtain different angles of swing of

	disk diameter					
	6°		3°		2°	
ratio	entry	exit	entry	exit	entry	exit
1.25	0.83	0.87	0.95	0.96	0.98	0.99
1.38	0.71	0.79	0.90	0.93	0.99	0.95
1.50	0.71	0.73	0.90	0.91	0.95	0.94
1.63	0.71	0.67	0.89	0.89	0.94	0.93
1.75	0.54	0.67	0.81	0.85	0.94	0.92
1.88	0.54	0.61	0.80	0.83	0.90	0.92
2.00	0.54	0.57	0.79	0.79	0.90	0.89

Table 4/1 Diameter of disks to fit over the escape-wheel arbor to produce a total arc of the pallets (excluding supplementary arc) of either 6° or 3° for various centre distance/escapewheel radius ratios and a 30-tooth escapewheel. For small swings the two disks are virtually the same diameter. (See Fig 4/24 to calculate the disk diameters for escapements of different proportions)

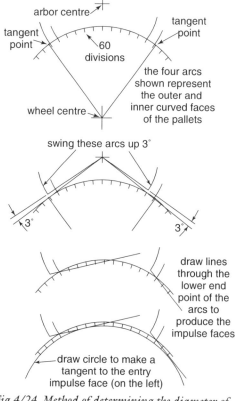

Fig 4/24 Method of determining the diameter of dics for making deadbeat pallet for precise lifting arcs. Note that for clarity the circle for the exit pallet is not shown, as it is almost the same as that for the entry pallet

the crutch, for a given centre distance/wheel radius ratio. They are based on a wheel diameter of unity (with unstated units of measurement). The method of defining these disks shown in **Fig 4/24** may be used to obtain values not given in the table.

Two centres are drawn for the pallet and wheel arbors and a circle representing the wheel is drawn on the latter. The circle is divided with twice the number of teeth, to mark both the tooth tips and the mid-points of the tooth spaces, and with centre line over one of the divisions. (It does not matter if the wheel has an even or odd count, and it is not necessary to consider which divisions mark the tooth tips and which the mid-points — they simply mark all the possible working positions of tips and mid-points.)

Draw tangents from the pallet centre to the outside diameter of the wheel and note where they touch (tangent points). For Table 4/1 the outer radius of the pallets was placed nearest to the tangent points — this is simply the designer's choice. Draw arcs centred on the pallet centre to the divisions closest to the tangent points and to the neighbouring divisions (towards the centre). These arcs represent the inner and out curves of the pallets without any clearance or drop.

The outermost entry arc is rotated about its centre by the angle desired for the total pallet swing (excluding suplementary arc), lifting it from the wheel division. A line representing the impulse face is drawn from the lowest end of the outer arc to the lower end of the inner arc (which coincides with the top of a division). This line is extended so that a circle can be drawn about the wheel centre to make a tangent to it. This circle is the diameter of disk needed to produce the impulse face.

Similarly on the exit side, swing the inner arc on anticlockwise to lift it from the wheel circle and so produce the disk needed for the exit impulse face. In many cases the difference between the disks for entry and exit will be too small to have any practical effect.

• **Impulsing Arc**
It must be noted that the arcs referred to in the table apply to the pallets and crutch and not necessarily to the pendulum. Some regulators have pendulums hung above the pallet arbor, such that the pendulum swing is only half that of the crutch, but thsi causes friction between the crutch pin and the pendulum.

A typical impulsing (or escaping) arc for a precion regulator is about 1 degree either side of the vertical, with a supplementary arc of about $\frac{1}{2}$ degree, giving a total pendulum swing of about 3 degrees. The clockmaker making a replacement escapement must decide for himself the swing needed. The beat plate and also the count of the pinion leaves in the going train are a good indication of what was originally intended. Pinions of not less than twelve leaves (except on the escape pinion) are usually found in a true regulator with a total swing of 3 degrees. Semi-regulators — high-quality clocks that were nevertheless not accurate to the few seconds a year required of a true regulator — often used pinion counts nearer to a longcase's eight leaves and a total pendulum swing of 6 degrees. The pendulum swings quoted include the lock.

For a given amount of lock, the locking angle becomes smaller as the centre distance between the arbors is increased. A regulator with a thirty-tooth escapewheel, a 5 per cent lock and a centre distance equal to twice the escapewheel radius will have an angle of lock of 0.17 degrees (10 seconds of arc).

On the other hand, if the centre distance is decreased to one and a half times the wheel radius with the same amount of locking (5 per cent of the pitch), the angle of lock becomes 0.27 degrees (17 seconds of arc). It might seem that the amount of work done in overcoming locking friction is affected by the distance between centres, as the moment arm for the frictional load on the pallets increases with increasing centre distance. However, the larger moment arm occurs when the escapement has the greater distance between centres and the length of time that this affects the escapement is smaller. Overall, the amount of friction remains substantially the same for different centre distances.

The centre distances are chosen for the clockmaker's convenience, not as a function of the escapement's efficiency.

• **Grinding the Impulse Faces**

This is a modification of the previous method, so that the impulse faces may be machined on a grinder or a grinding attachment on a lathe. The impulse faces are defined by disks centred on the *pallet* arbor (rather than on the escapewheel arbor) that will produce the same tangents for the impulse faces as the disks defined earlier.

Mark the tangents from the heel of the entry pallet to a disk on the escapewheel arbor, as given in **Table 4/1**, as just described. Take these marks and extend a line across the brass plate (**Fig 4/25**).

A circle centred on the pallet arbor must now be found to which this line forms a tangent. Though geometric construction may be used to find this tangent circle, it is just as easy to draw a circle with dividers based on the pallet centre to just touch the line through the heel and drop-off point.

This is repeated for the exit pallet, where, depending on the escapement geometry, a circle of a different diameter than for the entrance pallet may be necessary.

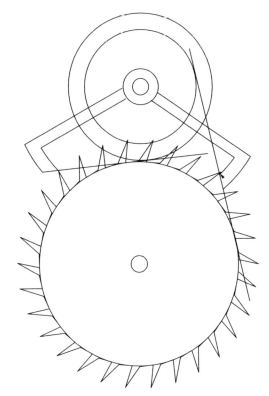

Fig 4/25 Tangent circles to the impulse faces are drawn centred on the escapwheel arbor and these are then used to produce disks centred on the pallet arbor

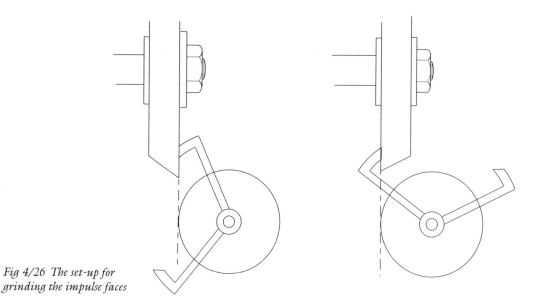

Fig 4/26 The set-up for grinding the impulse faces

		disk diameter			
		30-tooth		32-tooth	
ratio	angle	entry	exit	entry	exit
1.25	2°	0.20	0.10	0.19	0.18
	3°	0.26	0.18	0.27	0.25
	6°	0.41	0.35	0.46	0.46
1.50	2°	0.40	0.30	0.41	0.40
	3°	0.54	0.45	0.57	0.56
	6°	0.79	0.75	0.86	0.84

Table 4/2 Diameter of disks to fit over the pallet arbor for a total impulsing arc of 2°, 3° or 6° and two centre distance/escapewheel radius ratios. Different disks are needed for 30-teeth escapewheels, but for 32 teeth they are virtually the same

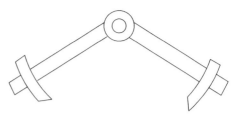

Fig 4/27 Vulliamy-type adjustable deadbeat pallets can have their impulse faces ground without reference to the heel

Alternatively the values in **Table 4/2** may be used. This gives the disk diameters for thirty and thirty-two teeth wheels, with two ratios of centre distance/escapewheel radius and two angles of total swing (not crutch semi-arch).

A grinding wheel is set up as shown in **Fig 4/26**, the radius of the circles just drawn representing the distance between the pallet centre and the working face of the wheel. The pallet should lie flat on the table of the grinder and allowed to rotate about the arbor axis. When the impulse angle of a pair of pallets of the fixed type is being made by this method the surface is ground until it just touches the heel of the impulse face.

For a one-off repair this is not a particu-

larly useful method. However, if the pallets are of the type that consist of separate pieces of curved steel set in a body and capable of being adjusted to give the correct locking (Vulliamy-type, **Fig 4/27**), the system is quick and easy since it is not necessary to take careful note of the heel position.

A simple (although time consuming) jig that forms a guide for stoning the impulse faces by hand is shown in **Fig 4/28**. Since the stone will bear on this as well as on the pallets, it should be made from hardened steel and the stone should have a good flat surface and be much wider than the pallets — so that the guide controls the alignment of the stone easily. Basically it is good for lightly-worn pallets or very small ones, and it is a 'one-off'. It cannot be expected that another escapement requiring the same size of jig will be found. However if the guiding surfaces are made of

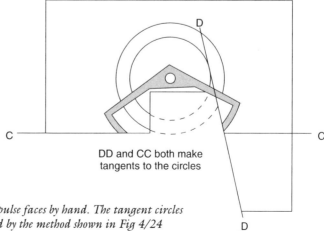

DD and CC both make tangents to the circles

Fig 4/28 A simple jig for grinding impulse faces by hand. The tangent circles are found from Table 4/2, or calculated by the method shown in Fig 4/24

tungsten carbide and mounted on sub-plates so that they can be adjusted to form tangents to a range of circles, the jig can be made useful for many years of workshop use.

The geometry of the deadbeat escapement is complex — the foregoing chapters make it capable of being produced without very expensive tooling — and a small error will give uneven drop, probably uneven locking too. If, at the end of the work, it is found that there are small errors the piece should not be discarded in disgust. *Small* errors are acceptable, so long as the escapement works cleanly without catching on the top of the escapewheel teeth, and locks positively. Comparison with antique examples will prove the truth of this.

Machining Pallets

So far the making of the inner and outer radii by machine tool has not been considered. **Fig 4/29** shows a form of pallets that, because of the offset of the arms, allows the radii to be bored out to calculated dimensions on a lathe rather than marking them out and then filing. Non-distorting, high-carbon steel (eg gauge plate) must be used for these pallets.

Small escapements (such as used in watches and platform escapements) have to be calculated in their entirety — the outer and inner radius (this is relatively easy, see **Fig 4/30**),

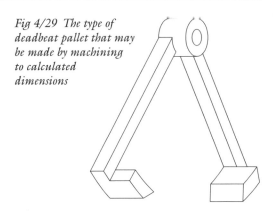

Fig 4/29 The type of deadbeat pallet that may be made by machining to calculated dimensions

the angles of lock and impulse, and one or two other little matters. These all require precise geometry, a means of very accurately measuring the angles, and do not come within the scope of this book.

For the normal clockmaking workshop only the calculation of the radii of the inner and outer curves (and the tangent circles for the impulse faces) are of any practical use.

Fig 4/30 shows how the inner and outer radii are calculated. The circumference of the escapewheel is divided into twice the number of equal divisions as there are teeth; it is not necessary to know which ones actually represent tooth tips. A tangent is drawn to determine which of the marks comes nearest to the tangent point and then angle A is calculated by counting the number of divisions from the

Finishing & Heat Treating Pallets

To finish the pallets, polish outside and inside radii and the impulse faces, and coat with ordinary soap to protect them during heat treatment. This is exactly the same process as already used on other escapement pallets. This is a hardening process and the pallets should be left without any tempering treatment, although stress relieving at about 150-200°C is a worthwhile insurance against damage to the pallet arms.

Raise both pallets to bright red heat, but not so high that the metal gives off sparks. Hold it at this temperature for a couple of minutes and then dip the tips only into water or oil. The former will produce a slightly harder surface in gauge plate, but the difference under workshop conditions will be indiscernible over the decades. Oil cools less abruptly and the small chance of developing cracks in the steel will be even smaller. After quenching polish the working surfaces and the sides of the pallet. Make sure that the hole for the arbor is clean of dust and oil, so that when it is assembled in the clock, Loctite or a similar adhesive can be used to fasten it in position.

Fig 4/30 Calculation of the precise dimensions of the dead faces when machining deadbeat pallets on a lathe

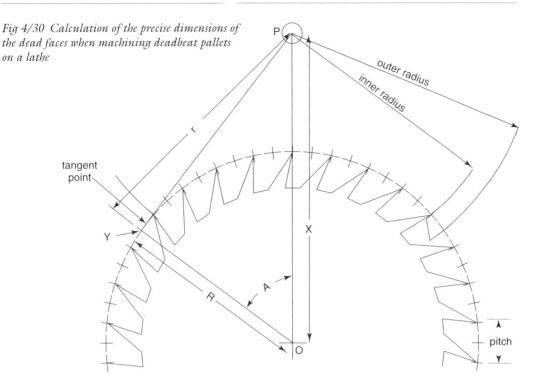

Divide the circle into twice as many divisions as there are teeth (60 divisions in this example).
Place the mid-point between two teeth, Y, as near as possible to the tangent point to give the outer radius of the pallets.
As Y is not necessarily on the tangent point, OPY may not be a right-angle triangle, hence

$$r = \sqrt{(X^2 + R^2 - 2XR\cos A)}, \quad \text{where angle } A = \frac{\text{number of divisions from vertical to Y x 360}}{\text{twice the number of teeth}}$$

R is the unadjusted radius of the entry pallet locking face and the exit pallet drop-off face.
To operate properly clearance the outer radius must be reduced by the clearance and the inner radius increased by the clearance

$$\text{clearance } C = \frac{\text{pitch}}{2} \text{ x } 0.05$$

centre line. The angle between any two divisions will be 360 divided by the number of divisions (not the number of teeth).

In the drawing there are sixty divisions, which results in 6 degrees per division. The nearest division to the tangent point is Y, and there are nine spaces from the centre line, hence A = 54 degrees.

The trigonometrical equation should not be allowed to complicate matters, as many electronic calculators are capable of dealing with functions such as cos. The figures can simply be fed in and the answer taken directly from the machine — so long as a rough check is then made with compasses to make sure that a decimal point has not been misplaced.

If the centre distance between the wheel and pallets is not already set by an existing clock, it is recommended making it 1½ times the escapewheel radius. The number of teeth on the wheel is decided by the train-wheel calculations and pendulum length, and whatever the result this method of making the pallets will cope quite happily.

Making Vulliamy-Style Pallets

The determination of the dimensions of this variation of the deadbeat is exactly the same as for the other type pallets, but since it can so easily be made on the lathe the dimensions calculated from **Fig 4/30** are particularly applicable.

The example shown in **Fig 4/31** is for a 30-tooth escapewheel of 25mm diameter and the centre distance of the arbors 1½ times the escapewheel radius. For an escapewheel of different diameter, all the calculated dimensions will be in direct proportion. The dimensions of the escapement, calculated to two decimal places, are:

escapewheel diameter	25.00mm
tooth pitch	2.61mm
centre distance	18.75mm
outside radius	13.95mm
inside radius	12.62mm

From the pitch the clearance C is calculated to be 2.61 x .05 x .5 = 0.065mm.

The corrected outside radius is therefore: 13.95 – 0.065 = **13.88mm** and the corrected inside radius is: 12.62 + 0.065 = **12.69mm**.

The two figures in bold type form the basis of the dimensions actually machined into the pallet body and the pallet ring of the Vulliamy escapement. For escapewheels of 25-35mm diameter and a pallet clearance of 5 per cent the manufacturing tolerances of the *pallet ring* can be taken as:

outside radius   + 0.00mm, – 0.02mm
inside radius   + 0.02mm, – 0.00mm.

Since these pallets will be made on a lathe it must be remembered that the dimensions and tolerances given above refer to radii — they must be doubled when considering diameters.

The clearances for the working of the escapement have been calculated, but the machined parts (the body and the ring) need their own clearances for one to fit the other. When making a one-off these clearances can be obtained by simply making the ring to the inner and out radii (and the tolerances) given above, and boring out the curved slot in the pallet

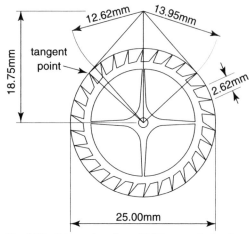

Fig 4/31 Dimensions for a Vulliamy-style deadbeat escapement

body until it will accept the ring.

However, if more than one escapement is to be made or if for any reason it is not convenient to use the ring as a manufacturing gauge for the body, manufacturing tolerances must be applied to the body.

The ring should be treated as the part that is made to the defining dimensions — which simply means that its needs determine which way the tolerances go. Since it must not encroach on the pallet tolerances (5 per cent and 10 per cent) this means that the outside radius may be a little smaller and the inside a little larger

The body provides the clearances that enable the ring to enter the slots. The fit should be considered as a sliding fit, which means that the tolerances on both parts of the escapement will not interfere when assembled. Otherwise the working surfaces of the pallet will be misaligned by the slots controlling their position along the pallet arms.

The tolerances for the *body* therefore provide additional clearance between the mating faces of body and ring:

outside radius: + 0.025mm, + 0.04mm
inside radius: – 0.005mm, – 0.02mm

When working with pallet clearances based on 10 per cent of the pitch these tolerances are doubled.

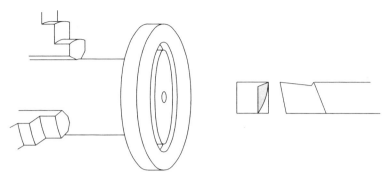

Fig 4/32 Large body blanks are best sweated onto a bar held in the lathe chuck. The shape of the lathe tool needed to bore the outer diameter of the slot is shown on the right

• **Turning the Body & Pallets**

The pallet body is usually machined from free-cutting brass — it has no need to be particularly strong and, when polished, provides a good looking contrast to the steel pallets. If the pallets are not large (not requiring a radius of more than about 35mm) they may be turned and bored directly from a bar of brass, but this does require a parting off blade that will reach to the centre of the bar and most clockmaking workshops may not have such a tool.

An alternative procedure is to tin a blank (with side to be tinned already faced flat) and then sweat it onto a faced bar that can be held in the chuck (**Fig 4/32**). This avoids the need to use a long parting off tool — and also accommodates large diameters of blank.

As can be seen, it is relatively simple to cut a slot to the dimensions required and to produce the hole for mounting on the arbor at one set-up so that all three diameters are absolutely concentric. The outer diameter of the slot requires a boring tool that resembles a small parting-off tool (**Fig 4/32**), with its left-hand side swept away in a radius to clear the sides of the slot being machined. **Fig 4/33** shows the outline of the pallet body against the turned blank that it is to be cut from.

It is not really necessary to describe this uncomplicated machining task in any greater detail except to point out that if an integral collet is wanted to steady the pallet body on the arbor this can be turned at the same time by using a thick blank. Which face the collet is turned on is a matter of choice, but since putting it on the opposite side to the slot re-

quires the provision of a clearance hole in the bar that it is sweated to, the mounting hole for the arbor should not be made until the pieces are sweated together.

In addition there should be enough clearance between the hole in the bar and the outside diameter of the collet to ensure that solder does not bridge the gap. Otherwise this will make the job of parting the two pieces after machining difficult. The outside of the collet can be machined to be concentric after all other machining is complete, by mounting the slotted blank on a temporary mandrel and taking light cuts over it.

A similar technique to the above is used for machining the pallet ring. It is not usually very convenient for the clockmaker to obtain high-carbon steel of a sufficient diameter to machine a complete ring but gauge plate (flat ground stock) is readily available. Since the pallets have to be hardened the steel must be specified as being 'non-distorting'.

A width of plate must be chosen that allows for the fact that the boring and turning of this material (which is fairly tough even in its annealed condition) are both 'interrupted' cuts. Bounce occurs as the metal hits the tool

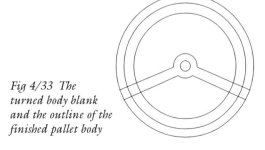

Fig 4/33 The turned body blank and the outline of the finished pallet body

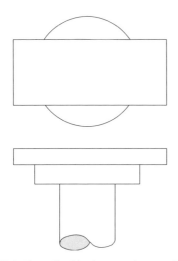

Fig 4/34 The pallet blank sweated onto a bar

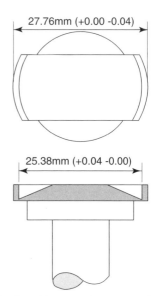

27.76mm (+0.00 -0.04)

25.38mm (+0.04 -0.00)

Fig 3/35 The pallets turned to precise dimensions

and there is a lesser variation in the position of the tool tip as it clears the trailing edge. These two effects leave areas of the pallets that must be discarded after machining.

The face of the ring should be machined and polished before turning and boring to make sure that this operation does not result in any damage to the finished dimensions of the inside and outside pallet faces. Use a lower lathe speed when finish-turning and boring than that usually recommended for this grade of steel with a high-speed steel (HSS) tool (70ft/min, 20m/min) to minimise the effects of the interrupted cut. Recommended speeds are 35ft/min and 10m/min.

Boring is also a trepanning operation (**Figs 4/34, 4/35**). If there is any doubt about machining the depth of the inside diameter accurately enough to avoid the piece breaking away before boring is finished, extend the diameter of the brass facing that it is sweated to so that the ring is also held by the solder. This is a weak support, only capable of sustaining the smallest of cuts, so that care must still be taken by measuring the depth of the bore.

When both diameters are finished the areas affected by bounce should be determined by measurement and then marked with a felt-

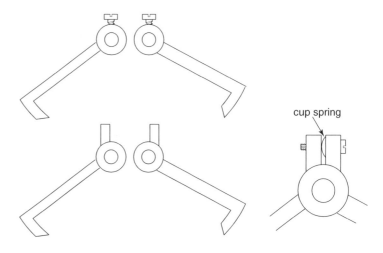

cup spring

Fig 4/36 Alternative types of adjustable deadbeat pallets

ip pen so that they can be filed away before
he impulse faces are dealt with. Final parting
of the pallets from the rest of the steel is car-
ied out by rotating the chuck by hand and
carefully advancing the boring tool (still set
on its last cut), until the pieces come away.

The rough corner that is left should be
chamfered with fine emery paper supported
on a round brass bar. Polishing the bore and
he outside curves is carried out in the same
fashion, finishing on flour paper (1000-2000
grit), a flat support being used for the outside. This can be made easier by 'gluing' the
pieces to the end of a shaped brass bar with
shellac.

The establishment of the impulse faces is
achieved by mounting in the body and using
he methods described earlier. Adjusting
Vulliamy pallets is discussed on pages 125-128.

Apart from Vulliamy pallets there are other
adjustable variants of the deadbeat escapement
(**Fig 4/36**). Here the pallets are made as separate arms that are locked to the arbor independently, either by means of screws or Loc-
ite, or by soldering one arm to the arbor and
fixing the position of the other in relation to
it by a screw.

Bent-Strip Deadbeat Pallets

Since the nature of a bent-strip escapement is
hat the pallets are made from steel that is easily
bent to shape before hardening, the strip has
little thickness. As a result the impulse faces
are relatively short and this leads to the de-

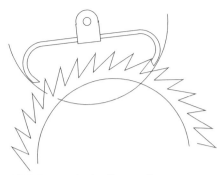

Fig 4/37 Bent strip deadbeat pallets

signer using a wheel with a short pitch and
rather large drop.

The effect of a large part of the wheel's
rotation failing to pass energy to the pallets
(during drop) is that the movement has to
have small pivots, efficient gears (lantern pinions for instance) and have rather more energy available to it than is the case in movements with either solid or Vulliamy-style pallets.

The pallets (**Fig 4/37**) are significantly different to bent-strip recoil escapements, so that
there is small chance of confusing the two
types of clock, but they are *very* similar to the
half-deadbeat employed in American clocks by
the Ingraham and Gilbert companies.

A deadbeat bent-strip escapement has locking faces that are truly so — they closely conform to a circular arc centred on the pallet
centre. The half-deadbeat however has a
slight amount of recoil on the entry pallet

deadbeat

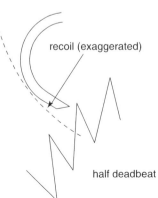

recoil (exaggerated)

half deadbeat

*Fig 4/38 Comparison between
deadbeat and half-deadbeat
bent-strip pallets*

because, if the faces do conform to a true arc, the centre is above the pallet centre (**Fig 4/38**). On the exit side this produces draw, pulling the pallets in towards the wheel. Limited recoil is seen in Berthoud's escapement and at least one horologist (W. J. Gazeley) defines a recoil anchor of this style as a 'half deadbeat'.

Because of the large amount of drop and

the fact that there is not, apparently, a short-span bent-strip deadbeat (or half-deadbeat) escapement, the impulse angle may be set to the same tangent circle for entry and exit. This circle appears to coincide with the crossing out rim in both Ingraham and Gilbert types. It produces a steeper impulse angle than is common for solid pallets — probably a necessity given the size of drop.

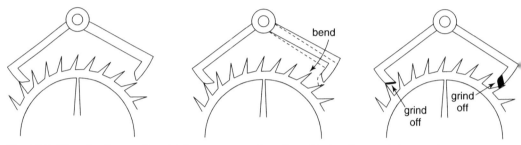

Fig 4/39 Worn deadbeat pallet with long arms may be adjusted by bending and the impulse faces ground, but only if less than 0.010in (0.25mm) is removed

3 Repairing & Adjusting Deadbeat Pallets

Repairing Graham Deadbeat Pallets

It is sometimes possible to repair Graham pallets. The simplest method can be applied when the arms of the pallets are relatively long and

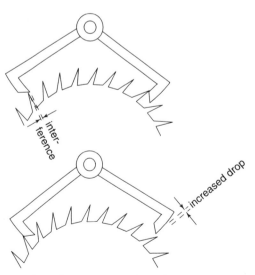

Fig 4/40 The effect of grinding the impulse faces is to cause interference on the entrance pallet (top) and increased drop on the exit pallet (bottom)

allow a slight amount of bending inwards (**Fig 4/39**). The impulse faces are then ground or stoned.

However the escapement geometry is severely affected by this. Because the arms bend rather than rotating about the pallet arbor centre, the inner and outer radii are no longer true arcs on one, or possibly both, pallets. This leads to an increased drop on one and interference between tooth and pallet on the other (**Fig 4/40**). As can be seen it is only possible to repair pallets successfully if the amount of stoning required is no more than about 0.010in on each impulse face, and it is necessary to stone the inner radius too. The procedure must be approached with caution and the result examined critically before judging the repair to be adequate.

One satisfactory way to correct badly worn solid pallets is to make shaped pieces of hardened steel and solder them in place (**Fig 4/41**). It is easiest to begin with rectangular sections for the inserts. This gives a better shape for the joint, making a seat for the in-

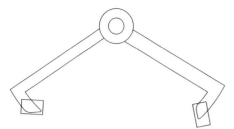

Fig 4/41 When using rectangular inserts to repair worn deadbeat pallets, the new locking faces must not have a joint where the escapewheel tooth rubs

ert that is more secure than the simple spring-steel slip utilised in repairing a recoil pallet. The seating should be filed to suit the rectangle and then the latter roughed out to avoid excessive stoning after it has been hardened and soldered in position.

The joint between the insert and the original metal must be clear of the region swept by the escapewheel teeth, otherwise the soft material will wear into a valley that will badly affect the smooth running of the escapement.

This is not an easy repair to make — particularly on small escapements where the difficulties of handling tiny inserts are great. In that case it is probably easier to make a new pair of pallets and, if retention of the original design is not important, to replace them with pallets of the Vulliamy type. Alternatively, new nibs fitted to the arms with screws, similar to those shown in Chapter 7 for repairing a pinwheel escapement (**Fig 7/11**), may be used.

Adjusting Vulliamy Pallets

Vulliamy escapements, of course, usually only need new pallets and the making of these is discussed in the preceding section. The arrangement of Vulliamy pallets within the clock plates and their adjustment can be seen in **Fig 4/42**. The shaded disk represents the eccentric bush which raises and lowers the arbor — often only one end is so equipped, with the result that the pallets are tilted when adjusted in this way, but the effect is small and of no real consequence.

Fig 4/42A shows the pallet arbor at the proper centre distance from the escapewheel

and with the pallet nibs extended the correct amount from the body. Both working conditions are illustrated: entrance and exit for a lock and drop of 5 per cent of the pitch and a semi-arc of 2 degrees. In **Fig 4/42B** the eccentric bush has been rotated clockwise to lift the arbor so that the centres are too far apart. On the left it can be seen that the entrance pallet has lifted off the wheel, while the exit pallet is in recoil because the exiting tooth has missed the lock. On the right the same thing happens to the entry pallet. Note that if the pallets are extended towards the wheel the right-hand diagram can be made to lock after the exit pallet drops, but the left-hand diagram simply jams.

It must be remembered that there is a fixed distance between the working tooth tips which must correspond with the heel (locked) and drop-off points of the pallets. When the pallets are extended or retracted the distance between heel and drop-off points is altered and no longer corresponds with the fixed distance on the wheel. The distance between the wheel teeth is reduced if the outside diameter has to be machined because of tooth damage.

Under that circumstance the pallets can be extended until measurement with vernier callipers shows that the distance between heel and drop-off points (across the two pallet nibs) is a close match with the distance between the working teeth. *Note that different teeth are involved for the two positions of the pallet body and the distances are therefore also different.*

In **Fig 4/42C** the pallet arbor is on the correct centre but the pallets are withdrawn — it can be seen that if the entry pallet is extended (either pallet would do, but this gives similar extension to both) it will move into the correct drop-off point. The arbor in **Fig 4/42D** is too low and an attempt to correct this by withdrawing the pallets results in recoil on the exit pallet.

Setting the pallet so that the distance between heel and drop-off matches the distance between the relative teeth when lock is applied is a first step in correcting Vulliamy pallets. The height is then changed until the es-

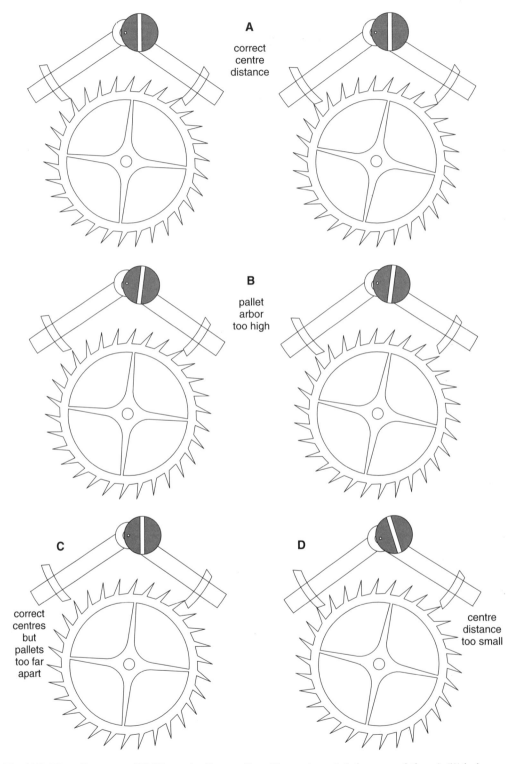

Fig 4/42 The adjustment of Vulliamy deadbeat pallets. The semi-arc is 2 degress and there is 5% lock

capement works, or until it becomes clear that a small adjustment of the pallets will make it do so.

• An Alternative Method of Setting Vulliamy Pallets

If the movement is disassembled and the plate, pallet and wheel arbors can be manipulated in full sight, then the Vulliamy escapement can be adjusted by establishing the centre distance first (**Fig 4/43**).

The two arcs for the pallets, inner and outer have been extended so that they cut the full circle of the escapewheel from side to side. This is the track that the pallets must follow when they are adjusted — there is no other. Consequently if the centre distance is adjusted until these arcs are equidistant from the nearest tooth tip and the nearest midpoint of the tooth pitch (as shown), the centre distance must be correct.

The actual position of the pallets themselves is unimportant because there is nothing that can be done to them that will either increase or decrease the true drop of the pallets, which is the movement that the escapewheel tooth

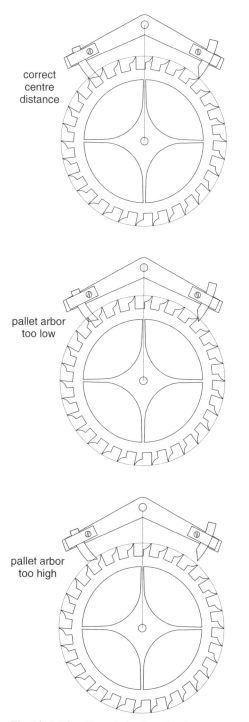

correct centre distance

pallet arbor too low

pallet arbor too high

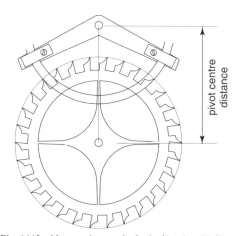

Fig 4/43 Alternative method of adjusting Vulliamy pallets. As the pallet radii is fixed there is only one correct distance between the pivot centres. Adjust the centres until the curved surfaces of the pallets (with allowance for clearance) pass through the tooth tips and the mid-points of the tooth pitches. All subsequent adjustments are made to the pallets — not the centre distance

Fig 4/44 The effect of altering the pivot centre distance (clearances not shown). It can be seen that if the centres are wrong then no amount of adjustment to the pallets will correct matters

makes to strike the locking arc of the pallet at entry or exit.

It should be noted that if there is any discrepancy (ie if one pallet has inner and outer arcs that are not continuations of the other), then this method cannot be used — and it is doubtful that the escapement is as the maker designed it. The pallet centres are shown raised and lowered from the proper position in **Fig 4/44** to show the error that will result.

If the entry pallet has an impulse angle that makes a tangent to a circle of about 80 per cent of the wheel diameter it is probably correct and can be used to check the exit impulse face. To construct the exit impulse angle:
• With the lock set on the entry pallet mark a point on the exit pallet outer arc that corresponds with the wheel circumference — this defines the toe.
• With the toe of the entry pallet on the tip of a tooth mark the exit pallet inner arc where it crosses the wheel circumference.
• Below this mark, and by an amount that equals the lock on the entry pallet, mark the heel of the impulse face.
• Join heel and toe to form the impulse face.

A simple set-up using the clock plates and two turned collars to support the wheel and the pallet body in the pivot holes is illustrated in **Fig 4/45**. This enables the repairer to make

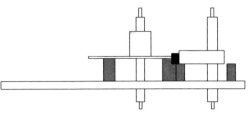

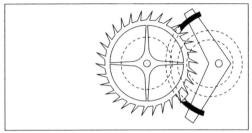

Fig 4/45 Supporting the whel and pallets using the clock plates and two turned collars

a very accurate adjustment of the Vulliamy pallets. As an alternative a piece of brass plate can be drilled with holes to suit the arbor diameters, one of them drilled into an eccentric bush for adjustment.

If there is any reason to believe that the existing entry impulse face is not at the original angle it will need to be defined by the probable arc of the crutch — refer to the description of making the escapement on pages 113-115.

4 Deadbeat Escapements — Faults & Comments

Tangent Points
It is frequently stated that the placing of the acting teeth relative to the escapewheel is important, and in earlier pages that has been disputed — or at least it has been claimed that it is not vitally important to place the pallets so when making or repairing the escapement.

Fig 4/46 examines the difference between the two extreme situations. In A the pressure of the escapewheel tooth is truly radial to the pallet circle; this is the case when the acting tooth is at the tangent point of the wheel's circumference. In B the pressure is shown taking place at a point on the pallet circle where it barely engages the circle — a touch more

and it would miss it completely. Though the second situation may apper to be absurd, there are characteristics which are the same in both:
• The wheel tooth is locked.
• There is no tendency for the pallet circle to rotate under the influence of the tooth. There is no draw or recoil.

From the point of view of a clockmaker wishing to make a deadbeat escapement there is nothing wrong with the second arrangement — if we ignore the impossibility of obtaining any sort of impulse!

What is disastrously wrong is that an enormous load is placed upon both pallet and wheel arbors. This situation is very close to

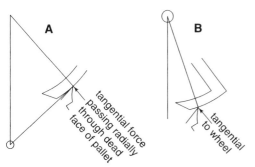

Fig 4/46 The effect of the active escapewheel teeth being at the tangent point (A), and where it is not (B). Despite the extreme situation shown in B the dead face will still slide past without exerting any force on the tooth other than friction

that of the linkage of a knuckle press — if a common pivot was substituted for the point of contact then it would *be* a knuckle joint.

All the intermediate positions from this to the condition of radial pressure produce lessening loads on the bearings until the minimum is reached at the tangent point of the escapewheel. This is the total of the effects produced by straying away from this preferred point.

Since friction is the load multiplied by the coefficient of friction, the frictional losses of the escapement will be smallest when the tangent point is used to place the acting teeth. The timekeeping of the escapement is affected by friction, or more explicitly, changes in timekeeping are affected by proportional changes in friction (usually brought about by the effects of age and temperature on the lubricant).

It is an interesting thought that if the loading of the circular face is increased by moving away from the tangent point the effects of changes in lubrication may be a smaller proportion of the total frictional losses. Timekeeping may not be affected so adversely. Of course if the pressure is so great as to break through the lubricating film, lubrication will not be of any value anyway!

The loading of the escapement is borne by the pivots as well as the working surfaces of course. For that reason any escapement designed with very fine pivots (and hence employing very low frictional losses) must have the acting teeth placed as close as possible to the tangent point.

CHAPTER 5
The Brocot Escapement

1 General Description of the Brocot Escapement

Brocot escapements are just as unrestricted in their proportions as any other escapement, although there are tables published of 'correct' proportions. The escapement devised by Achille Brocot of Paris (1817-78) and was manufactured under license during the lifetime of the patent and since that time, by any number of makers in France, America and Germany. Nineteenth-century French marble clocks often have a visible escapement on the front of the clock and as the pallets are usually made of an semi-precious stone, such as the deep-red cornelian, they are most attractive. Each manufacturer made his own decisions as to the centre distances of the escapewheel and pallets, to suit the disposition of the rest of the train and the overall dimensions allowed by the case. Brocot escapements with short centres work just as well as those with a greater distance between wheel and pallet centres.

Generally it will be found that this escapement has its acting teeth at or near the tangent points because the contact between tooth and pallet is virtually point contact, and as will be seen later in this chapter, the position of the acting teeth may produce draw or recoil, according to their position.

Fig 5/1 is an undimensioned drawing of a typical Brocot escapement. The distance between the drop-off points is exactly so many and a half pitches of the escapewheel teeth. The escapewheel teeth must drop a small amount onto each pallet (they must have clearance), and when one pallet is locked the other must just have dropped. It is almost a deadbeat escapement, the positioning of the acting teeth (as stated above) affecting the degree to which this is true.

The pallets of the Brocot are half cylinders, the flat part forming the drop-off face, and the highest point of the curved surface (in relation to the tooth) locks the escapewheel (**Fig 5/2**). In consequence the centre of the pallet must lie on the outside circle of the wheel at locking, and the other pallet, as usual, is poised on the top of another tooth. Although these pallets may be called pins, the Brocot is *not* a pin-pallet escapement, as the action is quite different.

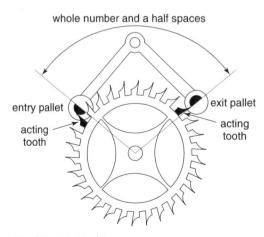

whole number and a half spaces

entry pallet

acting tooth

exit pallet

acting tooth

Fig 5/1 A typical Brocot escapement

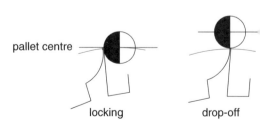

pallet centre

locking

drop-off

Fig 5/2 Position of Brocot pallets during locking and drop-off

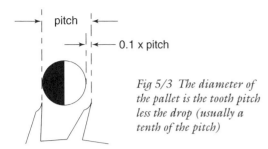

Fig 5/3 *The diameter of the pallet is the tooth pitch less the drop (usually a tenth of the pitch)*

The drop of the Brocot pallet can be expressed in the same manner as with the normal Graham deadbeat escapement, ie 5-10 per cent of the pitch. For the pallet to operate it must occupy no more than half the space between two adjacent tooth tips. In practice there must also be clearance for the pallets to avoid interfering with the teeth. The normal means of arriving at a pallet size that provides the clearance or drop is to make it a half cylinder with a diameter equal to the pitch less the drop (**Fig 5/3**).

Since the Brocot escapement locks on the midpoint of this half cylinder, the impulsing arc is defined by a line from the pallet arbor to the bottom of the pallet when it rests on the top of a tooth and another line to the midpoint of the cylinder when it lies on the cir-

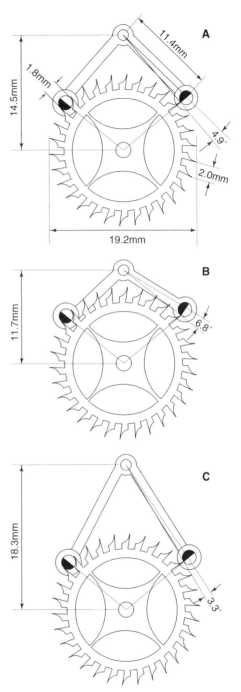

Fig 5/5 *The dimensions of a Brocot escapement for a thirty-tooth escapewheel of 19.2mm diameter. B and C show the effect of moving the pallet arbor. In addition to the obvious change in impulse arc, moving the tangent points away from the acting teeth also alters the amount of draw and/or recoil*

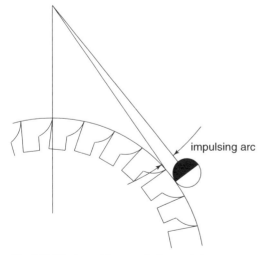

Fig 5/4 *The impulsing arc is the angle between lines from the pallet arbor to the point of contact on the pallet at locking and where the pallet circle touches the escapewheel perimeter*

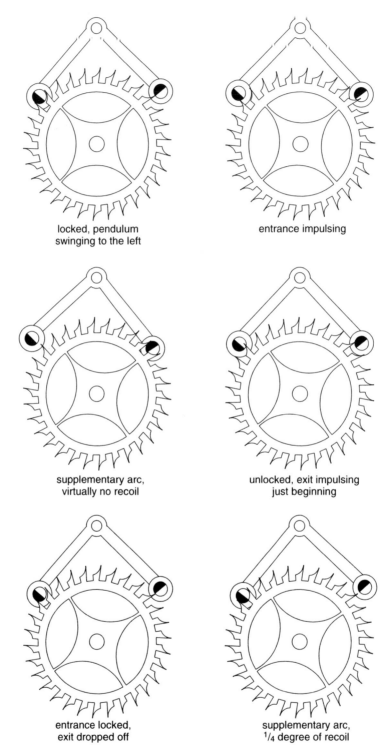

Fig 5/6 The action of a Brocot escapement during one complete oscillation of the pendulum. Note that in the final diagram the space behind the tooth is too narrow to accept the pallet on the entrance

cumference of the escapewheel (**Fig 5/4**). It must not be forgotten that the midpoint of the pallet is defined by the outside circle of the escapewheel when the pallet is locked and not by a line drawn to the centre of the pallet from the arbor centre.

Consequently the geometric construction of the pallets at drop-off must mark this point on the pallet perimeter and then swing it through the arc necessary to place the bottom of that circle on the escapewheel perimeter. The temptation is to believe that the point lies along a line from the pallet centre to the arbor centre.

The Geometry of the Brocot Escapement

Fig 5/5 shows a dimensioned Brocot escapement to establish the values for drop and to illustrate the effects of changing the height of the pallet arbor centre.

The escapewheel diameter is 19.2mm, hence the pitch of the teeth is 2.0mm and 10 per cent of this produces a clearance or drop of 0.2mm, giving a pallets that are 1.8mm diameter. The centres for the pallets are placed

on a 11.4mm radius from the centre of the pallet arbor. The pendulum's minimum arc will be a little less than 5 degrees, which is normally expressed as a semi-arc of 2½ degrees.

Figs 7/5B and **7/5C** show the same wheel, but with a modified pallet body to accept a distance between the centres of 11.7mm and 18.3 mm respectively. It can be seen how this affects the swing of the escapement and consequently the pendulum. The short centre distance produces a swing of 6.8 degrees, and the long centres 3.3 degrees.

Although it calls for precise drilling the Brocot is probably the simplest escapement to design and make. **Fig 5/6** follows the escape pallets through one complete oscillation.

Although the pallet enters the rectangular space behind the tooth on the exit side this is only because the flat of the pallet swings away from the right-hand side of this slot. It should be noted that because this effect is reversed on the entrance pallet (the pallet flat twists towards the right-hand side of the slot), the space is too narrow to accept the pallet.

2 Making the Brocot Escapement

The Body & Pallets

There are two ways in which this can be tackled. The pallet body can be marked out from an existing escapewheel, or alternatively the whole escapement can be drawn in a large scale (10:1 for instance), and the position of the holes for the pallet diameters taken from the drawing and marked out on the actual pallets. In both cases the pallet diameters are calculated first.

Almost all manufactured pallets are true half cylinders and so their diameter is calculated by measuring the distance between two tooth tips (ie the pitch), and subtracting the amount decided on for clearance or drop. When the cylinder is halved the pallets will measure (from flat to crest of arc) half the pitch less half the drop.

There is a disadvantage in this, though it is more theoretical than practical in most cases.

A true half cylinder presents no impulse angle to the escapewheel tooth immediately before drop-off and very little indeed for a measurable distance before that point. As a consequence, the actual drop is more than the calculated 10 cent of pitch. This is not noticeable in the usual size of escapewheel (10-25mm), but if the wheel is larger than about 30mm an alternative calculation for pallet size is probably better. In the latter case the pallet diameter is equal to the pitch of the escapewheel and half the drop is taken from it after it has been halved. This results in the drop-off moving round the arc of the semicircle that represents the section of the pallet, and a positive, if very small, impulse at drop-off (**Fig 5/7**).

The purpose of the drop is the very necessary one of allowing the components of the escapement to slide past each other — if there

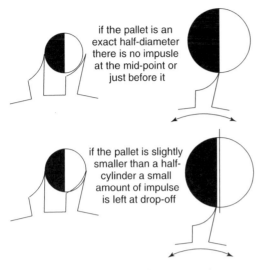

Fig 5/7 The effect of pallet diameter on the impulse at drop-off

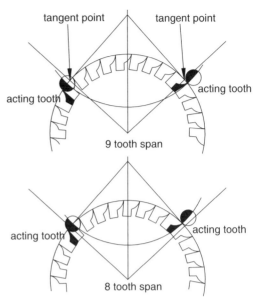

Fig 5/8 The Brocot escapement for spans of nine and eight teeth. The pallet centre line can be set to the left or the right of a tooth, but the displacement is a quarter of a pitch in each case

is no drop it will not operate. It is better to work on the tight side as far as drop is concerned, for it can always be increased by stoning or filing the flat of the pallet, with no unwanted effects in the operation of the escapement.

Marking the Pallet Body Directly
It is presumed that the pallets are to be made to suit an existing clock and that the distance between escapewheel arbor and pallet arbor, and the wheel diameter is already determined. If the entire escapement is new it is best to decide upon these parameters first and then proceed as if making a replacement pallet body.

A piece of brass plate is marked with the existing centre distance and a centre line drawn between the two. The position for the wheel centre is then drilled so that the escapewheel can lie flat on the brass plate, with the topmost tooth to the left or right of the centre line by a quarter of a tooth pitch. For the proportions used here, if the topmost tooth lies to the right nine spaces will be spanned and eight spaces if it lies to the left. The acting teeth are chosen as the two teeth lying closest to tangents struck from the pallet arbor centre (**Fig 5/8**).

For convenience the holes for the pallets are placed with their centres equidistant from the pallet arbor centre, ie the pallet hole centres lie on a common arc struck from the pallet arbor centre. Note that in this case A has less difference between the radii to each locking point than B.

When the entry pallet is locked its centre lies on the wheel circumference and the periphery of the exit pallet is resting on it. This is the configuration that was shown in **Fig 5/1** and advantage can be taken of this by making a specially formed punch to centre dot the pallet holes. The punch (**Fig 5/9**) has a diameter equal to the tooth pitch and is machined to leave a small pip at its centre. It is then halved by filing a flat across it

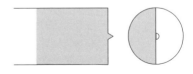

Fig 5/9 Special punch for centring pallet holes

An arc is drawn from the pallet arbor centre to pass through the midpoint between the acting tooth on the entry side and the next tooth to the right, and the tip of the acting tooth on the exit side. If the arc does not cut these two points then the placement of the centre line is inaccurate and should be corrected by swinging similar arcs from the midpoint and exit tooth tip. The wheel must be clamped to the brass plate during these operations, of course, and the arc is not continuous but interrupted by the body of the wheel.

The special punch represents the pallets with no clearance or drop and if its point is placed on the arc and the curved surface of the half cylinder touches the tip of the acting teeth at entry and exit, it will mark the centre of the pallet housing holes on the pallet body.

It will be necessary to twist the punch on the entry side away from the expected 'lie' of the pallet, otherwise it will strike the back of the wheel tooth. This makes no difference, it is the curve of the punch and its centre that are important in establishing the proper position of the holes that will be drilled to accept the pallets.

The plate can now be drilled through these centre dots and either used to make the pallet body, or used as a jig for a number of them.

• **Materials & Methods**

Though the Brocot pallet assembly is simple, there are one or two things that must be taken into account. One is the metal that is used. It is best made from brass, not only because it is an attractive metal and the traditional one for the body, but also because the right brass enables the clock maker to drill the holes easily and accurately — and give a good finish to the surfaces.

Most Brocot escapements are fitted to French clocks and these made use of cast brass, (about 67 per cent copper, 29 per cent zinc and 4 per cent lead). It cuts well, takes a fine polish and has a more yellow appearance than modern 60/40 brass (despite containing more copper). Old scrapped longcase clock plates are a good source for cast brass and, sadly,

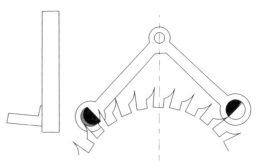

Fig 5/10 If the pallets are not set square in the body they will not be in the correct position with respect to the escapewheel

there are plenty of such plates to be found at clock fairs.

Ease of cutting is important, because it is imperative that the holes are drilled accurately. Modern 70/30 brass does not have lead in it to make it machine easily and as a result tends to draw up around the drill and cling to the rubbing surfaces. It is more difficult to produce a clean hole that does not wander away from the marked centre in modern 70/30 brass than in modern 60/40 brass which is free cutting. In the absence of cast brass it is better to forego the advantage of correct colour for the more important one of ease of drilling.

It is also important that the metal is held correctly while it is being drilled. If it is not held firmly and presented so that the drill enters at a true right-angle to the surface, then the pallets will lean and will not take up their proper position relative to the escapewheel (**Fig 5/10**).

To ensure that there is the largest surface for clamps to bear down upon and for support, all drilling should be done before making any attempt to reduce the size of the blank or cut out the shape of the body. So long as the drill quill (shaft) is truly at right-angles to the table or base, then the holes can be placed in the pallet body accurately. A centre (Slocombe) drill must be used for starting the hole and may, with advantage, be used for drilling clear through provided that the clearance flutes are not completely buried in the thickness of the blank so that swarf is prevented from leaving the hole.

• **Fixing the Pallets in the Body**

Traditionally the pallets are held in position with shellac, obtainable from clock supply houses and (in flake form) from painters' and decorators' suppliers. It should not enter the hole in the pallet body but simply adhere as an annulus around the pallet diameter. The full diameter of the pallet should be a good sliding fit in the body. This allows adjustment, since shellac softens with a modest amount of heat and this allows the pallet to be twisted in its socket. If the latter is too loose it will not align the pallet properly with the escapewheel teeth.

• **Ball Sizing**

If the pallet is machined from a ground steel bar (silver steel or drill steel) with a nominal dimension it may be possible to obtain a ball bearing of the same size. Sizing a hole by forcing a hard steel ball through it after drilling, produces an accurate and highly-finished bore. A little light polishing on the pallet diameter will then produce the clearance necessary for a push fit.

The hole should be drilled to about 95 per cent of the ball size and a support and punch

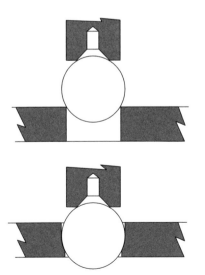

Fig 5/11 Forcing a ball from a bearing through a hole to size it accurately

(**Fig 5/11**) made so that the ball may be pressed through the body using the jaws of a vice. The holes should be finished with a small chamfer at each end for the shellac to sit in.

This is also a very good method of sizing holes for pivots in new clocks, or for clocks where the pivot has to be replaced and it is possible to choose a pivot size suitable for a ball-sized hole.

Making the Pallet Body from a Drawing

Because the Brocot escapement has no impulse faces to be machined or filed relative to the acting teeth of the escapewheel, it can be manufactured by determining the position of the holes and turning the pallets, (and halving them) to precise measurements. This in turn makes it feasible to make even a 'one-off' by drawing the escapement out in a large scale and then placing the holes from the dimensions alone.

A scale of 10:1 is large enough to resolve the position of lines and centres accurately for marking out with scribers, dividers and centre punches. A scribed line can be placed to an accuracy equivalent to half the width of the lines on a steel rule — generally about 0.12mm or 0.005in. (A sharp sewing needle held in a pin vice makes a good scriber.) A sharp pencil can be placed to an accuracy of about 0.25mm (0.010in). A drawing of ten times full size should therefore enable the clockmaker to determine measurements that are somewhat more accurate than the dividers and scribers can achieve.

Of course a computer-aided draughting system (CAD) will produce dimensions of a very high accuracy indeed — far beyond the reach of mechanical tools.

The centre line is drawn and the centres for both arbors accurately placed on it. After drawing the outside diameter of the wheel it must be divided into twice the number of teeth divisions (to obtain the mid-points of the tooth spaces as well as the tips). This is best done by drawing as large a circle as will fit on the paper on the same centre as the wheel circle and dividing this. Any draughting errors

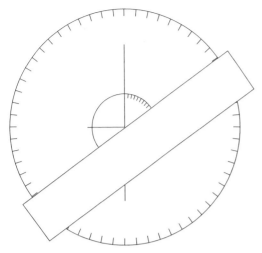

Fig 5/12 Dividing the escapewheel by scaling down a large drawing

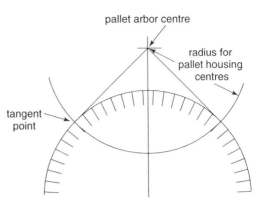

Fig 5/13 Draw tangents from the pallet arbor centre to the outside of the escapewheel and use the nearest divisions to set the radius for the centres of the holes for the pallet housings

that occur will then be scaled down as the divisions are transposed onto the smaller circle using a steel rule lined up with the divisions and the centre dot (**Fig 5/12**). Line up the midpoint of one space with the centre line. Since there are twice as many spaces as teeth this midpoint defines a quarter pitch. Although only a few of the marks are used in the geometric construction, a full half circle, terminating at either end of a diameter, should be drawn to confirm that the divisions are precise fractions of the circumference.

Draw tangents from the pallet arbor centre

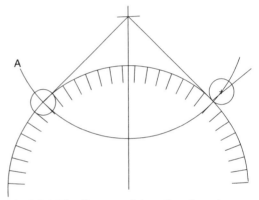

Fig 5/14 The diameter of the pallets (ignoring clearances) are drawn equal to the tooth pitch and their centres are placed on arc A

For a pallet span of 7½ teeth and a 30-tooth escapewheel, the angle between B and C is 45°. R is tangential to the escapewheel periphery, so B is at 90° to R. The triangle is isoceles so R=B. L is the sum of the escapewheel radii and the radius of the housing.

The radius of the housing is half the distance between two tooth tips (0.1045 for a 30-tooth wheel of B=1). Hence L=1.045.

Angle between C and R_0 is Z, where

$$\cos Z = \frac{C^2 + R^2 - L^2}{2LR} \quad \text{assuming } R=R_0.$$

Angle Z is calculated. Angle Y is Z = 45°, hence the distance between the housing centres is found from $D^2 = 2R^2(1-\cos Y)$

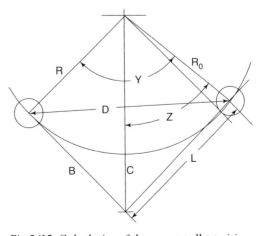

Fig 5/15 Calculation of the correct pallet position

to the wheel circle. The nearest divisions to these tangents are chosen to define the radius that the centres of the pallets lie on, but there must be an odd number of divisions between these divisions (**Fig 5/13**).

For the purposes of geometric construction the clearance necessary to the pallets may be ignored and circles drawn with diameters equal to the full pitch. Hence compasses are set with their points on two adjacent marks and the circles drawn with that setting (**Fig 5/14**). It will now be seen that irrespective of whether the span of the pallets is an odd number of pitches or an even one, the drawing automatically positions the teeth when the acting teeth are drawn in.

To position the centres of the pallets properly, the diameter is calculated and corresponding circles positioned at lock and drop-off, ie pallet centre on wheel circumference and pallet circumference on wheel circumference respectively (**Fig 5/15**).

To produce the actual pallet body, measure the distance between the centres on the drawing and convert them to working figures by applying the scale. These form a triangle whose corners are the pallet arbor centre and the two pallet centres, and since two sides correspond to a common radius it will be an isosceles triangle.

The shape of the body is of little importance except for appearance, so construct it around these three holes, and make it attractive. Though the body sits behind the wheel (ie not in the same plane) and so cannot strike the tops of the teeth, it does swing and there must be no interference with other parts of the mechanism, such as arbors, wheels or cocks.

If it is intended to make this size of Brocot escapement again, the holes may be transferred to a piece of gauge plate which can be used as a jig for drilling other pallet bodies. With a properly made jig, the Brocot escapement can be made by unskilled labour.

The Brocot pallet body often has 'turning' around the base of the pallets, and this can be formed with a piloted cutter made in the lathe

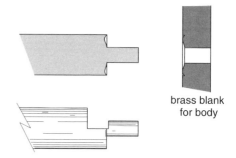

brass blank
for body

Fig 5/16 Cutter for producing ornamental turnings on a Brocot pallet body

(**Fig 5/16**). Harden the cutter and then hold it in a pillar or bench drill (preferably one fitted with a depth stop to give identical effects) to produce the turnings. This operation should be carried before the shape of the pallet body is cut out otherwise there is a risk that the power of the machine may twist the brass body out of shape.

• **Pallets**

The range of 'jewel' pallets that is available is limited. If there is one that is close to the pallet holes that have been calculated, the drawing may be modified to allow for this when positioning the pallet centres. This may well alter the drop allowed for the escapement, but a Brocot will work quite happily with a larger clearance (up to about 20 per cent of the pitch). By twisting the pallet in its housing a certain amount of adjustment can be made to the drop (**Fig 5/17**).

Note that the drop will not be reduced if the physical drop-off of the pallet moves to the right (for a clockwise rotation of the wheel) of the radial line from the wheel arbor. This is because the 'bottom' of the curved surface drops the pallet instead of the drop-off point.

It is possible to use a larger pallet diameter without being forced into this measure and reducing the breadth by stoning the flat until what remains of the original pallet is less than half a diameter and produces the correct drop. This will make sure that impulse is being given until the moment of drop-off. This solution does not result in the drop-off shifting from

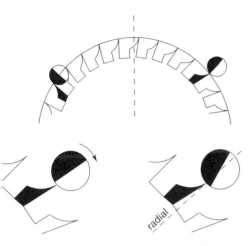

Fig 5/17 If the pallets are a tight 'fit' on the escapewheel the drop may be increased by twisting them. Twisting past the radial from the wheel centre merely transferes the drop-off from the flat to the 'bottom' of the pallet curvature. It increases the chance of fouling the back of the tooth, but it does not increase the drop

the flat of the pallet to the curvature at the bottom.

If stones are not available or not desired, the pallets can be made from hardened and polished steel. Friction will be a little less (unless the jewels are of artificial ruby) and on an existing clock this may result in the pendulum swinging a little wider than usual.

Fig 5/18 shows the making of steel pallets. It is not necessary for the pallet to be of the same diameter from end to end. The end that is designed to fit into the body should be made to suit the diameter of hole drilled in the body — and that depends on the size of drills available. Broaching to fit the pallets should be avoided since the holes will then be tapered and the pallets be able to wobble.

The pallets are hardened 'dead hard', though if they are stress-relieved at 150°C (302°F) in a domestic oven they are less likely to break in service. Pallets have been made of brass as a repair but the result is poor. There is a great deal of wear on the pallets as the escapewheel rotates — in fact if there are thirty teeth there is thirty times as much wear on each pallet.

After hardening the pallets must have their circular surfaces polished with flour paper and any oil removed — so that the shellac will adhere. It is usual to polish the flats too, but this is purely for appearance's sake.

Making a Brocot Escapewheel

In most cases it is the escapewheel that has suffered in the Brocot escapement. This happens even more frequently in the visible version because the wheel is usually of a very elegant and very delicate shape (**Fig 5/19**). The teeth get broken or bent — and then bent

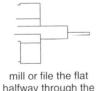

mill or file the flat
halfway through the
diameter and polish the flat

turn the stock to suit
the housing in
the pallet body

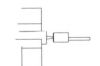

part almost through but
leave attached, chamfer
the edge of the parting,
harden the pallet, polish
and break from the bar

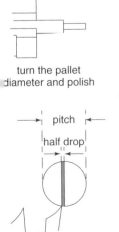

turn the pallet
diameter and polish

pitch

half drop

Fig 5/18 The stages in making steel pallets for a Brocot escapement. The lower diagram shows that if the pallet diameter equals the pitch and the flat is half that diameter less half the drop, then there will be a residual impulse at drop-off

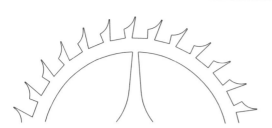

Fig 5/19 The usual shape of Brocot escapewheel teeth

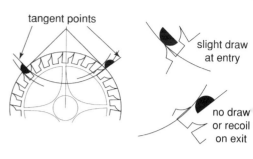

again. Pallets, on the other hand, are fairly robust and are mounted in the pallet body with shellac, which allows slight adjustment when it is warmed with a moderately hot (and clean) soldering iron.

Apart from determining the number of teeth and the outside diameter of the wheel, the shape of the escapewheel teeth should be left until it is known exactly what the proportions of the escapement will be. The form of the tooth can then be designed to be as sturdy as the necessities of operation will allow.

• **The Escapewheel Teeth**

The shape of the front of the tooth must be arrived at by studying the operation (on paper), of the escapement. It is no good simply using an arbitrary rake. As the wheel teeth pass through entry and exit the design should ensure the wheel remains as static during locking as possible. **Fig 5/20** demonstrates the effects of changing the proportions of the escapement when locking at entry and exit — and the result of moving the acting teeth far from the tangent points mentioned earlier. It is always worthwhile drawing out the entry and exit condition for locking and drop-off. Note that it is possible to avoid recoil at drop-off and the early part of the supplementary

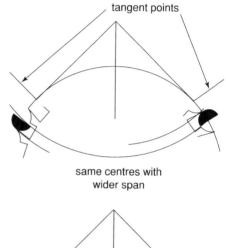

Fig 5/20 The effects of changing the proportions of a Brocot escapement, and the effect of moving the acting teeth far from the tangent points. With a wider pallet span there is no recoil or draw at entry, but pronounced draw at exit. With the centres raised there is a little draw at entry and heavy recoil at exit

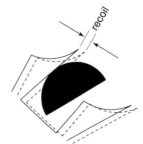

Fig 5/21 Recoil may occur after the pallet has bitten deeply into the tooth space

arc, but the wheel can be so designed that recoil *or* draw results after the pallet has bitten deeply into the tooth space (**Fig 5/21**).

Arcs are drawn centred on the pallet arbor and just touching the curved side of the pallets. These, of course, trace the path of the point of contact as the pallet swings from locking during the supplementary arc.

This is only true for normal proportions of escapement. If the geometry is examined losely it will be seen that the point of contact moves around the curve as it swings. Unless the escapement is of very unusual proportions, this is an effect that is barely measurable, but it may be of consequence if a very large escapement is designed.

To avoid recoil the raked face of the tooth must approximate to this curved path. It will be seen that the rake that satisfies this requirement is not necessarily the same for both entry and exit. Since, in practice, this is an impossibility, the amount of recoil or draw that is acceptable (or desired) must be decided upon and that rake used for cutting the teeth.

From a practical point of view it is easiest to define the rake by the diameter of a circle at the centre of the wheel that is tangential to the rake line (**Fig 5/22**). Then, when cutting the teeth it is only necessary to set the line of the cutter above the centre of the wheel by the radius of this circle.

Typical Brocot pallets have a rectangular slot 'behind' the clearance curve of the tooth tip. This portion of the tooth space must be large enough to accommodate the width of the pallets to allow for over-swinging of a pendulum. Over-swinging and a friction fit crutch is frequently the method built into the movement by the maker for putting the pallets in beat — it is not simply a safety device.

The back of the dropping tooth must clear the free pallet during the impulsing of the other. Because the curve that represents the path of the pallets cuts into the back of the entry pallet and away from the back of the exit pallet it is necessary to consider each pallet in turn as drop occurs, taking care to make sure that the impulsing pallet remains in con-

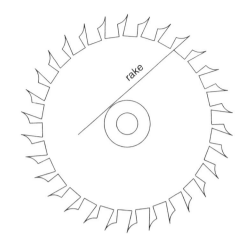

Fig 5/22 A convenient method of specifying the rake is to draw a tangent to a small circle centred on the escapewheel arbor

tact with the acting tooth. Usually an included angle at the tooth tip of about 30 degrees blended into an arc is enough to ensure clearance (the drop helps of course). This is translated into a curve so that the body of the tooth is not cut away unnecessarily where the tooth moves away from the pallet.

Two stages of cutting are needed for the form of tooth shown: the slot and the backing curve. It is best to cut the curved surface first since this has a long cutting surface and transfers greatest loading to the blank. Clearly it is better to ensure that this occurs when the blank is still sturdy and not weakened by partly-cut teeth. The slot is cut with a tool rather like a parting tool with only a short length of cutting edge. If the order is reversed the pressure upon the blank from making the curved cut the last one is very likely to curl

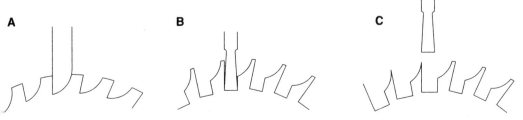

Fig 5/23 The delicate Brocot escapewheels should be cut in stages with two different cutters

the tip of the tooth forward. **Fig 5/23** shows the progressive cutting of a wheel with two fly cutters.

The fly cutter is ideal for this type of wheel cutting, as it is easily made from silver steel (drill steel). Because the cutter is revolving in air for most of its path it remains cool and can be used at high speed (2,000-5,000 rpm). The details of making and using a fly cutter can be found in Chapter 12.

The Brocot escapewheel is often quite thin and care must be taken to choose a hard-rolled brass and it must be supported during cutting. It is usually sufficient to soft solder the blank on to the end of a piece of brass rod that has been turned to provide a diameter that is just cleared by the fly cutter when the deepest cut is made. If this does not prove adequate two blanks can be soldered together and then soldered to the end of the rod. This does have the advantage of producing a spare escapewheel at very little additional cost. A future repairer will appreciate a spare wheel wired to a pillar.

Missing Wheel

If the wheel is missing it must be calculated from the wheel and pinion count of the rest of the train and the length of the pendulum. In all likelihood the escape pinion will have wandered off with the escapewheel as well. The calculation for the number of teeth in the escapewheel and the pinion will only produce the ratio for the two missing gears, such as 32:8 or 36:9. It will be necessary to assume the count of one of the two before the count of the other one can be calculated, but bear in mind the following:
• The pinion is very probably the same count as the next pinion in the train.
• If the pallets are present, even damaged, the pitch of the escapewheel teeth may be approximated by measuring the span of the pallet centres.
• The outside diameter of the wheel may be

surmised by the space available to it.
• Dividing the probable diameter of the whee by the pitch will indicate the proper whee count, working back from that will give th pinion count — which is of course, a whol number.

The formula for calculating the ratio be tween the escapewheel and pinion is:

$$\frac{EW}{EP} = \frac{N}{2} \times \frac{TP}{CW} \times \frac{1}{TW}$$

N = beats of the pendulum per hour.
The number of teeth or 'count' of each of th gears is:
EW = escapewheel
EP = escape pinion
TW = third wheel
TP = third pinion
CW = centre wheel.

The number of beats per hour is depend ant on the length of the pendulum, measure from just under the suspension cock to th centre of the pendulum bob. A table of pen dulum lengths and beats is shown on pag 215.

Alternatively, the pendulum length may b calculated from the following formula:

$$N = \frac{3600}{\pi} \times \sqrt{\frac{g}{l}}$$

L = pendulum length in inches or mm
N = beats per hour
g = acceleration of gravity in inches/sec/se or mm/sec/sec.

If the pendulum is missing there should b clues as to the probable length from marks o the case, the total height available and possi bly stamped figures on the movement. French clock will have the pendulum lengt (suspension to centre of bob), marked in unit that approximate to inches, a German one wi be marked in centimetres, and an America one will be marked in inches — if marked a all. Very few British clocks used the Broco escapement.

3 Repairs to the Brocot Escapement

The Pallet Body

If there is severe damage to the body there is usually no option but to make a new one following the pattern of the old. However it is always possible that damage can be corrected if it is a simple matter of the body having been distorted slightly by a previous repairer using a screwdriver to open the span or pliers to close it (**Fig 5/24**). Such a repair will consist of simply squeezing the pallet body in a vice with wooden guards on the jaws (**Fig 5/25**) or placing a brass wedge in the slot to open the arms of the body. See pages 145-146 for a full description of these adjustments.

The degree to which the body is opened or closed is governed by the geometry of the escapement, and the pallets must be checked against the escapewheel as correction proceeds so as to meet the same criteria that have been discussed in the previous section 'Making the Brocot Escapement'. Clearly the pallets must be already mounted in the body and set parallel to each other and to the escapewheel arbor. It may be necessary to warm the shellac used to hold them in their housings and to twist them, but, as has been seen, there is not a great deal of adjustment available.

If the pallets are damaged they will need to be replaced by making new ones, but it may be of advantage to leave them in place (always bearing in mind the amount of damage they have suffered) while the body is manipulated to correct the geometry.

The Brocot is essentially a pretty escapement and the body is almost always intended to be well finished and good-looking. If the damage has left the body serviceable but rough, it should be brought back to original condition or replaced entirely.

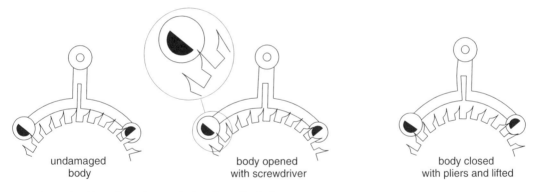

undamaged
body

body opened
with screwdriver

body closed
with pliers and lifted

Fig 5/24 The effect of opening or closing the pallet body

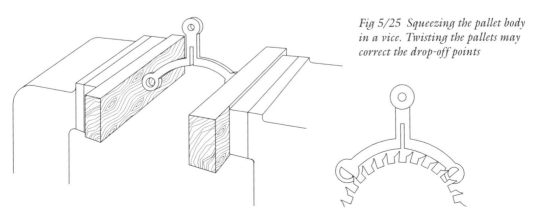

Fig 5/25 Squeezing the pallet body in a vice. Twisting the pallets may correct the drop-off points

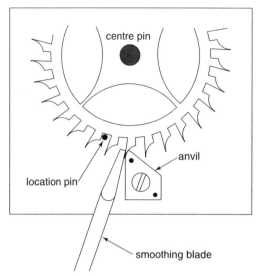

Fig 5/26 Jig for straightening escapewheel teeth

Damaged Wheels

There is not a lot of tooth damage that can be put right on a Brocot escapewheel. They are so delicate that quite minor accidents can be irrepairable.

Teeth that have been bent over at the ends can be straightened by squeezing with flat-nosed pliers, ensuring that one jaw of the pliers lies flat along the front of the tooth while the other is drawn along the curve, gradually pressing the tooth tip flat against the first jaw. This is only practicable if a few teeth are damaged, say a quarter of the total. If there are more than this the time taken in straightening the teeth and checking their pitches afterwards will approach the time taken to make a new one — and the result will not compare favourably with the alternative.

As a more precise way of reforming the teeth of the escapewheel the jig shown in **Fig 5/26** can be made. There is a hole to accept the arbor, another to accept a pin that registers against the rear of the tooth (close to the root where damage almost certainly has not occurred), and a small shaped anvil behind the tip of the tooth. The method of use is to place the wheel on the jig with the tooth for correction pressed hard against the register and

then to stroke the tip with a screwdriver blade until it is lying flat against the anvil. This jig is also very useful for checking the pitch of the teeth and since the anvil need only be made from brass it is easily modified to deal with different wheels.

• Broken Tooth Tips

Since the Brocot escapement is often fitted with adjustment on the centre distance between pallet and wheel arbors, the loss of a small amount of tooth tip can be corrected by turning the wheel and making all teeth the same height before resetting the height and the angle of the pallets.

The wheel must be turned at the top speed of the lathe and rather than use a turning tool a fine file should be steadied on the tool post and gently lowered until it just touches the rotating wheel teeth. As an alternative a very fine file can be mounted vertically by soldering it on the end of a piece of brass which can then be held in the tool post (**Fig 5/27**).

The wheel should rotate so that the front of the tooth advances towards the tool or file, and any burr is left on the back of the tooth where it can be removed without affecting the pitch. After turning or filing, the back of each tooth must be dressed to remove the burr, with 400 grit emery paper on a small stick.

As much as 10-15 per cent of the pitch can be removed from the diameter in this way and still leave the escapement within the limits of the adjustment available by altering the centre height and twisting the pallets in the body. The drop will be increased and it is very probable that it will be uneven.

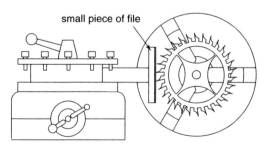

Fig 5/27 Topping the escapewheel teeth to the same height

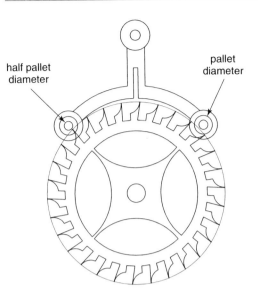

Fig 5/28 When adjusting the centres place the pallets over the wheel so that the perimeter just touches circles that are half the pallet diameter

half pallet diameter

pallet diameter

• Adjusting the Centres

When the wheel diameter is altered the geometry of the escapement is changed too. This subject is also dealt with in Section 2: 'Making the Brocot Escapement'.

When the repairer has reason to believe (from scratch marks and a damaged eccentric bush) that the height of the pallet arbor and the span of the body are not as they left the factory, a definite plan should be followed in examining the escapement, otherwise adjustments may be made without actually establishing precisely where the fault lies. A haphazard series of corrections will eventually put the escapement right, but a lot of time will be wasted and, in all probability, the damage to the surface of the metal will be increased.

• Remove pallets and escapewheel from the movement.

• Drill a small piece of plate to accept the escapewheel and pallet arbors and install the wheel so that it lies flat on the plate.

• Lay the pallets over the wheel so that the perimeter crosses the pallet diameters halfway between the centre and the lower circumfer-

ence (**Fig 5/28** makes use of two circles half the pallet diameter).

• Adjust the pallets until their drop-off faces point directly at the centre of the wheel.

The pallets are now reasonably accurately placed if the body is in its original condition. In this case the wheel can be put back into the movement and the pallet arbor installed as well.

Now the height can be altered until the pallets are properly placed, (or nearly so) in the escapewheel. If this cannot be done the body has been altered, so proceed to the next step:

• Study the width between the drop-off points (**Fig 5/29**) and match it against the span over the acting teeth. The span should, of course, be so many and a half pitches at the periphery of the wheel.

• Spread or close the body until the span complies with this rule.

• Small adjustments can now be made to the

Fig 5/29 An approximate test for damage to the body is to check the space between the drop-off points against the span of the teeth, which should be a whole number and a half. Any error from having to guess at the alignment of the drop-off faces will have little effect. It will be clear whether the span of the body matches that of the teeth within the small adjustment obtained by twisting the pallets in their housings

set of the pallets and the height of the pallet arbor centre until the correct configuration is achieved.

Care must be taken when opening or closing the span of the body — it is most likely to be a casting. Closing is best done in a vice (protecting the metal body with aluminium or wooden jaw guards). An estimate is made of the amount that the body needs to be closed by and a piece of scrap brass cut to the desired finished distance placed between the pallet *housings* — *not the pallets.* The existing distance over the pallets is recorded and the housings squeezed towards each other until they touch the piece of brass.

The result is measured after taking the body out of the vice and the scrap brass reduced by whatever amount the pallets still need to be closed by. There is, of course a certain amount of spring in the body, which is the reason for doing the job in several bites.

The body may be opened by making a brass wedge that fits the slot at the centre and having no more than about 0.010in (0.25mm) taper over the length of the slot. It ought to be twice as long as the slot so that the end can

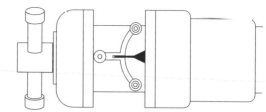

Fig 5/30 Opening the body of a Brocot escapement by use of a brass wedge

be filed off to allow the wedge to open the slot a little more at a later stage. The end of the wedge and the top of the pallet body is squeezed between guarded vice jaws.

Fig 5/30 shows the method, but the shape of the wedge does not need to be as well defined as this. A broad base is necessary for stability and the working taper must be carefully matched to the width of the slot and the amount of movement that is needed; apart from those criteria the wedge can be any scrap of brass plate.

Everything must be taken slowly however, with consideration of the results of each step. It is not a difficult job — just a painstaking one.

3 The Brocot Escapement — Comments & Faults

Though the Brocot escapement is reliable it is easily damaged. The pallets are brittle, the teeth delicate and the adjustments are a temptation to 'twiddlers'. However a damaged Brocot is fairly obvious, even when it is enclosed between the clock plates. A broken pallet (they tend to snap rather than chip) is not easy to hide and the bent over teeth of a damaged escapewheel can often be felt with a finger nail. Short teeth are usually accompanied by bent ones and turned over tips.

Minor faults are difficult to determine in the short time available in a saleroom, as a Brocot in good condition will run without a pendulum since its locking is not as positive as with a Graham deadbeat escapement. It is therefore no test of the clock to note whether it runs without a pendulum. However the enthusiasm with which it runs when no pendulum is present is an indication of condition — it should not 'gallop away'.

If it locks very positively there is probably significant draw on the pallets and, since this is not a common manufactured state, the buyer should be suspicious.

Minor faults are those that can be put right by adjusting height and pallet settings.

It is not so easy to see whether a Brocot escapement has locked properly as it is with with a Graham deadbeat. If the wheel tooth does not drop directly onto the centre line of the pallet, the escapement will operate erratically. Otherwise it is a very reliable escapement with no other foibles.

Some very strange repairs are made to clocks (drawing pins instead of pallets for instance) so that it is worth peering in between the plates to see if there are large quantities of shellac or some other substance around the pallets and to see if there is solder on the body. Both are indications of trouble and poor repairs.

The author has only had experience of one really large Brocot escapement and that was designed by a fellow clockmaker. The wheel was about 12in (300mm) diameter and the large eight-day clock operated very well on a weight of about 12lb hung on a pulley.

From the point of view of the clockmaker the Brocot is probably the easiest escapement to make and, because the pallets can be placed in correct relationship to the teeth by the use of a drilling jig, lends itself to simple batch production.

Finally, the Brocot escapement is capable of keeping very good time, certainly better than an anchor escapement and not far off the performance of a Graham deadbeat.

CHAPTER 6
Platform Escapements

The Graham deadbeat escapement is also used in platform escapements. Repairing these is more a matter of watchmaking techniques than clockmaking, since they are small and require the skills and techniques of a watchmaker. Therefore this chapter should be regarded as adjustment, not repair. However, it is useful for the clockmaker to be able to recognise the faults that call for specialised attention. If in any doubt as to your ability to deal with a platform escapement, then take it to a qualified watchmaker.

1 The Lever Escapement

The essentials of the lever escapement are shown in **Fig 6/1**. It consists of the pallets and escapewheel of a Graham deadbeat, a balance wheel and balance spring; connecting the two systems a lever that carries the pallets and impulses the balance wheel. The spindle or arbor of a platform escapement (or a watch or chronometer) is termed a 'staff' and in this case the plural is staffs — not staves.

Generally speaking the lever is not made with provision for adjustment of the position of the pallets after manufacture, consequently the escapement is in beat when (with no load on the escapewheel) the centre of the balance, the impulse pin and the lever centre are in a straight line. No deadbeat escapement will work if it has worn to the extent that the escapewheel teeth land directly on the impulse faces instead of locking. This converts the escapement to a rather poor recoil escapement- and this will take twice the energy to keep going as a Graham deadbeat.

The heels of the pallets should be inspected with a magnifying glass. There should be no rounding of the heel or a definite break across the line of its edge. A certain amount of wear on the locking and impulse faces can be sustained by the escapement. Clearly this lowers its ability to keep good time, but until damage to the heel is so great that the escapewheel tooth lands on a sloping face, it will keep working.

Since the pallets and lever are locked to-

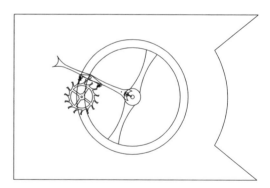

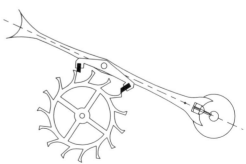

Fig 6/1 The lever escapement. In the top view the components are shown as transparent for clarity. Only the balance wheel, lever and escapewheel are shown, the cocks and balance spring are omitted

gether, both will move through the same an- gle. The fork at the other end of the lever delivers the impulse to the impulse pin and so causes the balance wheel to rotate. As the escapewheel turns, the fork thrusts the impulse pin over to one side and this then carries on in a circular path, temporarily leaving the fork. When the impetus given to the wheel has been used up it reverses its swing and the impulse pin re-enters the fork (which has remained waiting for it), carrying it towards the other side and allowing the escapement to operate, it then leaves the fork again on the opposite side.

Checking the Fork

If a finger is used *very* lightly to rotate the escape pinion in the working direction, the balance wheel should be entirely free of the lever immediately after the impulse pin rotates away from the fork, ie it is 'detached'. The little guard pin (**Fig 6/2**) must *not* touch the disk or roller that the impulse pin is carried on. It is a safety device that prevents the lever swinging back to the centre line if sudden movement takes away the pressure of the escapewheel on the pallets. Under that con-

dition the fork will still remain in position to catch the impulse pin when the balance makes its return swing.

Many of the other possible failings of the lever fork are difficult to see, but the most common fault appears when banking pins have been bent out of position by a previous re- pairer. These pins (there is one on either side of the lever), ensure that the fork is placed correctly during normal operation to accept the impulse pin without fouling (**Fig 6/2**). If they are too wide apart, the impulse pin may fall foul of the fork, if they are closed up fric- tion will result between the guard roller and the guard pin or the dart.

The banking pins also have an effect on the timekeeping of the clock because of the change in friction on the balance wheel if the guard pin or dart are allowed to rest on their respec- tive rollers after drop-off. The diagrams show that a guard pin is used in conjunction with a single roller (the one carrying the impulse pin) and a double roller with a dart — the second roller has a notch to clear the nose of the dart. There is also a notch on a single roller, to pass the guard pin as the lever accepts the impulse pin.

Shake

There should be a small amount of shake or freedom between the lever and the banking pins when the escape pallets lock (immediately after drop-off), a matter of just a few thou- sandths of an inch. The 'draw' (see below) of the pallets immediately after locking will move

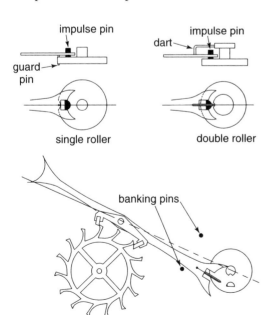

Fig 6/2 Guard pin and banking pins

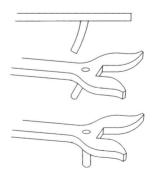

Fig 6/3 The guard pin should be straight, not bent

the lever from this position to the banked position (pressed against the banking pin) and waiting for the return swing of the impulse pin. If the balance wheel shows a tendency to shudder or stagger as it oscillates, the position of the banking pins is incorrect, or the fork itself is damaged. It is also possible that the dart or the guard pin has been modified by a previous repairer.

Most clock repairers will not want to tackle the shortening of a dart if it *has* been bent forward, but adjustment of a guard pin (**Fig 6/3**) is not difficult. Since the manufacturer intended it to be upright it is a matter merely of bending it straight again, or of replacing it if it is missing. It must be remembered that the actual freedom of the pallets at drop-off must remain very small or other problems will be introduced — only move banking pins by a tiny amount before checking their effect upon the lever and impulse pin. If the banking pins have a screwdriver slot in their tops they must *not* be bent, but rotated as they are eccentric.

'Draw' in Small Platform Escapements

Small platform pallets are usually made after the fashion of a watch escapement, that is they have 'draw'. A Graham deadbeat escapement used in a clock has locking faces that are true arcs struck from the centre of the pallets, and neither push the escapewheel teeth away during operation nor pull them in. A small escapement, such as in a watch, is often made so that the locking faces have a tendency to pull themselves down onto the escapewheel teeth (**Fig 6/4**). In this case the locking faces are not true arcs but straight lines, and the angle between this locking face and a tangent to the true arc of locking is generally 15 degrees. This avoids the chance of the pallet lever bouncing, which is more likely on exiting than entering.

Draw can be observed when the balance wheel is removed. Light pressure on the escapewheel pinion flips the pallets over, and if a the fork is touched with a very fine wire it can be seen that if the fork is then moved towards the centre line less than the amount needed to unlock the pallets, it pulls back against the banking pin when the wire is taken away. Hence it has positive locking. Large pallets (as in longcase and bracket clocks) have

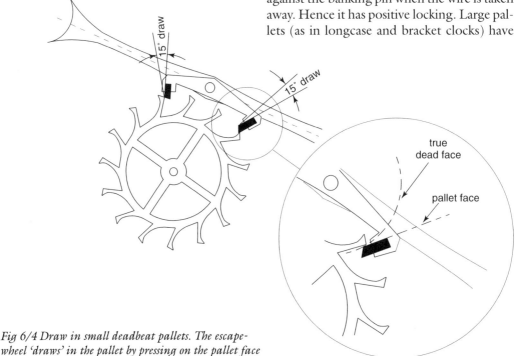

Fig 6/4 Draw in small deadbeat pallets. The escape-wheel 'draws' in the pallet by pressing on the pallet face

neutral locking and worn pallets have negative locking or recoil, the wheel throwing the pallets away from it.

Impulse Pin & Rollers

The pin must stand upright on its platform or roller. If it is leaning away from the perpendicular it will cause one of the following:
• Leaning to left or right of the fork reduces the clearance in the fork and cause binding.
• Leaning towards the balance staff increases the force needed to keep the balance rotating and increases the chance of it failing to make a clean entry into the fork on its return and then jamming or jarring.
• Leaning away from the balance wheel decreases the force needed to keep the balance rotating, but requires a larger arc from the fork in order to clear the impulse pin properly and obtain a full oscillation of the wheel. It will probably jam against the banking pins, and even when these are bent outwards causes the pallets to bite deeper into the escapewheel than it was designed to do.

When the impulse pin reaches the fork notch a cut-out on the roller (the disk supporting the impulse pin) is in position to allow the guard pin a space during the lever's proper motion. A double roller has a similar

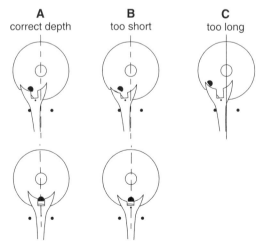

| A | B | C |
| correct depth | too short | too long |

Fig 6/5 The effects of the depth of the notch on the impulse pin (see text). The mid-position for C is not shown, as the fork cannot accept the pin

arrangement on the roller *not* carrying the impulse pin, to accept the nose of the dart.

There are three things to check at the moment that the impulse pin leaves the notch:
• That pressure on the escape pinion causes the pallets to draw the lever over to the banking pin.
• That the guard pin is not in contact with the roller while pressure remains on the escape pinion.
• That the impulse pin does not scrape along the horns adjacent to the notch (very unlikely).

When the balance wheel is swinging back towards the lever and the impulse pin is about to enter the notch, there are again three things to check:
• That the lever is still hard against the banking pin.
• That the guard pin or dart is opposite the cut-out provided for it on the roller.
• That the impulse pin enters the notch cleanly and just clears the corner, neither scraping nor butting onto the horn, nor missing it by a clearly visible amount.

Damage to a fork is obvious under a magnifying glass, and becomes more obvious if there is a clear view of the entry of the impulse pin as the wheel rotates slowly. The brass forks of a Seth Thomas, or a mass-produced German clock with separate lever and pallets, can be tidied up by careful work with a very fine escapement file after spreading the metal slightly with a small hammer. But it is only a matter of 'tidying up'; gross damage is irreparable with a hammer and file, only the effects of wear can be tackled this way. The jaws of the fork must just allow the impulse pin to enter and exit cleanly without striking the corner or end faces. In **Fig 6/5** the three conditions of the notch are shown:

A The lever is in good condition and the impulse pin just clears the corner of the notch.
B Metal has been removed from the end of the notch so that it is now too shallow and the pallets will not operate properly.
C The lever has been 'stretched' so that the notch is too deep — if it does operate there will be a knock as the impulse pin hits the edge

of the throat and the pallets will not operate reliably.

Note that the impulse pin is not a bare semi-cylinder (which would increase the clearance in the notch as it entered or left), but a cylinder with a flat ground on it just sufficient to clear the horn. The position of this flat (on the cylinder) is defined by the notch mouth as the impulse pin leaves or enters.

Whether the protection is a guard pin and single roller or a dart and double roller, the balance wheel must be completely detached during the time that it is not being impulsed. *Nothing must touch any part of the roller, staff or wheel.* (The balance spring can sometimes catch on the wheel or one of its spokes during the oscillation.)

Adjusting the Beat & Repositioning Platforms

Platform escapements can be readily lifted off the clock and still maintain a proper relationship between the parts of the escapement. It is always best to study the platform while it is off the movement so that it is certain that there is no loading on the escapewheel to affect the

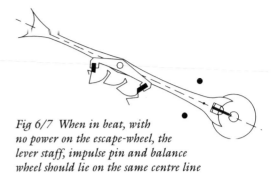

Fig 6/7 When in beat, with no power on the escape-wheel, the lever staff, impulse pin and balance wheel should lie on the same centre line

assessment of its 'beat'. **Fig 6/6** shows the position of the lever at the time of locking on alternate beats — the features are a little exaggerated to illustrate the action.

The lever and balance are in beat (and for most platform escapements this means that the pallets are also in beat) when the centre of the balance wheel, the centre of the lever staff or arbor and the impulse pin are in line (**Fig 6/7**). This is only true when the platform is free of external forces as described above. If these centres are not in line the escapement can be put in beat by adjusting the centre collet of the balance spring.

The degree of error (judged by the amount that the balance wheel needs to rotate to correct matters), should be observed. Then the complete assembly of balance wheel, spring and balance cock is removed from the platform by releasing the cock (the Z-shaped piece of brass that supports the upper end of the

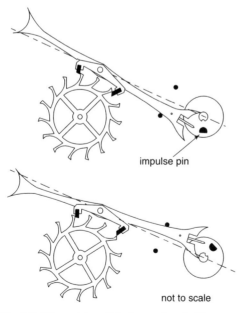

impulse pin

not to scale

Fig 6/6 The position of the lever when locking on alternate beats

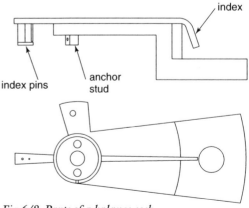

index

index pins

anchor stud

Fig 6/8 Parts of a balance cock

balance staff, **Fig 6/8**). The balance wheel will only come clear of the lever by careful and gentle wriggling. It is permissible to lift the wheel out of its station by holding the cock, but *pulling* at the wheel while doing this will probably distort the balance spring — gentleness must be emphasized again.

It will be seen that the collet to which the inner end of the spring is attached is a split cylinder that can be freed from its position on the staff by expanding the split. A finely ground screwdriver (or a piece of pivot steel with a wedge ground on the end) can be gently pressed it into this slot so that the spring is freed from the staff and the balance wheel can be rotated the amount needed to correct its position on the platform.

It must be borne in mind that the pivots of the staff are very slender (unless they are conical pivots similar to **Fig 6/22**), and when making this adjustment it is necessary to take great care with both the pivots and the spring itself.

The results of the adjustment are tested by holding the cock and lifting the balance wheel into place in the lower bearing (in the platform). The lever must be so positioned, and the balance wheel so offered, that the impulse pin enters the fork of the lever before the lower pivot enters the bearing. By resting the cock on the platform when the balance wheel is properly in position and tenderly lifting the wheel to be parallel with the platform, it is possible to test the correctness of the new spring collet position.

The balance wheel should rotate easily even though the cock is not fastened down and should be governed by the balance spring. If the three centres previously mentioned (balance staff, impulse pin and lever staff) are in line, the top pivot of the balance staff can be eased into the bearing in the cock, the cock set in place and the fastening screw slowly tightened up.

Gently swing the balance wheel by puffing at it with a rubber bulb or rotating it with a wisp of paper and only tightening the screw of the cock while the balance wheel is swinging. If the pivot does not enter its jewelled

bearing properly this swinging will come to a stop before the cock is pressing so hard on the pivot that the latter is broken or bent. Despite this being a slow and fiddly task it becomes faster with practice and, more importantly, will prevent a catastrophe.

The same process should be followed if the escapewheel and lever are removed. In this case the balance wheel will have been removed first and the platform will be bare of working parts when the escapewheel is replaced. This must spin when puffed and kept rotating as its cock is tightened. The lever is more awkward to test, but it should fall from side to side as the platform is rocked if all is well. A broken pivot is very expensive to have repaired!

Once the balance spring is adjusted so that the three centres are in line, the balance wheel will make even beats both clockwise and counter clockwise. If the sound of the escapement is still offbeat, the fault lies with the pallets, which will be worn, chipped or (in the case of jewelled ones) shifting in their housing. Correcting these faults lies in the purlieu of a watchmaker rather than a clockmaker.

Pivots & Bearings
The operation of any platform is affected by the pivots, bearings and the shake that must always exist in a clock movement. In **Fig 6/9**

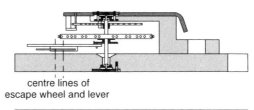

centre lines of
escape wheel and lever

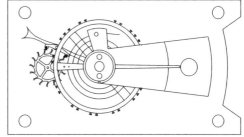

Fig 6/9 Cross-section of a lever platform escapement

a common lever platform is shown in section. All the moving components, balance wheel, lever and escapewheel, must lift on a whisker and drop down again immediately they are released.

Pivots and pivot bearings must be inspected. Bent pivots are easy to diagnose, since the staff will refuse to lift and drop freely, but worn pivot jewels are not common and really call for experience to judge their condition. However the jewels should be carefully inspected with a magnifying glass. Cracked or disintegrating bearings are more common than worn ones and quite clear to any eye and this information will help in obtaining a rough idea of the cost of repair from a specialist.

The jewelled bearing (**Fig 6/10**) consists of two main components — the pivot hole itself and an end jewel that caps it and which supplies axial support for the pivot and prevents any part of the staff coming into contact with the pivot hole. (The pivot of a normal clock arbor has shoulders that may bear on the inside of the clock plates and produce much greater frictional losses than the end-jewelled staff of a platform escapement.)

These end bearings must be smooth and have no pits or cracks. An attempt may be made to polish out pits with an Arkansas stone, and afterwards polish the end stone. Cracked end stones can be readily replaced from a wide range of standard stones, but it may be necessary to modify the little plate that either holds or retains the jewel (**Fig 6/11**) to accommodate a new one.

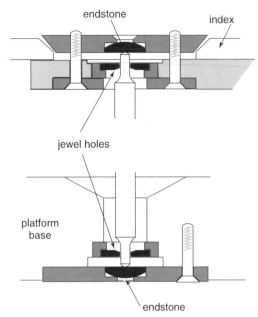

Fig 6/10 Details of jewelled bearings

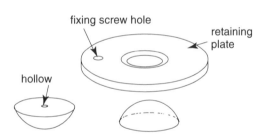

Fig 6/11 A hollow worn in the endstone must be stoned out and the jewel refitted

2 Cylinder Platform Escapements

Although the cylinder escapement is not a Graham deadbeat (though he was involved in its design) it *is* a type of deadbeat escapement and this is a convenient place to discuss it.

There are three moving parts or sub-assemblies to this escapement: the escapewheel, the balance wheel and the balance spring (**Fig 6/12**). In the enlarged view of the escapewheel and balance staff (**Fig 6/13**) it can be seen that the latter is hollow and cut away so that the teeth of the wheel bear on it. The hollow staff (or cylinder as it is properly termed) forms the pallets of this escapement; remaking them is a job for the specialist, but there are some adjustments provided in the platform.

The test for wear is precisely the same as for any deadbeat, the escapewheel is checked to see that it actually locks and does not recoil.

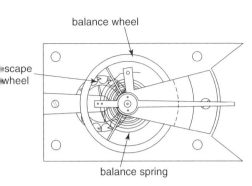

balance wheel

escape
wheel

balance spring

Fig 6/12 The cylinder platform escapement

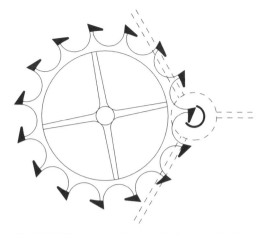

Fig 6/13 The escapewheel and balance staff of a cylinder platform escapement

Rolling the escape pinion lightly with a finger will cause the teeth to contact the cylinder and give the balance wheel a part rotation as one tooth or the other impulses the cylinder. Note that, like any other pair of deadbeat pallets, the cylinder has an entrance and an exit (termed outside and inside respectively) and both must be capable of locking. If one side locks the balance wheel must be rotated manually until it impulses as a result of the finger pressure on the escape pinion, and then locks on the other side. A more precise assessment of the state of the locking — if it is not obviously failing — follows.

The amount of locking on a cylinder escapement is about 5 degrees of rotation of the balance wheel. This can be measured conveniently while the platform is still mounted on the wound-down clock. The contrate wheel is rotated to operate the escapewheel in its proper direction until a tooth drops off the cylinder. Mark the position of the pin on the rim in respect of the platform and reverse the rotation of the balance wheel until the escapement drops again. Mark this point too. The angle between each of these two marks and the centre of the balance should be about 5 degrees. On a 20mm diameter wheel this amounts to a circumferential interval of a little less than 1mm (0.87mm by calculation). A circumferential interval of less than 0.5mm indicates bad wear. More than 1mm indicates that the locking is too great and the balance wheel needs to be moved away from the escapewheel (see next section). This is an unu-

sual fault and the result of poor adjustment by a previous repairer.

The Balance Chariot

When a cylinder escapement wears it is often possible to squeeze a little more life out of it by moving the centres of the balance wheel and escapewheel towards each other. This increases the depthing of the escapewheel and cylinder — it will only accommodate a *small* amount of wear at the entrance and exit to the cylinder.

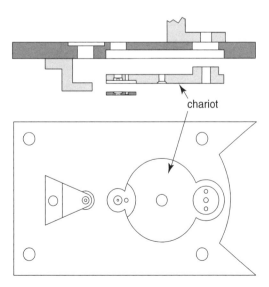

chariot

Fig 6/14 The balance chariot

Since replacement cylinders are so difficult to come by nowadays, extending the life by a few years, even at the expense of good time-keeping, is often thought worthwhile by the customer.

Increasing the depth of the escapewheel is achieved by shifting the bottom bearing of the balance wheel which is let into a 'chariot' (**Fig 6/14**) on the underside of the platform. The fastening screw for this chariot is released and the chariot slid towards the escapewheel. It will be stiff, will not move far (about 0.25mm) and may already have been moved to its limit by a previous repairer.

The chariot also carries the cock for the top pivot of the balance wheel, so that shifting it does not tilt the balance wheel. It may be necessary to slacken the holding screw for this cock before the chariot will move, the clearance between the faces of the chariot and the platform are necessarily small and the tiniest bit of dirt left from a previous repair or examination will lock the chariot to the platform. Manufacturers usually provided enough movement to allow one or two adjustments for wear (though this was not the main reason for providing the chariot, which was to set the locking to 5 degrees of the balance vibration).

Taking up wear in this way will change the drop onto the locking faces. Since one locking face is the outside of the cylinder and the other the inside, the terms 'outside shake' and 'inside shake' are fairly obvious. After changing the depthing of the cylinder and escapewheel the outside shake will decrease and the inside increase — they will no longer be equal. If a difference in the shakes is noted, this is a strong indication that the escapement is worn and has been re-depthed.

The escapement is faulty if either lock fails on any tooth. It is quite possible to keep a cylinder escapement in operation with either the outside or the inside locking failed, but its timekeeping rate will be variable and it will stop at the slightest provocation.

Setting the Cylinder Escapement in Beat

The escapement is set in beat by moving the

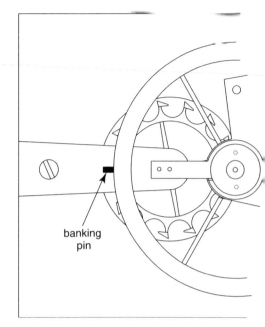

Fig 6/15 When the cylinder escapement is in beat the banking pin should lie on the centre line of the platform when all power is removed

balance spring collet in the same manner as the lever escapement. However, on the balance wheels of most of these platforms there is a restraining (banking) pin that is intended to prevent the balance wheel rotating too far. (It catches on a projection inside the balance wheel cock, **Fig 6/15**.) This pin should lie on the long centre line of the platform when

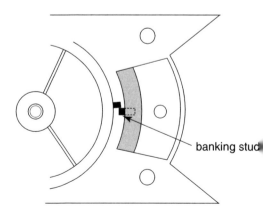

Fig 6/16 The banking pin should catch positively on the banking stud and not jam on it

all power is removed; the wheel is then in beat.

When receiving a cylinder escapement back from a repairer, always check to ensure that when the cylinder sounds as though it is in beat, the pin on the balance wheel rim lines up with the centre line in the unpowered condition. If the wheel has not been properly aligned with the new cylinder the rotation of the balance is reduced, and this simple way of setting it in beat has been compromised (so has the banking). The outside and inside shakes should also be checked to ensure that the repair has not simply consisted of moving the chariot.

Note that if the banking pin does not project far enough for the stud in the cock to catch it positively (**Fig 6/16**) there is a probability that one will jam on the other. The balance wheel must be taken out of the platform and the old pin extracted, replacing it with a longer one. Care must be taken during the extraction because it is very easy to mangle the protrusion so that it cannot be extracted and the rim of the balance must be drilled for a new one. This is not a good solution as it makes the banking slightly uneven, unless it is possible to drill into the broken pin itself rather than to one side.

3 Depthing Platform Escapements

In most clocks where the platform escapement lies in the same plane as the train wheel arbors, there is a contrate wheel that has adjustment for longitudinal position. This adjustment is a screw mounted in a small cock or falseplate on the back plate of the clock. It has a flat end that bears on the end of the contrate pivot (**Fig 6/17**).

When a platform is reinstated on the clock movement, this adjustment should *not* be used for obtaining a proper depth between contrate wheel and escape pinion because it affects the end shake (movement of the arbor between the plates) and this should remain unaltered by any repair to the clock. If, for any reason, the overall length of the contrate arbor has changed, this adjustment screw can be used to ensure that the arbor shakes just

enough to be totally free of any pinching between the shoulder at one end and the screw at the other.

Depthing the escapewheel pinion and the contrate wheel (or a normal wheel if the platform is mounted vertically on the back plate) is achieved by moving the whole platform to give the best meshing of the two gears.

Ideally, meshing should be tested when the escapewheel is free of the rest of the escapement and there is no power on the rest of the train. A lever escapement must have its lever removed to carry out depthing in this way and this is only a practicable method if the repairer is confident of refitting the lever while the platform is in place on the clock plates.

In practice repairers often judge whether the depthing of a lever platform is satisfactory or not by putting a tiny amount of power on the train, loosening at least three of the mounting screws and tapping the ends of the platform with the wooden handle of a small tool (file, brush, small hammer, etc) until the largest swing or vibration of the balance wheel is obtained.

The mounting screws are tightened one by one, making sure that the vibration of the balance wheel does not reduce after tightening any of the screws. If this occurs the platform must be adjusted again, tightening the screws in a different order so that whatever

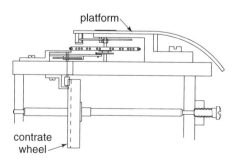

Fig 6/17 End-shake in the contrate wheel pivots is adjusted by a screw

distortion is causing the problem is minimised. It may seem to be literally 'hit or miss', but the method works well with practice. There is not usually sufficient movement in the mounting holes to allow the pinion to come out of mesh, but this is a danger that must be anticipated and checked.

Depthing the cylinder-type of platform is much easier. *There must be no power on the train.* If the balance wheel and spring are removed the escapewheel will be completely free to rotate when the contrate wheel is turned very gently by hand. Depthing can be tested as the platform is screwed in place, with no difficulty at all. Then the balance wheel, spring and cock are replaced, gently turning the contrate wheel to facilitate the entry of the pallet into the cylinder.

4 The Balance Spring & Index

Both types of platform employ a balance spring of course and these only differ in quality and style. Their attachment to the staff, pinning and indexing are essentially the same.

The common balance spring is a flat spiral, while good quality ones have the outer coil lifted away from the plane and bent in a calculated form towards the centre of the staff (Breguet springs). Whether the spring is flat or has this 'overcoil' is only of academic interest, because making or remaking a balance spring is beyond the scope to this book. In any case, it is quite difficult nowadays to find a supply of balance springs suitable for old platforms. Most repairers match old stock springs to platforms when a balance spring is destroyed or too short, but old springs are not the best material on which to try and form an overcoil.

It has already been pointed out that the inner end of the spring is clenched into a split collet that is then pushed onto the staff. If any adjustment has been made to the beat of the balance (ie the split collet has been rotated) the height of the outer end of the spring must be checked against the stud that it will be pinned to. If necessary the collet should be spread again with a thin wedge so that it can be moved along the staff to bring the outer coil into position. If the fastening of this outer coil in the stud is carried out when it is either lower or higher than the hole it is pinned into, the spring will be distorted, will vibrate in an uneven fashion and probably jam in the pins of the index as it is used to regulate the clock.

The balance should be supported in the cock with the spring in place but not pinned, yet allowing the outer coil to pass through the hole in the stud and the indexing pins. If the outer coil is properly shaped it will be a true arc concentric with the staff, and when the balance is rotated slightly the outer coil will slide through the index pins and the hole in the stud. This is the perfect case and where old battered springs are concerned 'near enough' may have to be accepted. However when the outer coil is pinned into the stud is imperative that the index can be used without grabbing it. Usually a slow careful movement of the index will enable the index pin to slide along the outer coil quite satisfactorily.

Concentricity of Balance Spring Coils

It is most important that the coils of the balance spring spiral evenly around the staff, so that as the latter oscillates the spring as a whole stays centred and does not compress on one side and expand on the other **Fig 6/18**. The effect is brought about by the outer coil being drawn out of its true arc by the stud or despite making a true arc when held by the stud, there is a definite pull on the rest of the coils by the pinning of the outer coil.

Rating the Balance Spring

The rate of the spring is altered by sliding the index pins along it and either lengthening or shortening that part of the spring that is free to vibrate. This is not quite as simple as it appears.

In **Fig 6/19A** the outer coil is shown relatively tightly gripped by the index pins. If the

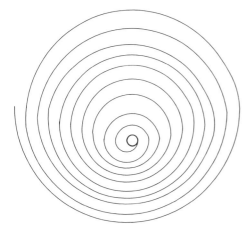

Fig 6/18 A balance spring strained so that it is eccentric

index is moved (and if the index pins slide properly along the coil), the spring will be shortened or lengthened and the length of the spring will remain constant whether the balance wheel makes a 'long' arc or a 'short' arc. It must be appreciated that the energy fed to the escapement is not constant, hence the arc or part-rotation of the balance will become greater with increasing power to the impulse or shorter with a decline in power. A long arc takes more time than a short arc, so the latter will result in a gaining rate.

Fig 6/19B shows the index pins opened so that the outer pin will only touch the spring when the balance makes a long arc. This has the effect of shortening the spring part way

through the beat and speeding up the vibration. This effect can be used to reduce the tendency of a clock to run at a losing rate when fully wound and the balance makes long arcs, and at a gaining rate when run down and producing small arcs.

If both pins are opened so that neither touches the spring it will behave as if there was no indexing and moving the index will have no effect. The timekeeping rate of a given balance and spring depends upon the length of spring vibrating and, of course, the index ought to be set to its central position on the platform for correct rate, so that there is adjustment up and down for changes in rate due to temperature and friction.

The common method of achieving this is to set the index to the midpoint, unpin the spring and slide it in and out of the anchor stud until the rate is right. The spring is then pinned in this position. However it is possible to use the width between the pins to set the clock (when the index is centred) for accurate timekeeping. Clearly it is more convenient to vary the width between the pins than to fiddle about with the position of the end of the spring within the stud. It is, of course, necessary to have a small losing rate when the index pins are not touching the spring.

Badly damaged springs *can* be reshaped using two pairs of tweezers, but this is only worthwhile if the amount of damage is slight. Coils that have been twisted with respect to

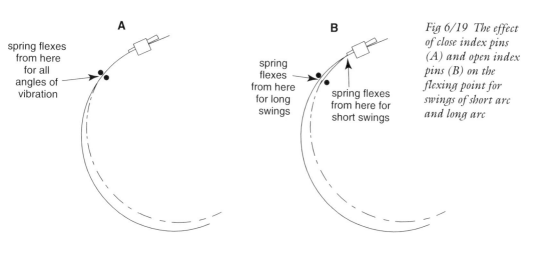

A

spring flexes from here for all angles of vibration

B

spring flexes from here for long swings

spring flexes from here for short swings

Fig 6/19 The effect of close index pins (A) and open index pins (B) on the flexing point for swings of short arc and long arc

each other and kinked rarely respond to this method of reshaping. Fine springs can have their outer coils smoothed and brought to a decent spiral by trapping the coil between a stout piece of pivot steel and a brass plate and then carefully drawing it through with tweezers while keeping the plane of the spiral vertical (**Fig 6/20**). Unfortunately most platform escapements have springs that are too stout in section to respond well to this.

Finding replacement springs for old platform escapements is not easy. The newcomer should practice adjusting balance springs on an old, large alarm clock (most have spares available), or a broken platform escapement that is not worth renovating — there are any number of these available.

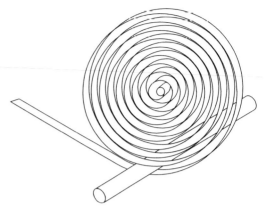

Fig 6/20 Fine balance springs may be reshaped with care

5 Cleaning a Platform Escapement

The platform escapement is too delicate a mechanism to clean in the same way (and definitely not in the same bath) as the rest of the clock. It should be partly dismantled by removing all the cocks and those end stones that are easily removed. The end stone for the top pivot of the balance wheel is held by two screws under the cock — which also keeps the retaining cap for the index in place. The balance spring needs to be unpinned before these screws can be undone safely.

Platforms do not often become stained and a degreasing fluid is frequently sufficient for cleaning. It is imperative that the fluid leaves no deposit on the metal or jewels. Watch rinsing fluids are excellent and as is any alcohol that is 100 per cent pure (with no methylated spirits additive); it should be fresh — not already used on another escapement.

After soaked the parts in the rinsing fluid use a puffer to blow away the excess, soak up fluid from the spring and jewel holes with a touch of non-acidic paper, and then leave in a warm place to dry out thoroughly. Most platform escapements are large enough to accept a light synthetic oil (5-6 centistokes/sec), but if the balance wheel is smaller than about 15mm a synthetic watch oil is better.

Lubrication should be carried out *before* reassembly by placing a dot of oil on each pivot and two or three escapewheel teeth. Under no circumstances should the balance spring be contaminated with oil.

It is worth repeating the instruction to keep the escapewheel and balance wheel rotating while the cocks are tightened down and to make sure that the lever is equally free.

6 Alternative Lever Escapements

A number of American and German clocks have lever escapements that are not mounted on platforms, but have the lever and pallets attached separately to an arbor or staff (**Fig 6/21**). It is easy for the pallets of this style of escapement to be out of beat even though the balance wheel is *in* beat. The balance wheel should be attended to first and the balance spring shifted on the staff until the centres of the balance wheel, lever and impulse pin are all in line when unloaded.

At that time the pallets should be half way

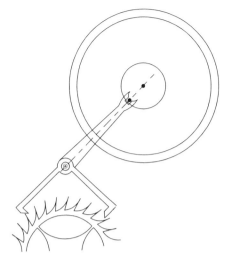

Fig 6/21 Lever escapements that are not mounted on platforms are in beat when the three centres are in line as the acting tooth is halfway through impulse

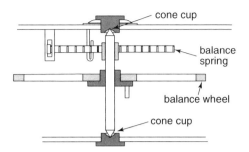

Fig 6/22 Conical balance staff bearing as used in cheap clocks

through their operation, they should be un-locked and the teeth of the escapewheel will have progressed to the approximate middle of the impulse face. A club-foot wheel com-plicates matters, since impulsing is not com-plete until the two incline planes of the wheel and the pallet have come free of each other. However, the width of the club-foot tooth and the length of the pallet impulse face should be disposed evenly about a common centre — which is much the same as a pointed escape-wheel tooth resting at the midpoint of the impulse face.

The pallets are moved on their arbor until this disposition is achieved when the balance is unloaded (ie the impulse pin is not pressing to left or right).

Conical Bearings

The simple balance wheel with a cone-ended staff appears in a number of cheap clock move-ments and can give very satisfactory service over decades — probably getting on for a cen-tury in some cases. Since it is a cheap move-ment it is often the first type that a beginner tackles. Fortunately it is a robust device and in the larger examples the process of disas-

sembly is fairly obvious. However, there are a number of things to be said about the clean-ing and setting up of the balance wheel that will make the repair easier to carry out.

The first is that the cones are, of course, bearings — and they are efficient as long as the points of the cones are the only part of the staff to make contact with the rest of the clock. **Fig 6/22** shows a typical cone-ended balance staff and the cups that hold it. Over the years this clock will have been lubricated and the oil in the cups will, in all probability, have gone hard (cheap clocks, for obvious reasons, are not serviced as often as more expensive ones). This old oil (which behaves much like lacquer) will not readily clean out in the cleaning tank — it really is too hard in most cases to do anything much except turn into a sticky, tarry mass at the bottom of the cup. If an attempt is made to run the clock like this, the 'tar' will reduce the angle through which the balance swings, to the point where it either stops altogether or runs very fast.

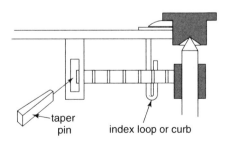

Fig 6/23 The balance spring is held in place with a taper pin

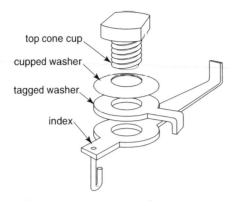

top cone cup
cupped washer
tagged washer
index

Fig 6/24 Components of a cone bearing

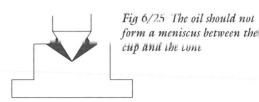

Fig 6/25 The oil should not form a meniscus between the cup and the cone

To clean out the tar the balance wheel must be removed from the clock. The taper pin or wedge that holds the end of the balance spring is removed (**Fig 6/23**) and the spring is slid out of the index loop or slot (depending on the manufacturer). The balance is now quite free to rotate — apart from striking the forked lever — and can be removed from the clock plates. Either of the cups may be unscrewed to release the staff and the easiest one is usually the one that also supports the index arm. **Fig 6/24** is an exploded view of the parts that are involved — the cup itself, a cupped spring, a 'tagged' washer and the index arm,.

The balance wheel is removed in the same way as in the case of the platform escapement. This must be done carefully to ensure that the fork and the impulse pin are not damaged as they part. It should be encouraged to emerge using tweezers, so that it does not snag anything or leave the end of the balance spring hooked around another part.

The inner, working surface of both the cups (one still in the plate, the other with the removed parts), are now visible. Thick black tars are obvious to the naked eye, but often the oil has dried out to form a faintly coloured lacquer that is less easy to see.

The end of a matchstick or piece of peg wood is used to clean away any solid or near-solid residues. Shape the end to form a three-sided pyramid that can be twizzled into the cups to cut the tar out of the bottom of the cone. This may need to be done two or three

times, recutting the pyramid in between, before the cup is absolutely clean.

The cups should be lubricated now. If it is done when the cones are seated inside there is a probability that oil will form a meniscus between the sides of the male and female cone which will slow it down and give a short arc (**Fig 6/25**). Just enough oil to moisten the bottom of the conical hole is quite sufficient and the easiest way to ensure this is to place a drop of oil in the cup and then pull out the excess with the pointed end of a matchstick.

Repointing the Cone Ends
Fig 6/26 shows the balance wheel assembly, consisting of a staff with conical points at each end, the balance wheel with its impulse pin and the balance spring. Also shown is the sort of damage at the end of the staff that should be looked for. What should be a sharp cone with the very slightest radius on its tip now has a worn surface that looks like a facet, but in fact is part of another cone that is no longer concentric with the staff. In most cases there is plenty of adjustment between the cups and the staff to allow for remaking the ends of the staff to produce cones that are truly concentric and sharp. It is a matter of stoning away the worn cone.

There is no way of repairing or refurbish-

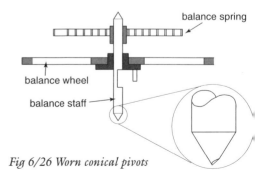

balance spring
balance wheel
balance staff

Fig 6/26 Worn conical pivots

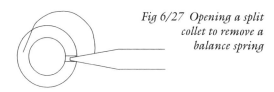

Fig 6/27 Opening a split collet to remove a balance spring

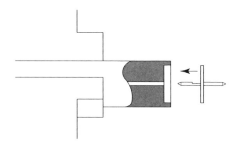

Fig 6/28 Support the balance and staff in recess bored in a piece of brass held in a lathe chuck

ing the seating itself, unless the repairer is willing to go to the lengths of annealing the steel, re-sinking the female cone, polishing and hardening. It is rarely worthwhile, as making a new one take very little longer, even if the threads in the clock plate also have to be remade. Fortunately, the seatings appear to be less prone to wear than the ends of the staff, and resharpening the latter is a simple matter.

In order to spin the staff in a lathe (or drilling machine if no lathe is available), the balance spring must be removed. This is a simple process since it is attached to the staff by the same method as any platform escapement. The inner coil of the spring is clenched into a split collet that is a friction fit on the staff, and all that is needed to slip it off is to expand the collet slightly by pressing a wedge into the split and move it along the staff. The wedge may be a screwdriver with a conveniently sized blade or a piece of pivot steel ground to suit the split (**Fig 6/27**).

Before this is done however, it will make reassembly much simpler if the staff between the spring and wheel is marked with a fine-point felt-tip pen. This will show how far down the staff the spring was originally fitted and — if a scratch mark is made opposite the split in the inner collet — what the original disposition of the spring was in regard to the staff. If this is not done, unnecessary time will be spent putting the balance in beat after reassembly by twisting the split collet around the staff.

The wheel and staff may be supported in the lathe by machining a small piece of brass with a counterbore to accept the outside diameter of the wheel and a hole that is a slide fit on the staff (**Fig 6/28**). This reduces the strain on the staff to a minimum, and is necessary as that there is a cut-out on the staff just above the wheel which weakens it considerably. The wheel is held in place with shellac, warming the brass with a small flame and rubbing a stick of shellac onto it until there is a film of stickiness on the face.

There will be enough of the original cone left to guide a stone or backed-up emery paper and keep the new surface concentric while the staff is spun in the lathe. In fact the wear on the point of the staff is normally very small. A steady hand and a good eye is needed if this is done without some form of guide for making new cone to the correct angle. Alternatively, a simple guide made from a disk of brass which is slipped onto the staff and turned and chamfered until a straightedge lined up on the surface of the cone point just touches the chamfer (**Fig 6/29**), makes the task easier.

The lathe should be run as fast as possible (though no faster than about 5,000rpm) and stones or emery paper used that range from about 120 grit down to flour paper. When a sharp point is produced it is touched lightly with an Arkansas stone and a tiny (barely visible) radius made on the end.

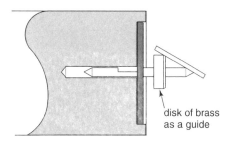

disk of brass
as a guide

Fig 6/29 Reshaping a worn cone pivot

CHAPTER 7

Other Deadbeat Escapements

1 The Escapements of 400-Day Clocks

The best 400-day clocks have Graham deadbeat escapements, sometimes with solid pallets, sometimes with separate steel pallets in a brass body and sometimes with pin pallets. They operate in much the same way as in a larger clock, but with a lock of about 15 per cent of the pitch and a drop of the same.

The tooth tips of the escapewheel are rela-

tively thick (about 7½ per cent of the pitch) and the impulse faces are steeper than the usual Graham deadbeat. In fact they are similar to the impulse faces seen on recoil anchor escapements, making an angle of about 45 degrees to the tangent at the outside diameter.

Because of the large drop, lock and the thickness of the tooth tip, the impulse faces drawn as a tangent to a common circle will

escapewheel = 20 teeth
tooth tip width = 1 degree from centre of wheel (linear measurement = 0.026)
drop = 2 degrees from centre of wheel (linear measurement = 0.052)
adjust radii A by -0.013
adjust radii B by +0.013

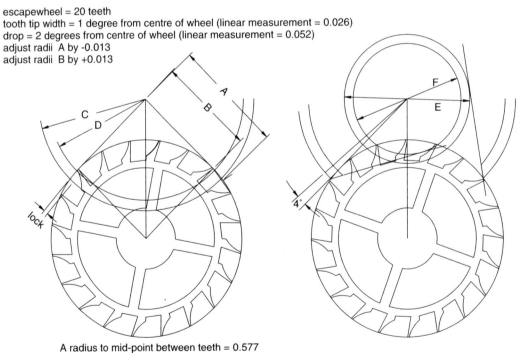

A radius to mid-point between teeth = 0.577
B radius to acting tooth = 0.500
C pallet outside radius = 0.564
D pallet inside radius = 0.513
E exit tangent circle = 0.654
F entry tangent circle = 0.562
lock = 0.020

Fig 7/1 Dimensions for manufacturing pallets for a 400-day escapement with a twenty-tooth escapewheel

have a high degree of error. In **Figs 6/1** and **6/2** the two most common counts of escapewheel (twenty and fifteen teeth) are drawn out with the tangent circles for entry and exit centred on the pallet arbor. Because almost all of these clocks are mass produced it is possible to provide proportional dimensions that will work with most examples.

In both cases the dimensions are stated on the basis of a wheel diameter equal to 1. It is assumed that the drop-off point of the entry tooth and the locking point of the exit tooth are at, or near, the tangent point. Both impulse tangents are shown in the marking out position (when the pallet is about to unlock). For information on using the impulse tangent circles refer to the making of a Vulliamy-style set of pallets (pages 120-123). It is still more convenient to translate these into linear measurements for machining and measurement.

Adjustment of the Pallets

Separate pallets are, of course, Vulliamy-style and the comments on the adjustment of that type of escapement also apply here. The centre distance (pallet arbor to escapewheel arbor) is adjustable, as is the position of the locking and drop off points.

If the pallet positions in the body are correct, raising the centre of the pallet arbor will:
• reduce the locking
• increase the drop on entry
• decrease the drop on exit.
Lowering the centres from the original set-

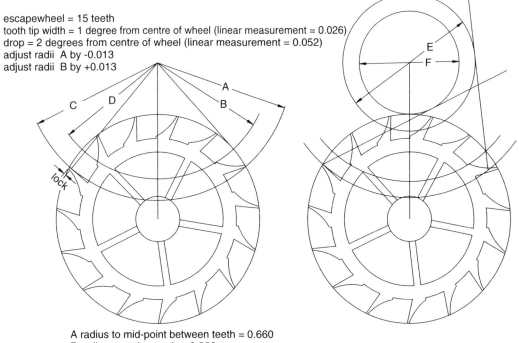

escapewheel = 15 teeth
tooth tip width = 1 degree from centre of wheel (linear measurement = 0.026)
drop = 2 degrees from centre of wheel (linear measurement = 0.052)
adjust radii A by -0.013
adjust radii B by +0.013

A radius to mid-point between teeth = 0.660
B radius to acting tooth = 0.556
C pallet outside radius = 0.647
D pallet inside radius = 0.657
E exit tangent circle diameter = 0.494
F entry tangent circle diameter = 0.562
lock = 0.012

Fig 7/2 Dimensions for manufacturing pallets for a 400-day escapement with a fifteen-tooth escapewheel

In both diagrams all dimensions are for an escapewheel of unit diameter. The entry drop-off points are approximately tangential from the pallet centre. The swing of the pallets gives 4 degrees of impulse and a total swing of the upright post of 6 degrees (3 degrees semi-arc)

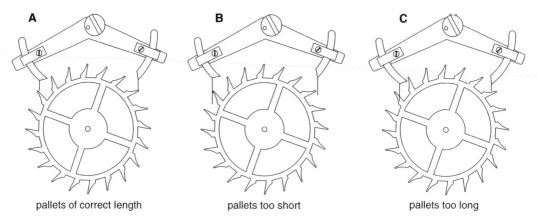

Fig 7/3 Adjusting the pallets of a 400-day escapement. Set the pallets to the width shown in A and raise or lower the pallet centre until correct locking is obtained at locking and drop-off. Check for both beats and ensure that the drop-offs and lock are similar.

A The vertical projection from the heel of the entrance pallet falls on the incoming tooth at the correct depth for locking, and the one on the right falls at the correct drop-off point.

B The vertical projection on the left misses the incoming tooth, as does that on the right.

C The vertical projection on the left falls onto the incoming tooth much too deeply for proper locking, and the one on the right shows excessive drop

ting will produce the opposite effects and shifting the pallets in the body will not correct either.

If the height of the centre is correct, extending the pallets will:

• increase the locking
• reduce the drop
• probably refuse to clear the teeth.

Since the pallets are part of common, concentric, circles the only effects of choosing between the adjustment of exit and entrance pallets are seen in the position of the upright stalk. The pallets should be set so that the stalk moves equally about the vertical centre line.

A certain amount of imagination is needed when adjusting this small escapement. The eye needs to compare the distance between the heels of the pallets and between the drop-off points, with the distance between the acting teeth of the wheel (**Fig 7/3**). In a large escapement the pallets can be laid over the wheel and this comparison made directly — in a small one it is a matter of using a magnifying glass and visualising the pallets placed over the wheel teeth. The pallet positions are correct (if the impulse faces have not been touched)

when lock and drop for the entrance equals those for exit.

When it is not known that either the centre distance or the pallet position is correct, it is probably best to lift the centre distance and set the pallet positions using the drawings in **Fig 7/3** as a guide. Then lower the centre again until the lock and drop can be checked physically. Most 400-day clocks with Vulliamy pallets have viewing holes in the back plate, opposite the pallets.

It is important that the screwdriver used to adjust the eccentric bush containing the pallet arbor pivot hole is a good fit in the slot. This bush is often very tight in its housing and, being made of brass, is easily damaged.

Repairing Worn Impulse Faces

There is hardly anything that can be done to recover a worn pair of solid pallets of this size. They need to be remade or, if spares are available, replaced.

Making solid pallets of this size is difficult, and the originals were ground in large batches to close tolerances A great deal of accurate hand work is involved in reproducing them.

In fact, if there is no obvious reason to avoid modifying the design of the clock, it is easier to make the replacement in the Vulliamy style using the instructions on page 122.

Vulliamy-style pallets (separate pallets) can have their impulse faces stoned and then replaced in the brass body. Though almost all the pallets fitted in Vienna regulators are ground at one end for entry and for exit at the other, it is curious that the pallets for 400-day clocks are hardly ever double ended. Hence there is not the option of turning them end for end and swapping them in their housings. Since the main thing is to have the impulse even on entry and exit, a close estimation of the circle that the impulse faces make a tangent to is sufficient to allow the use of the stoning technique used for the making of replacement pallets (pages 113-123). As mentioned earlier the tangent circle for most 400-day pallets is similar to that of a recoil escapement (0.71 the escapewheel diameter) and this is often the approximate diameter of the crossing out circle.

The pallets on 400-day clocks have a stalk mounted on top that impulses the fork attached to the suspension wire (**Fig 7/4**). This stalk is a frequent source of trouble. It must of course, be secure, without any looseness or wobble. More than that though, it must have the correct relationship to the pallets.

The stalk must move to either side of the vertical by an equal amount as the pallets clear the escapewheel. This may seem fairly obvious, for the suspension hangs vertically and the escapement cannot be properly in beat if it makes an unequal movement between entry and exit. Unfortunately this is disguised somewhat by the need to obtain an equal angular movement of the fork about its position of rest. **Fig 7/5** includes a plan view of the fork, and for perfect operation the suspension must hang from a line that is at right angles to the plane of the escapement and on the mid-point of the action.

If the suspension is out of line then the relationship between the swing of the torsion pendulum hanging from it and the swing of

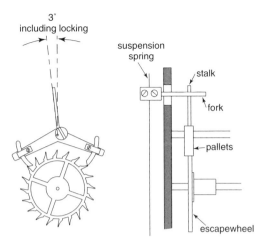

Fig 7/4 A stalk on the top of the pallets impulses a fork on the suspension wire

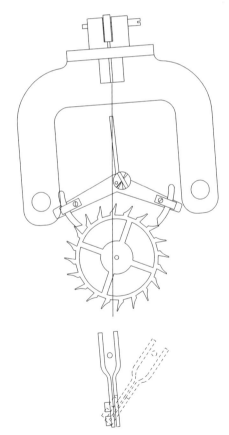

Fig 7/5 If the suspension does not hang from a point vertically above the centre line of the arbors, then escapement will be out of beat. The lower part of the diagram shows the fork in plan view

the pallet stalk can never be truly in beat. The suspension may be held away from the true line by the back cock (**Fig 7/5**). Because the actual suspension is often higher than the line between the mounting screws — and because there is a large clearance between the screws and the screw holes — the suspension wire can be made to hang to one side or other of the correct line by tilting the back cock.

Normally the suspension and fork are judged to be in beat by watching the swing of the pendulum and the action of the pallets. The rotation of the pendulum is closely observed and when the escapement unlocks, its position noted. (This can be managed conveniently if the pendulum is only given just enough impetus to lock and unlock the pallets). If the pendulum has reached a similar point on the other side when the escapement unlocks again, then it is in beat.

This is only correct if the relative position of the suspension and pallets is as stated above, otherwise the actual movement of the fork is uneven at each beat. The intervals may be equally balanced about the centre of the pendulum, but the amount of energy transferred at alternate beats is not the same and the clock is less efficient than it should be. This is a main explanation for those 400-day clocks that apparently should go — but do not. This is rather similar to lever escapements that have the fork and the pallets mounted as a friction fit on an arbor and the need to have both pallet and balance wheel in beat.

The view from the top of the clock should always be checked to see that the suspension, pallet arbor and centre of rotation of the pendulum are in line. The matter is not one of great precision, but quite gross inaccuracies can be found sometimes in old 400-day clocks — probably as a result of them being dropped, or of having something dropped onto them.

2 The Pin-Pallet Escapement

The working surfaces of the pallets (the impulse faces) in this version of the deadbeat escapement are simple pins of relatively small diameter. The pin-pallet escapement escape-

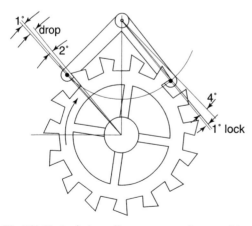

Fig 7/6 Typical pin-pallet escapement for use with a pendulum. The lock is about 1 degree, or half the pin diameter (shown exaggerated). The free movement of the escapewheel (drop) includes half the diameter of the pins; in this case a total of 3 degrees

ment should not be confused with either the pin-wheel escapement, discussed in the next section, or the Brocot escapement discussed in Chapter 5.

Since pins can provide only a small amount of impulse from their own surface, the major part of the impulsing is provided by incline planes on the tips of the teeth. The effect is much the same so far as actual impulse is concerned. **Fig 7/6** shows the make up of the total impulse action and the increased amount of drop that must be employed to clear the non-working side of the cylinder.

Lock, draw and recoil become considerations of the geometry of the escapewheel teeth alone (**Fig 7/7**) and the escapewheel for a pin-pallet will be quite different to a club-footed wheel of similar size. Since pin-pallet escapements are often much the same size as club-footed ones there is a temptation to repair a cheap clock by cannibalising another, but it will not work.

Replacement pins for the pallets should be hard and polished and the best material that

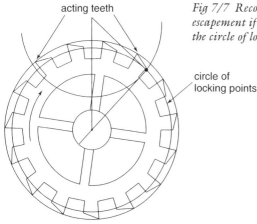

acting teeth

circle of
locking points

Fig 7/7 Recoil or draw can be almost eliminated in a pin-pallet escapement if the pallet centre is arranged to make a tangent with the circle of locking points at the acting tooth

is readily available is pivot steel. As there is a limited range of pivot steel diameters a slight difference in diameter from the original is acceptable. However this will result in the pins being sloppy in their housing. Loctite or a similar adhesive may used to make up for this, but the pin must be supported during the time it takes for the adhesive to set so that they are exactly square to the face of the pallet body in both planes.

3 The Pin-Wheel Escapement

This is an escapement which has entry and exit pallets on the same side of the centre line between arbors (**Fig 7/8**). As a result the action of the tooth in moving the incline plane of the pallet is much easier. It is a similar effect to that of the action of gears taking place after the line of centres — as opposed to before that line. It is a simple sliding and lifting and there is no crushing.

The escapement shown has pallet arms of different lengths and so is likely to have different torques at entry and exit. However, it is possible to make these similar by adjusting the impulse angles and placing pins on both sides of the wheel so that the pallets arms are of the same length.

Drop

If the pins are round in section or any form which does not allow drop off to occur immediately the end of the impulsing plane is reached, the the drop of the pin-wheel escapement is larger than that required by the conventional Graham deadbeat (**Fig 7/9**). To remove this disadvantage pins are often made of triangular or half-round section (**Fig 7/10**). With care and the employment of banking, the escapement can be made with Brocot pallets (see Chapter 5).

A particular advantage of the pin-wheel es-

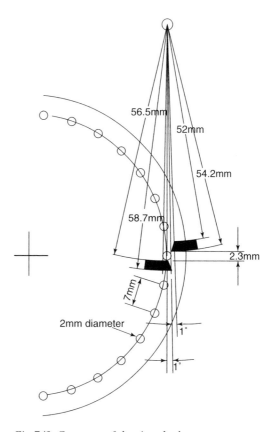

56.5mm
52mm
54.2mm
58.7mm
2.3mm
7mm
2mm diameter
1°
1°

Fig 7/8 Geometry of the pin-wheel escapement. The dimensions refer to a typical escapement

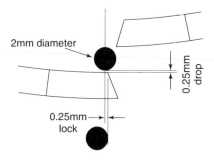

2mm diameter

0.25mm
drop

0.25mm
lock

*Fig 7/9 Round pins result in an increase in drop
over that in a conventional deabeat escapement*

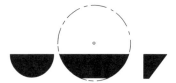

*Fig 7/10 Alternative pin cros-sections to give a
reduced drop*

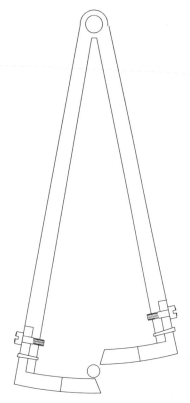

*Fig 7/11 Replacement pallet nibs screwed onto the
ends of the pallet arms*

capement is that is easy to make, only the passage of the pins through the 'gate' (formed by the exit and entry pallets and the locking faces), is critical. Adjustment of the height of the pallet arbor is only necessary if the clockmaker wishes to keep the acting teeth close to the tangent point.

Repair of the pin-wheel escapement is usually easier than the normal deadbeat escapement of the Graham type. The arms of the pallets are often quite thick enough to allow the attachment of new nibs or pallets ends (**Fig 7/11**). It is worth noting that Graham arms are sometimes thick enough to also allow this type of repair.

Long pallet arms produce a small swing of the pallets (for a given impulse) and conse-quently there is a tendency for the escapewheel to 'skip' through the pallets if a light pendulum is employed. However, if draw is applied to the pallets this can be avoided, and the use of straight pallets instead of curved ones makes the manufacture of these pallets very simple indeed. Interposing a spring between the pallets and the crutch or pendulum will make the use of draw practicable and a little ingenuity would make this into a gravity escapement.

CHAPTER 8
Gravity Escapements

1 General Description & Early Gravity Escapements

In the escapements that have been dealt with in the previous chapters, the pendulum is driven directly by the force that drives the gear train. The energy, or impulse, to keep the pendulum swinging comes from the spring or weight and is passed to it via the gears, escapement and crutch. As a result of the varying frictional losses in this path, the pendulum does not receive a constant impulse. Since the pendulum is not isochronous, any change in energy passed to it results a change in the angle of swing and the length of time taken for one beat, so it loses or gains in a varying fashion.

It is clearly an advantage to arrange for an unvarying force to impulse the pendulum and the only way this can be attained is to use the train to 'top up' a separate system that *then* impulses the pendulum. The pendulum is detached from the train.

There are two common methods. The first uses a 'remontoire', which is a spring or weight-driven subsidiary drive direct to the scapewheel. The main train feeds energy to the remontoire and that, being a very simple system in terms of points of friction, feeds a much less variable amount of energy to the pendulum. The remontoire governs the rate at which the train and the hands rotate, but it does not allow the main gear train to directly affect the pendulum.

The second system is much simpler in theory. Two pivoted bars or arms that rest on the pendulum rod are lifted, one at a time, into position by the main train. One arm is held away from its free-hanging position until the pendulum at the end of its swing touches it, releasing it from its static position.

The pendulum is then driven in the opposite direction by the dead weight of the arm — now resting on the pendulum rod. The gravity arm for the return beat is lifted into its 'charged' position by the train when the active active is released and allowed to drive the pendulum.

The impulse to the pendulum is derived from the gravitational force of the arm and is therefore independent of the train. The impulse is metered by the mass of the arm, the amount it has been raised and any frictional losses associated with impulsing and unlocking.

The latter point is where theory proved difficult to apply, as early gravity escapements failed to either lock reliably, unlock with invariability, or in some other way fail to be both reliable and constant in force.

Many names are associated with the development of the gravity escapement, but a few of these ought to be excluded because the direction of their development is not clear. One of these is Ferdinand Berthoud, whose escapement is described as a detached pendulum type, but in fact it is still impulsed directly by the main train. Though later French makers altered it to be more 'free', they did so by way of remontoires.

In **Fig 8/1** it can be seen that the pendulum carries a projection A which accepts impulse from the escapewheel when the weighted or spring loaded lever B on the right is pulled from its locking position by the swivelling hook C. The first diagram shows the escapewheel locked and the pendulum swinging towards the vertical centre. The second shows the escapewheel unlocked and impulsing the

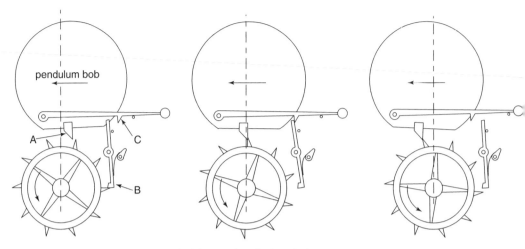

Fig 8/1 Berthoud's detached escapement

pendulum. Before the impulse is finished the detent pulls free of lever B, which then drops down to await and lock the escapewheel tooth. When the impulse has finished the pendulum carries on a little further due to its momentum and then swings back, the detent lifts over C and it is then in position to begin the cycle again.

A modified version of this system could make use of the escapewheel to raise lever B, which would then be unlocked by the pendulum swing and impose the impulse by virtue of its own weight drawing the hook to the right. So far as the author knows, this is a modification that has not been tried.

Clockmakers associated with gravity escapements and approximate dates for their invention are:

Alexander Cumming (about 1770)
Thomas Mudge (just prior to 1774)
Ferdinand Berthoud (about 1760)
W. Nicholson (1784)
Simon Goodriche (1799)
J. M. Bloxham (about 1800)
William Hardy (about 1800)
Edward Massey (1803)
Gustav Horstmann (about 1854)
Lord Grimthorpe (about 1854)

Thomas Mudge's Gravity Escapement
Of the above clockmakers, Thomas Mudge was the first to achieve a gravity escapement with any degree of reliability — but that was insufficient to make it anything more than a step on the way to a successful gravity escapement. It is stated by Abraham Rees to be a development of Nicholson's escapement which is said to have preceded it.

Fig 8/2 shows that the escapement consists of an escapewheel and separate pallets that are raised by the escapewheel teeth to a locked position. Attached to each pallet is a gravity arm — a weighted rod (in this case its own weight) — that is in a position where it can rest on the pendulum rod when it swings from the vertical. The sequence of operation is:

• The pendulum is swinging to the right towards the already raised gravity arm and its attached pallet. The pallet is locking the escapewheel.

• The pendulum strikes the gravity rod, raising it, unlocking the pallet and continuing a little on its path.

• Immediately the escapewheel is unlocked a tooth impulses the left-hand pallet, raising it until the wheel locks again.

• Meanwhile, the gravity arm on the right is lying on the pendulum rod and its mass is now urging it on its downward swing.

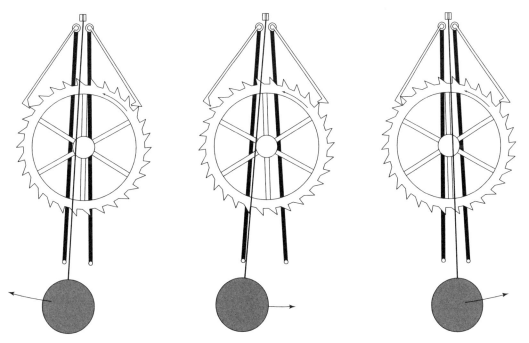

Fig 8/2 Mudge's gravity escapement

- This impulse from the gravity arm is cut off at a precise point as the pallet strikes the root diameter of the escapewheel.
- The pendulum swings to the left towards the raised gravity arm on that side.

The escapement is theoretically sound in that a invariable impulse is given to the pendulum for a measured distance, Unfortunately it was prone to tripping. If the drawing is studied it will be seen that the radius at which impulse takes place and that of locking are virtually the same. If the locking is to be secure and have a low unlocking force it must be at the end of a relatively long radius.

However, to provide this by means of a large diameter escapewheel also increases the driving force needed by the escapewheel (since this too will be at a large radius), and at a disadvantage in lifting the pallets.

Bloxham's Gravity Escapement

About a generation later J. M. Bloxham addressed the matter of the required difference between the impulse and unlocking radii.

In this escapement the functions of impulsing the gravity arms and locking are separated, although they are, of course, fixed in relationship to one another. Locking and unlocking takes place on a large diameter wheel, with impulsing on a much smaller one (**Fig 8/3**). The compound wheel (for impulse and locking) is driven by the train, and the gravity arms carry locking pallets that catch the teeth of the locking wheel. Horizontally extended projections from the gravity arms are engaged by the teeth of the impulsing wheel and in turn carry pins that bear against the pendulum rod when impulsing.

The diagrams show the pendulum swinging to the left, having just finished receiving impulse from the gravity arm on the right.

- The wheels are still locked by the gravity arm on the left, and the other arm is in position to be lifted by the small wheel when the pair are unlocked.
- The pendulum strikes the left-hand gravity arm, unlocking it.
- As the pendulum continues its swing the right-hand arm is raised by the rotation of the compound wheel.

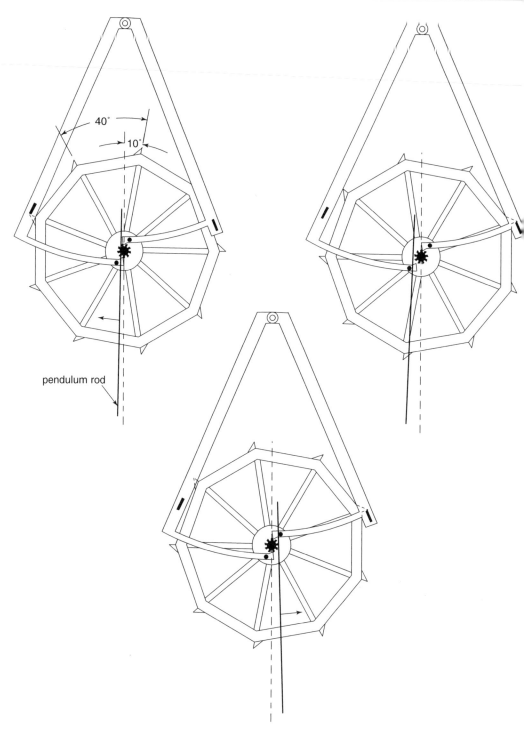

40°

10°

pendulum rod

Fig 8/3 Bloxham's gravity escapement

• When the wheel has rotated through 20 degrees the right-hand arm catches and locks the wheel and lifting ceases.

• The gravity arm is now ready to give impulse to the pendulum when unlocked on the opposite swing.

Although the functions of locking and impulse have been given different radii, there is a fault in the impulsing which led to the escapement tripping. There are nine teeth on the locking wheel (and nine on the lift, of course), with a relatively small rotation of the wheels between each beat and the wheels themselves were heavy. Hence variations in friction led to slight differences in the timing of the locking block catching and the arm being lifted — there is no control over the relative speeds of these two actions.

(The detail drawing of the lifting wheel shows that the tops of the 'teeth' are angled — it is presumed that this is how it would have been done in practise, otherwise the pin on the gravity arm could strike the top of the tooth during impulse and introduce another variable.)

The frictional forces are better arranged, but this engineering detail of impulse and locking leads to a tendency for the escapement to fail in locking. Although Bloxham succeeded in adjusting matters so that it would work in a clock, it was very critical and gave other clockmakers great trouble.

Gustav Horstmann's Escapement

Fig 8/4 illustrates Horstmann's variation of Bloxham's escapement. It is in effect an inversion, but the locking and impulse pallets are formed by two Vs and the locking V is fixed in relationship to the pendulum. As a result it is not possible to have both sides of the locking wheel unlocked as a result of tripping.

The impulse V is attached to a crossbar from which hang two small weights and it is the regular application of these weights to another crossbar attached to the pendulum rod that gives the latter its impulse. The operation is:

• The pendulum swings to the left, away from

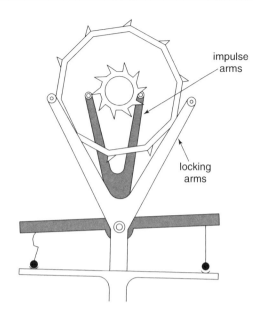

Fig 8/4 Horstmann's gravity escapement. (From Watch and Clock Makers in the City of Bath *by Ian White)*

the vertical. The locking wheel is unlocked and the linked impulse wheel is about to tip the crossbar carrying the weights anticlockwise.

• Impulse has taken place and the weight rests on the left-hand side of the pendulum rod's crossbar.

• Having finished its impulsing the wheel is now locked on the left-hand side.

• The weight impulses the pendulum towards the vertical and as the rod passes it the wheel begins to unlock on the left.

• Fully over to the right and impulsing starts again on the right, the linked wheels turn and are locked after the weight has been laid on the right-hand side of the pendulum crossbar.

By report this escapement worked well, the impulse V was adjusted by banking pins and one turn of the escapewheel gaves twenty beats of the pendulum as opposed to six beats in Lord Grimthorpe's escapement— this is a decided advantage in terms of the gearing of the train. The author has no information on the timekeeping abilities of the escapement, but it would appear that variations in lubrication will not effect the pendulum.

Since the vertical position of the weights will determine when they are applied to the pendulum, any tendency for the thread to vary in length will alter the rate. Also locating pegs must be provided to keep the length of the lever arm constant, to ensure that the weights land in the same place each time. This would seem to be the major fault and the use of a non-expanding metal tape, such as the Invar variant used in 400-day clocks, would correct this error. Nevertheless it was Lord Grimthorpe's device that was installed in the Westminster clock and the only reference to Horstmann's that the author has seen is in *Watch and Clock Makers in the City of Bath* by Ian White.

2 Grimthorpe's Gravity Escapement

The success of the gravity escapement depended on engineering design, and Lord Grimthorpe identified and corrected the practical faults of previous designs that were fine in theory, but failing in practice.

As in all these escapements, the gravity arms are made to pivot as close to the flexing point of the suspension as possible. This ensures that longitudinal relative movement between the pendulum rod and the gravity arm resting on it is minimised. Bloxham's escapement is illustrated as being pivoted on the same centre line as the pendulum, but since the two arms are necessarily adjacent on the pivot there is a risk of transfer of motion from one to the other if they are not kept totally free of dirt and deteriorating lubricant. Grimthorpe used independent pivots close set on each side of the suspension spring.

The gravity escapement that Grimthorpe developed has six teeth (or legs) arranged on two arrays of three. Later versions had six (in a single array), four and three legs. Everything was made as light as possible and, very importantly, a large fly or air brake was attached by spring friction to the escapewheel arbor. The device was thus allowed to move through a larger arc before locking, it had a fly to control its speed and its low weight allowed it to be accelerated at a speed that was determined more by the fly than the mass of the escapewheel. One more feature eliminated the tripping that had plagued earlier gravity escapements, and that was the mounting of the fly. Since it was held in place by friction applied by a spring, the fly was able to continue its forward motion at the moment of locking.

This held the leg against the locking pallet and prevented it bouncing away. Without this refinement it would still be possible for the escapement to trip. The fitting of the fly is crucial to proper operation of this escapement.

The gravity arms are lifted by pins (usually the shanks of the screws that hold the leg assembly together) that register against flat faces on the end of extensions from the gravity arms.

Operation of the Double Three-Legged Gravity Escapement

Fig 8/5A shows the pendulum having just passed the vertical and swinging to the left.

• The right-hand gravity arm is resting against its banking pin and no longer in contact with the pendulum.

• The left-hand arm is resting on its banking pin and not yet contacted by the pendulum swinging towards it.

• The legs are locked on the left-hand arm. and a lifting pin is waiting on or near the vertical centre.

The drawing shows the legs (ie the escapewheel) ready to rotate clockwise.

In **Fig 8/5B** the pendulum rod has made contact with the left-hand arm.

• The left arm is raised slightly, unlocking the legs which then begin to rotate.

• A small amount of space is left between the lifting pin and the face of the extension from the gravity arms. This allows the legs to make a small amount of movement (accelerating quickly), before the work of raising the right-hand arm up to its locked position. The pendulum has reached its furthest swing to the left.

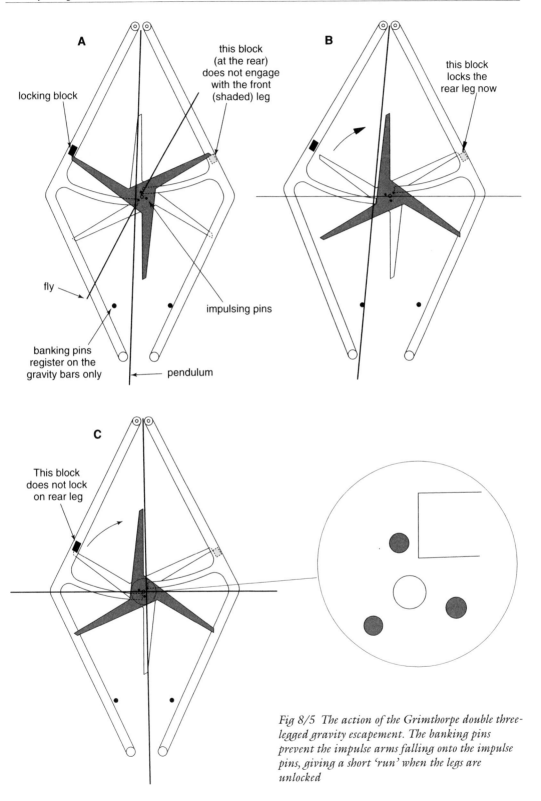

A

locking block

this block
(at the rear)
does not engage
with the front
(shaded) leg

fly

impulsing pins

banking pins
register on the
gravity bars only

pendulum

B

this block
locks the
rear leg now

C

This block
does not lock
on rear leg

Fig 8/5 The action of the Grimthorpe double three-legged gravity escapement. The banking pins prevent the impulse arms falling onto the impulse pins, giving a short 'run' when the legs are unlocked

• The weight of the left-hand arm is resting on the pendulum rod and exerting a force on it. It is impulsing the pendulum.
• The legs are rotating and raising the right-hand arm.
• As the arm lifts the leg approaches the locking position.

Fig 8/5C shows the end of the impulse and the pendulum swinging back past the centre.
• The pendulum has swung from left to right.
• The gravity arm on the left has reached the banking pin and swings no further.
• On the right the lifting pin is held hard against the face of the projection by the momentum of the fly, while the locking pallet is placed in position.
• The leg is held ready to lock by the lifting pin as the pendulum recovers its small supplementary arc and allows the locking pallet to secure the end of the leg.

This is a general description of the operation, but there are a number of small design details that are of interest to anyone making the escapement and these are discussed in Section 3 'The Gravity Escapement — Comments & Faults' on pages 181-184.

Maintenance of Grimthorpe's Gravity Escapement

The pallets or locking blocks must be free of dirt or any stickiness, and the surface that makes contact with the leg must be free from chips or any roughness. The legs themselves must be clean — not only on their mating surfaces, but over the whole of their surface. Because many gravity escapements are used in tower clocks, the dirt (stone grit and pigeon droppings) that tends to accrete makes a noticeable difference to the mass of the fly and the legs. The inertia of these parts is increased and this will affect the brief intervals of time between impulsing and locking, which in turn will affect the timekeeping.

The fly must be free to rotate (under friction) on the arbor. As pointed out earlier, the fly controls the speed at which the escapement

parts rotate (this is a matter of some dispute), but more importantly its *momentum* holds the leg against the locking block immediately after striking it. If the fly is too free the leg will be heard to bounce slightly on the locking block. On the other hand if it has no slip it will definitely bounce as the whole system of legs, arbor and fly comes to a sudden halt and recoils. Bouncing at the locking blocks will cause damage and possibly allow the escapement to trip if the impulse pin can pass the impulsing surface at the point of locking.

• **The Working Surfaces**
The locking blocks are often held in place with screws and arranged so that they can be adjusted. The locking surface must be parallel to the mating surface of the legs and be truly radial. Any possibility of an edge being presented to the leg must be avoided, because the closing velocity of the two parts is much higher than, for instance, a Graham deadbeat escapement. The result of an edge meeting a surface would be to chip the locking block or dent the leg — either will badly effect the ability of the escapement to unlock easily.

The impulse surfaces and pins should be treated exactly as in any other escapement, ie their surfaces should be smooth and free from dents.

Since the arms pivot about a fixed point or points, while the pendulum pivots about a series of points as the spring flexes, there is always a slight amount of relative motion between the rod and the contact pins of the gravity arms. This common surface must be smooth and if rollers are used on the contact pins, these must be kept lubricated — but *not* the actual contact betwen the pin and the arm, which *must* be kept dry to prevent sticking.

As with any clock mechanism, all moving parts must be free and move easily. All other faults that can appear in this robust — though rather noisy escapement — are design faults.

The escapement is a very good timekeeper and one that can withstand a great deal of rough usage — or at least a rugged environment.

Three-, Four- & Six-Legged Gravity Escapements

Lord Grimthorpe's escapement for the Westminster clock is described as a double three-legged gravity escapement — and the reason is quite clear from the diagrams and description — but there are a number of variants.

F. J. Britten is the major source for the older versions of the escapement, and his *Watch and Clock Maker's Handbook, Dictionary and Guide* illustrates a single three-legged escapement by Waldo and Lyman. This uses a triangle for impulsing directly onto two light wheels carried by the gravity arms. The locking blocks are set high up the arms and allow the legs to rotate through 60 degrees at each beat of the pendulum.

The four-legged escapement (**Fig 8/6**) was developed for use in regulator clocks, and has the legs rotating between two projections from the arms, one on either side. There are four pins on each side of the legs, with each grav-

ity arm lifted by the pins on one side. The banking pins are usually positioned high up the gravity bars for practical reasons, but would be better near the lower end of the gravity arms, as shown in **Fig 8/5**, if possible.

• **Thwaites & Reed's Six-Legged Escapement**
This development of Lord Grimthorpe's escapement has one or two advantages over the original double-three legged one and has been used in regulators. It has six legs and only impulses once every two beats of the pendulum, consequently the gearing of the train does not have to be so high. Also the wheels may be smaller and hence lighter, and the pivots smaller in diameter, thus lowering the frictional torque. The angular motion of the legs from lock to lock is less than 60 degrees (**Fig 8/7**), despite the claim (repeated earlier in this chapter) that a large part of the escapement's effectiveness depends upon the air-braking of the fly. Due to this reduction in angular motion during impulse, it seems unlikely that the fly reaches sufficient speed to have much effect as a brake. Also, as the escapement is typically used in smaller clocks than the Westminster clock, the fly is considerably smaller, reducing the braking effect still further. Nevertheless it still functions effectively to hold the legs firmly against the locking block as the fly slips against the spring friction drive on its arbor.

Only one gravity arm accepts impulse from the six lifting pins, the other being referred to as the neutral arm. In **Fig 8/7** the latter is on the right. The operation is as follows:

• As it passes the centre on its leftward swing

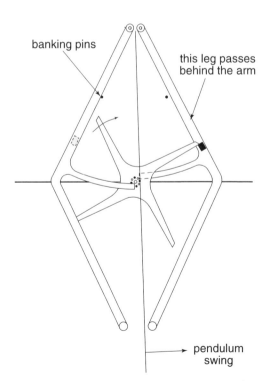

Fig 8/6 Four-legged gravity escapement as used in regulator clocks

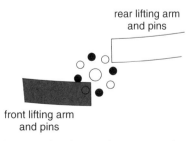

Fig 8/6a Detail of the impulsing pins and arms on the four-legged gravity escapement

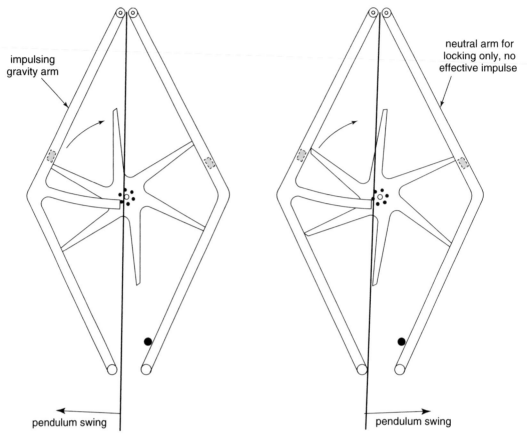

Fig 8/7 Thwaites & Reed's six-legged gravity escapement

the pendulum lifts the working bar, unlocking it and allowing the legs to make a small rotation (up to 30 degrees).

• This clears the lifting pin from the projection face and the leg locks on the locking block of the neutral bar (on the right).

• The pendulum swings to the right, followed by the working bar and receives its impulse.

• Passing the centre, the pendulum continues swinging to the right and lifts the neutral bar, unlocking it.

• The legs rotate, lifting the working bar and then locking on its locking block, while the projection rests on the lifting pin.

• During this time the pendulum swings back to the left, passing the centre after the working arm has been lifted and locked.

It is clear that the neutral bar contributes nothing to the energy being fed to the pendulum and, indeed, absorbs energy from it by way of frictional losses.

In order to keep these losses to a minimum the neutral bar must be kept as light as is consistent with reliably placing the locking block in the path of the leg. If it is too light it might well fail to drop in time with a seconds or half-seconds pendulum.

On the other hand, the interval for the legs to receive lift and lock on the working arm is measured by a full beat of the pendulum (whereas the double-three legged escapement must perform within a half-beat and rotate 60 degrees). The accelerating force required is smaller for comparable sizes of movement — and this, of course means that the weight or spring is lighter.

• Sinclair-Harding Gravity Escapement
In 1984 Mike Harding's company (Sinclair Harding) commenced work on developing a table clock with a six-legged gravity escape- ment based on the Thwaites and Reed design (**Fig 8/8**). As a result of space constraints within the movement, tests were made on dif- fering sizes of fly. It was found that unless the

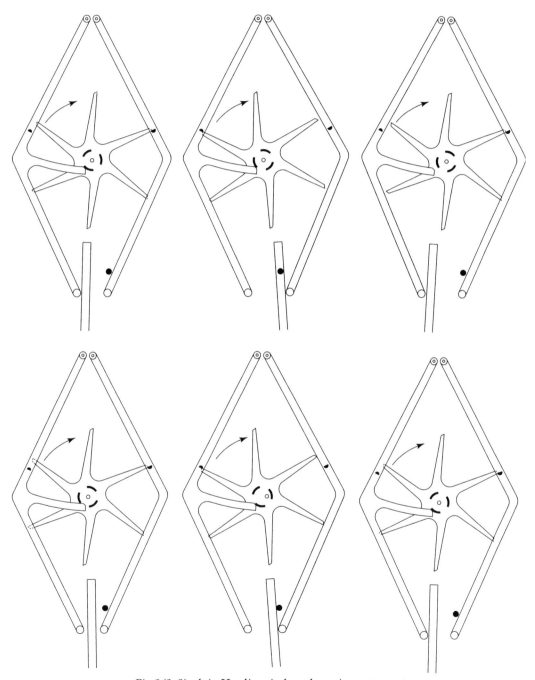

Fig 8/8 Sinclair-Harding six-legged gravity escapement

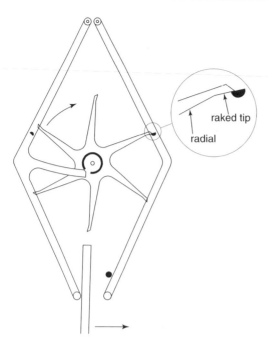

Fig 8/9 Modified Sinclair-Harding six-legged gravity escapement to give only one impulse per escapewheel revolution and with draw to the gravity arms

fly was very large it did not acts as an effective air brake and so an experiment was made using a small flywheel instead.

The flywheel prevented bounce at the pallets just as effectively as a large fly, tending to confirm that it is not braking that prevents bounce, but pressure at the locking block. The momentum of the fly or flywheel exerts a force on the arbor as it slips against the sprung friction disc between arbor and fly. This force keeps the leg pressed firmly against the locking block.

Two further developments were made. Firstly the pins were modified to allow dwell, or a period of no impulse, at every other beat of the working arm. When this was successful a further modification allowed only one working beat in six (**Fig 8/9**). This left the pendulum free for more than 83 per cent of the time, as only a part of the sixth stroke is employed in impulsing the pendulum.

Uniquely it was found that this six-legged escapement required a certain amount of draw on the locking blocks to be safe and a rake of 15 degrees was applied to the end of the steel legs, so that the blocks could be skewed to draw the gravity bar against the lift on the working bar and the banking pin on the neutral one.

• Gillett & Bland's Fifteen-Leg Escapement
In the 1870s Gillet and Bland of Croydon devised a gravity escapement for use in turret clocks, with three gravity arms and fifteen legs on the escapewheel. Only one leg provided the impulse, the other two being for locking and unlocking. The large number of legs helped to reduce the wheel count of the going train.

3 Gravity Escapements — Comments & Faults

The Gravity Arms
The gravity arms bear on the pendulum rod, adding their mass to it as it accelerates downwards due to gravity. Why does this add energy to the pendulum, so that when it returns on the opposite swing it reaches higher than its starting point and unlocks the system?

All masses within a gravity field fall with a common acceleration, when other factors such as friction and air resistance are eliminated. How then, does the additional mass of the gravity arm speed up the velocity of the falling pendulum and increase its kinetic energy?

In fact what is happening when the gravity arm is rested on the side of the pendulum rod is that the pendulum is changed — it is now a pendulum rod with two masses on it, the bob and the bar, and this can be represented as shown in **Fig 8/10**. Neither the main bob nor the gravity arm are free-falling masses. For the short space of time that the bar rests on the rod the pendulum behaves as if it is very slightly shorter, and its centre of mass is raised.

A short pendulum beats more quickly than a longer one and so the pendulum, in its changed condition, is travelling faster when it

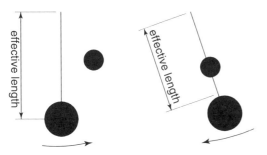

Fig 8/10 *When the pendulum rod contacts the gravity arm the effective length of the pendulum becomes shorter, and it swings faster. Energy is transferred to the pendulum when the gravity arm loses contact with the rod and the pendulum velocity is reduced. This energy causes the pendulum to swing through a slightly wider arc*

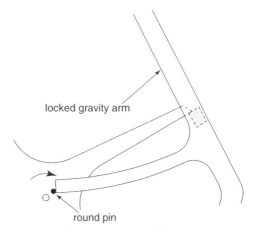

Fig 8/11 *The arrangement of lifting pin and gravity arm. A round pin must remain a small distance away from the edge of the lifting face to avoid danger of release due to vibration or bounce*

reaches the point at which the arm disconnects. Hence it has a greater kinetic energy than the original simple pendulum would have had, and so travels through a longer arc than the arc that it fell through when in contact with the gravity arm.

It may seem that this explanation is unnecessarily pedantic, but what difference does it make if we believed that the addition of the mass exerted an acceleration that made the pendulum swing faster? Consider what happens if the gravity arm, when struck by the pendulum rod, lifts away from it slightly at the moment that the pendulum begins its downward movement.

Will the gravity arm 'catch up' with the pendulum? It is in the same gravity field and if falling free would travel no faster than the pendulum rod. So a small lift off at the termination of the pendulum swing would be fatal to the system and the pendulum would not swing back to its starting position. However, the gravity bar is a short pendulum pivoted close to the flexing point of the main suspension and so it will naturally swing faster than the main pendulum — and catch up.

Now suppose that the gravity arm is long enough to contact the side of the bob. At first sight the small mass of the arm is being applied at a longer lever arm and will be more effective. In fact, of course, it is now a pendu-

lum of similar length and beat — it will not add any energy to the main pendulum and the system will fail.

It is possible to calculate the mass needed for a given length of gravity arm, using the general pendulum formula, but pendulum losses due to friction and air resistance are more complex and in practice it is more effective to make adjustments to the mass.

Lifting Pins & Faces

The lifting pins not only raise the gravity arm to the position at which it locks the escapement legs, but have to support the arm in that position (**Fig 8/11**).

The relative positions of lifting pin, lifting face, locking block and escapement leg are important to the operation of the escapement.

Britten's sketch of the double three-legged escapement indicates a blunt pointed lifting face on the gravity arm projection (though not for the four-legged or the Thwaites and Reed six-legged escapements). Since the lifting pins are cylindrical it can be seen that this would cause a problem (**Fig 8/12**). This must surely have been an illustrator's error, but it has been perpetuated in the extensively revised sixteenth edition (1978) for which all the diagrams were redrawn.

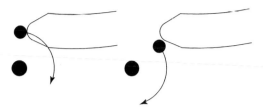

*Fig 8/12 A rounded nose to the lifting face of the
gravity arm will make the locking uncertain*

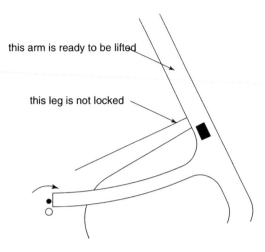

this arm is ready to be lifted

this leg is not locked

The normal arrangement of the lifting face
and pin is as shown in **Fig 8/13**. When a gravity arm is ready to be lifted, the leg is locked,
the pin is vertically above or below the centre
of the escapement and the lifting face is held a
short distance away from it by the banking
pin. This allows the escapement to make a
small arc of free movement before it begins
to lift the gravity arm.

*Fig 8/13 The usual arrangement of pin and
lifting face*

Because the lifting pin must hold the gravity arm in place, locking takes place before the
pin runs off the lifting face. This face should
be flat otherwise there will be a tendency to
kick the arm out of locking when the leg hits
the locking block, or a tendency to hold it
down against the pendulum and increase the
unlocking force needed. However, as has been
seen in the Sinclair-Harding design (**Fig 8/9**),
draw can sometimes be useful.

The lifting device in the Sinclair Harding
escapement is made by cutting spaces in a cylinder, so that the gravity arm can be supported
while unimpulsed beats of the pendulum are
made. The normal pins would not serve for
this purpose. If the cuts in the cylinder were
left with square edges it was found that they
would not rest safely between impulse beats.
At one point (the beginning of the neutral
beat) the gravity arm needs to make a very
small movement to ride up onto the cylindrical surface.

A small chamfer (actually an arc that
matches the circumference of the cylinder) is
cut on the rubbing edge of the impulse face.
This has the effect of making the action of the
escapement safe and removes the small lift of
the gravity arms just mentioned. **Fig 8/14**
illustrates the difference between a square-

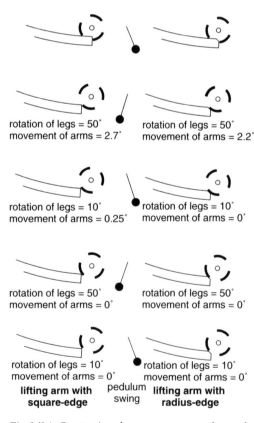

rotation of legs = 50°
movement of arms = 2.7°

rotation of legs = 50°
movement of arms = 2.2°

rotation of legs = 10°
movement of arms = 0.25°

rotation of legs = 10°
movement of arms = 0°

rotation of legs = 50°
movement of arms = 0°

rotation of legs = 50°
movement of arms = 0°

rotation of legs = 10°
movement of arms = 0°

rotation of legs = 10°
movement of arms = 0°

**lifting arm with
square-edge**

pedulum
swing

**lifting arm with
radius-edge**

*Fig 8/14 Comparison between a square-edge and
radiussed lifting face to the gravity arm on the
Sinclair-Harding gravity escapement*

edged arm (left-hand column) and a cham-fered arm (right-hand colum). Both the rota-tion of the cylinder and the angular motion of the gravity arm are given for each position of the pendulum.

Faults with the Gravity Escapement

There are not many characteristics of the grav-ity escapement that can be called horological faults. Though it is noisy and needs much more energy to drive than a Graham dead-beat escapement, it is a good timekeeper. It is not important for clocks to be efficient — as long as they do not actually run out of en-ergy.

Sinclair-Harding drove their version of the six-legged escapement by means of a fusee, so as to keep the locking pressures fairly constant. Since the pallets are unlocked by the up-swinging pendulum striking the gravity arms, any variations in the amount of friction at the pallets will alter the amount of energy removed at this instant. The amount of energy fed to the pendulum during impulse is almost un-varying (though there is friction at the gravity arm pivots to consider), and changes in un-locking will certainly affect timekeeping.

No matter where the arms are pivoted, there will be differential movement at the point where they contact the pendulum (un-less pendulum and arms are mounted on a common pivot). This movement may be small or large according to the geometry of the es-capement, but it is not a continuous move-ment.

When two elements of a bearing have rela-tive motion that stops and starts there is a higher frictional loss at each end of the cycle. It is often referred to as 'sticktion'. A simple demonstration is the difference between the force needed to start a mass sliding from rest and the force needed to keep it sliding. This must take into account inertia of course. Re-gardless of how short the relative motion is, there is a relatively high frictional force at the moment of commencing the movement. Af-ter that, of course, the energy lost is depend-ant upon the distance that the force is applied for, and a short travel will have smaller fric-tional losses than a long one. The use of light wheels of large diameter at the points of con-tact probably reduces the frictional work done.

However, friction force is directly propor-tional to the force applied, and in this case this is related to the impulsing force applied by the gravity arms. The mass of these bars must be sufficient to keep the pendulum swinging, but not much greater. Otherwise the frictional force will increase and variations due to changes in lubrication or coefficient of friction at the point of contact between bar and pendulum, will affect timekeeping.

Calculation of the effect of the mass and length of the gravity arms may be made by considering the pendulum to be a complex one (as already mentioned). Then, using the standard formula, the velocity of the bob at the time that the gravity arm leaves the main pendulum may be found. The kinetic energy of the pendulum is now increased and the ex-tent of the swing (taking into account the new complex pendulum that is formed when the other gravity arm, if any, is contacted) can be calculated. By reference to the amount of arc lost by the pendulum during actual tests, the effects are probably capable of more exact cal-culation than with more common escape-ments.

CHAPTER 9

Harrison's Grasshopper Escapement

The Harrison brothers are two of the most important people in the history of precision horology. John Harrison was born in Foulby, Yorkshire in 1693. Totally self-taught in clockmaking, he and his brother James brought a number of improvements to the art of timekeeping that were outstanding. It is not known how much of John's work was based on James's ingenuity, or indeed if any was.

John Harrison's chief work was in improving the effectiveness of the clock mechanism by compensating for temperature changes (using the differences in expansion of dissimilar metals), eliminating the need for frequent lubrication and cleaning of the train, and providing escapements that produced remarkably steady rates of timekeeping. His major achievement was the invention of a seagoing clock, the chronometer, that allowed great improvements to be made in accurate navigation.

This is not the place for a history of the Harrisons' contribution to horology (see the bibliography at the end of this book), but his so-called 'grasshopper' escapement for land-based clocks was such a remarkable departure from the art of his day that it demands to be described here.

The name 'grasshopper' was not applied by Harrison, but **Fig 9/1** demonstrates its aptness. It becomes more obvious when the escapement is seen working and the 'limbs' flip out of contact with the wheel or dip in to take impulse. Apart from its effectiveness the escapement is very attractive in its operation and although few clocks were made with it (being quite difficult to adjust), this escapement has attracted many amateur makers during the twentieth century.

It is unlikely that the reader will need to repair one, hence this chapter will deal with its operation and mechanical details only.

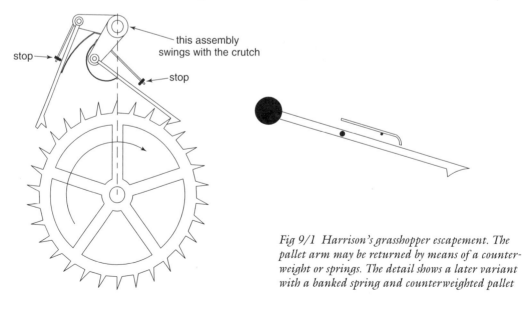

this assembly swings with the crutch

stop

stop

Fig 9/1 Harrison's grasshopper escapement. The pallet arm may be returned by means of a counterweight or springs. The detail shows a later variant with a banked spring and counterweighted pallet

1 The Operation of the Grasshopper Escapement

The major working parts of the Grasshopper escapement are two independent pallet arms and an escapewheel. Weights or springs are employed to ensure that the pallets assume their correct position during the swing of the frame that supports them. It is important to realise that Harrison intended that there should be no sliding contact between wheel and pallets at any time and that there is no drop. The pallets are either being impulsed or are in recoil — as long as the pendulum is swinging.

The impulse action does not, therefore, involve incline planes, nor 'dead' faces. It is entirely a matter of push and pull. If a fault in geometry results in sliding contact the escapement will fail to keep good time — or it may even fail to go.

Most references to this escapement state that it has a much larger working arc than the Graham deadbeat or the recoil anchor escapements. This is true of many of the illustrations, but it is not the whole story.

In the first place, it is fairly obvious that the escapement does not have to be mounted on a pivot level with the flexing points of the pendulum suspension. Consequently, although the arc of the crutch might be wide the pendulum does not need to have the same swing. Just as the Vienna regulator generally has a pendulum semi-arc of one degree or less while its escapement swings through two or three times that much, the pendulum associated with a grasshopper escapement can be mounted much higher than the latter's pivot.

In the second place the escapement can be designed to operate with a much smaller arc than the 15-25 degrees often quoted. This will be seen in several of the diagrams that follow.

Finally, although most illustrations show Harrison's escapement with a thirty-tooth escapewheel, he actually used counts as high as ninety, which decreased the working angle of the escapement by a factor of three. For reasons associated with the timekeeping of his device, Harrison aimed for escapement working angles that were four or five times the angular motion of the wheel for one beat of the pendulum.

Fig 9/1 shows the escapement receiving impulse on the swing to the right. This arrangement is Harrison's original with the pallets having separate pivot points carried on a swinging arm (the proportions are not a copy of Harrison's design however). The pallet arms, pivots and positioning springs are mounted on a frame consisting of two radial arms that may be either a single piece or may be capable of angular adjustment.

The geometry of the frame ensures that each pallet arm is held in position by two opposed springs, or by a counterweight and sprung stops. When the frame swings it dips each pallet in turn into the escapewheel. At the end of the impulse from one pallet, the other begins to recoil the escapement and instantly relieves the grip between the wheel tooth and the first pallet — *there should be no 'free' movement*. The positioning springs then flip this pallet out of the wheel's influence.

Fig 9/2 illustrates the operation of the escapement as the pendulum makes a full oscillation. Starting with the top-left diagram:

A The right-hand pallet has dipped into the wheel, the frame is making a counter-clockwise rotation and is being impulsed by the escapewheel.

B Impulse has proceeded far enough to dip the left-hand pallet into the wheel — it is about to cause recoil.

C The left-hand pallet contacts a wheel tooth, the pendulum is still swinging to the right (on its supplementary arc), and the right-hand pallet flips out of contact as recoil begins.

D Recoil ends, the left-hand pallet is gripped by the escapewheel tooth and now receives impulse. The frame is rotating clockwise.

E At the end of impulse the right-hand pallet is dipped into the wheel again, recoil starts and the left-hand pallet breaks free to flip up to its rest position.

The geometry of the escapement is quite

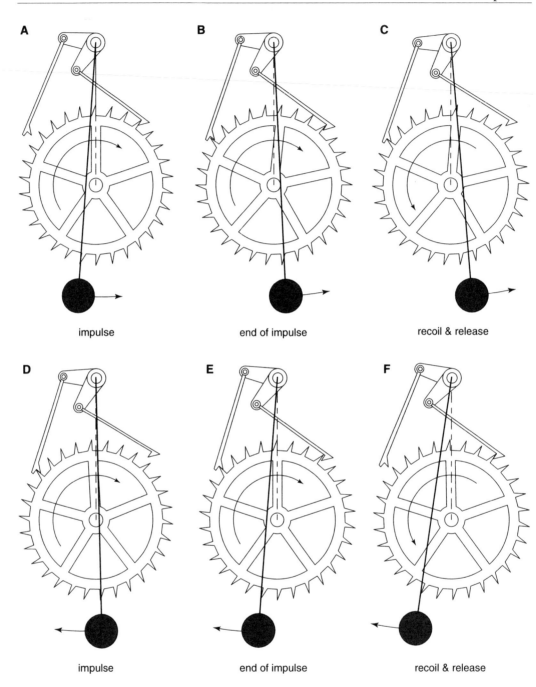

Fig 9/2 Operation of the grasshopper escapement

complex and is generally best defined by draw-ing out at a large scale or with a CAD pro-gramme capable of an infinite range of scale.

Although most published drawings of the escapement show the radial arms to be of simi-lar length, it would require a very careful ar-rangement of the proportions and angles to achieve a correct action with arms like this. In order that the escapement should produce similar impulse and recoil from each arm, the distance that the pivoted ends of the entry and exit pallet move through should be the same for each rotation of half a tooth pitch of the escapewheel.

Fig 9/3A shows the circumferential path of the pivot of the exit pallet and the angle of rotation (13.4 degrees) that is produced. In **Fig 9/3B** it can be seen that when the entry pallet is advanced by half a pitch a radial arm of the same length would rotate through the smaller angle of 10.1 degrees. A radial arm of 12.2mm is required in this case to produce

the same angle as the exit pallet.

(Although it is not shown in any of these diagrams the out-of-balance mass of the es-capement is balanced by a counterweight on a short rod.)

Alternative Arrangements of the Grass-hopper Escapement
Balancing weights with screwed banking pins may be used instead of springs. Harrison made use of banking pins and springs, the latter bearing on the pallet arms as they were re-leased from the wheel and absorbing the ki-netic energy of the moving pallet and coun-terweight. The pins banked the springs, so that after checking the upward motion of the pal-let it was returned to a precisely determined position. The frame may be altered too, so that the pallet arms are carried on a single pivot centre (Harrison made several versions of his geometry) — it is a simpler frame to make and can be made to have less mass.

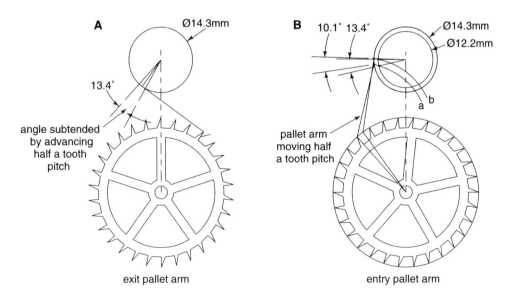

*Fig 9/3 The geometry of the grasshopper escapement. The layout of the escapement may require radial arms of unequal length to obtain the same impulsing angle. Arcs **a** and **b** equal the length of the pallet arm and are struck from the beginning and the end of the impulse. The proportions of the wheel diameter, pallet and wheel centres, pallet arm radii are all adjusted to obtain the required escapement arc. Within limits the proportions are not set to achieve a specific direction of thrust. To obtain similar exit and entry impulse angles the entry pallet arm is pivoted on the inner circle. Arcs **a** and **b** cut this circle at the position of the pivot at each end of the impulse*

2. The Grasshopper Escapement — Comments & Faults

Harrison's design flies in the face of what is generally held to be good escapement design and practice. It produces, or needs, a wide arc of operation and the pendulum is apparently exposed to a greater circular error than in most other escapements. In addition, the escapement is of the recoil type.

However, the fact that the pendulum and escapement are never free of one another, and that there is no sliding friction between parts of the escapement, produces a device where the components of the escapement and circular error can be controlled and balanced so that the effects of changing frictional loads and barometric changes on the rate of the clock are negated.

Any interruption to the swing of the pendulum may result in the freeing of both pallets and the consequent free running of the escapewheel, though the escapement can be designed to avoid this. Hence maintaining power is a necessity. The curious action of the escapement amazed and horrified most of his contemporaries — its efficacy must have irritated a large number too.

It is imperative that the pallets do not slide at any time. They are held by the tips of the escapewheel teeth and a slight indentation at the point of contact ensures that the releasing pressure of the springs or counterweights is a less critical balance of the gripping and releasing pressures. The escapewheel teeth must have rake (10-15 degrees as determined by drawing) to ensure that it is only the tips that engage the pallets. No lubrication is needed, and indeed it would interfere with the clean release of the pallet during recoil.

As has already been mentioned, this escapement may have the pendulum mounted higher than the frame pivot and thus produce a smaller pendulum arc. The point to make in connection with this is that there would then be a greater relative motion between the crutch (loop or pin) and the pendulum and larger frictional losses at this point. Since the disparity between the arcs of pendulum and crutch produces a larger sliding movement within the loop or slot, a horizontal link between crutch and pendulum with pivots to both might be needed.

Pallet Material

Harrison used lignum vitae for his pallets and this practice has been followed since. It is generally stated that this material is used because of its self-lubricating properties, but the pallets need no lubrication — that is the whole point of the escapement design. However lignum vitae is both a hard wearing and a resilient material and most probably assists the grip of the tooth on the pallet. Changing the pallet material to metals such as hardened steel or jewels might conceivably lead to bouncing. The slight indentation mentioned earlier would need to be machined into steel, whereas it occurs quite naturally in lignum vitae.

Critical Factors of the Grashopper Eascapement

The critical factors to be observed when making or inspecting a grasshopper escapement are:

• Contact between the pallets and the escapewheel must be continuous. One or other of the pallets must be in contact with a tooth while the pendulum is swinging.
• Contact between the wheel tooth and the pallets must occur only at the point of the tooth. The faces of the wheel tooth and the pallets must be angled so that at no time during their operation is there face-to-face contact.
• The travel of the pallets during impulse and recoil must be the same for entry and exit. This calls for precise measurement and manufacture, or the use of screw adjustment.
• No lubrication must be used on the pallets. Even synthetic oils and greases will gather dust and create stickiness.
• The escapewheel teeth should have a slight radius at the tip (no more than a hair's breadth), or the materials used must be so hard

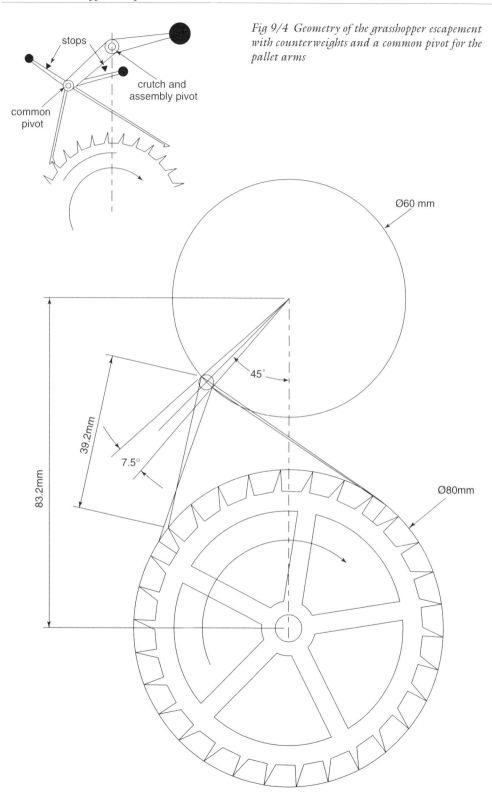

stops

crutch and assembly pivot

common pivot

Ø60 mm

45°

39.2mm

7.5°

83.2mm

Ø80mm

that there is no possibility of the wheel tooth cutting into the pallet and increasing the contact area.

- The pivot tolerances must be small to eliminate or minimise any free movement of the pallet arms. An increase in the radial arm of the frame reduces the effect of a given 'shake'.

3 The Geometry of the Single-Pivot Type of Grasshopper Escapement

Fig 9/4 shows a version of the grasshopper escapement that has pallet arms mounted on a single pivot. It is shown schematically with solid triangles for the screw-adjusted stops and solid circles for the counterweights.

As drawn the single pivot is supported on a relatively long radial arm, which produces an escapement with a working angle of about 7.5 degrees.

In the dimensioned diagram the single pivot is mounted on a circle with a diameter that is 75 per cent of the outside diameter of the escapewheel. The span of the pallets is a quarter of the wheel, and the position of the single pivot is 45 degrees to the frame/wheel centre line at the midpoint of the circumferential movement of the pivot. The distance travelled by both pallet arms during impulsing and recoil is almost precisely the same. It is hoped that the drawing clarifies this description and is sufficiently clear for it to be scaled and escapements made without too much difficulty.

In this drawing the length of the exit pallet defines the position of the single pivot at each end of its working travel. The distance between the pivot and the two positions of the escapewheel tooth is shown to be 39.2mm for both the beginning and the end of travel.

The next three drawings (**Figs 9/5, 9/6**

Fig 9/5 Adjustment of the single-pivot grasshopper escapement

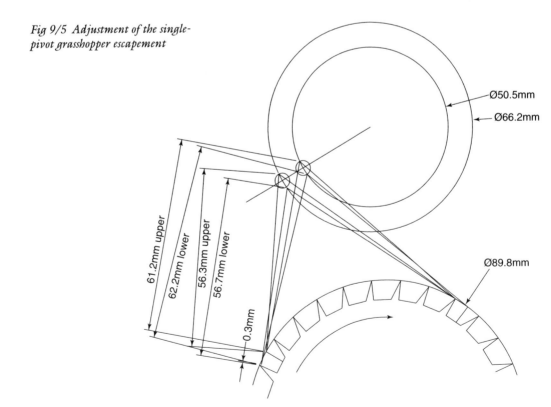

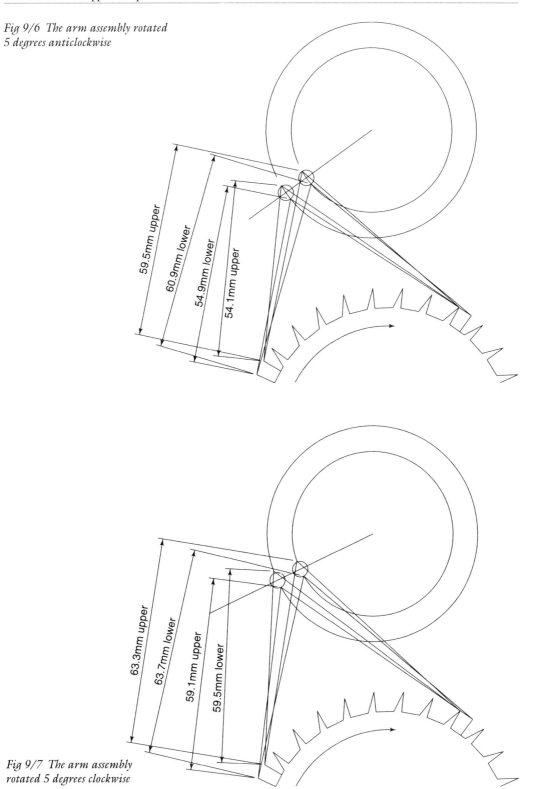

Fig 9/6 The arm assembly rotated
5 degrees anticlockwise

59.5mm upper
60.9mm lower
54.9mm lower
54.1mm upper

63.3mm upper
63.7mm lower
59.1mm upper
59.5mm lower

Fig 9/7 The arm assembly
rotated 5 degrees clockwise

upper	lower	difference
61.2	62.2	1.0
56.3	56.7	0.4
59.5	60.9	1.4
54.9	45.1	**-0.8**
63.3	63.7	0.4
59.1	59.5	0.4

Table 9/1 The distance between the escapewheel teeth at the entry side and the common pivot, at each end of the pallet arm travel

Fig 9/8 Obliquely applied impulse

and **9/7**) demonstrate the adjustment of a single-pivot grasshopper escapement. The length of the exiting pallet arm and the diameter of the wheel remain constant. The radial arm is considered as being screw adjusted and is shown with two pitch circles of 66.2mm diameter and 50.5mm diameter. In addition the arm is rotated with respect to the vertical centre line 5 degrees anticlockwise (**Fig 9/6**) and then 10 degrees clockwise (**Fig 9/7**).

As a measure of the effects of adjustment,

the distance between the escapewheel teeth on the entry side and the single pivot are given for each end of the pallet arm travel. For simplicity these are called 'upper' and 'lower'; these terms only apply to the drawing and have no relevance except for identification.

It will be seen from **Table 9/1** that the differences between these distances can be made both negative or positive as a result of adjustment. This indicates that at some point the difference become zero, and therefore the

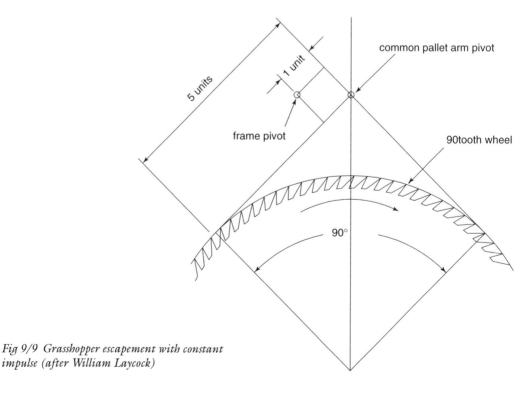

Fig 9/9 Grasshopper escapement with constant impulse (after William Laycock)

escapement is truly adjustable. When this value is zero there is no drop or free movement and the escapement is operating correctly.

Harrison's invention was made with the deliberate intent of controlling the escapement and, to a certain extent, the circular error. Many (possibly all) of his designs result in the impulse and recoil being applied 'obliquely'. That is: the direction of pull or push of the pallets is *not* nearly tangential to the circle that is centred on the frame pivot and which carries the pallet pivots. Instead the direction of these forces makes a tangent to a circle on the same centre, but very much smaller in diameter (**Fig 9/8**).

It can be seen that if the force applied at the circumference of the escapewheel is fairly constant, the force on the moment arm of the escapement frame will vary considerably as it makes its arc, increasing as the action moves through the impulse. Harrison stated that this increase should be in the ratio of 3:2 (a 50 per cent increase from start to finish).

The simplified explanation of the single-pivot grasshopper escapement given here owes a considerable debt to *The Lost Science of John 'Longitude' Harrison* by William Laycock. **Fig 9/9** is a geometric development based on Mr Laycock's suggestions for a constant impulse grasshopper escapement. It should produce a working arc to the escapement of 10 degrees or a semi-arc of 5 degrees. This layout achieves the small arc by the use of a ninety-tooth escapewheel and a neat geometry. The design given in **Fig 9/4** achieves this for a thirty-tooth escapewheel by using long radials on the frame, adjustment and a more widely-spaced wheel-to-frame centre. The latter design should be more tolerant of slackness in the pivots.

Mr Laycock's examination of circular error gives a very clear explanation of Harrison's aims. (See also A. L. Rawlings *The Science of Clocks and Watches* on this subject.)

CHAPTER 10
Pendulum Suspensions

The pendulum and its suspension work in conjunction with the escapement, forming a governing system that is virtually separate from the rest of the clock movement. The relationship between this governing system and the clock hands is obviously important, but its effectiveness is independent of the gear train, whereas its constituent parts, the escapement and the oscillator, are interactive to a degree.

It is for this reason that this chapter on suspensions and the following one on pendulums are included in a book devoted to escapements.

1 Suspensions for Vertical Verge Escapements

Christiaan Huygens is credited with having invented the crutch, pendulum and suspension in one design of clock in 1657. There are additional claimants, but these do not need to be discussed here. Prior to the pendulum the method of governing the movement of a clock was by means of a foliot or a balance wheel. The foliot is a bar pivoted halfway along its length with weights arranged along the arms. If the weights are moved out from the centre the device oscillates more slowly, if they are moved inwards it oscillates faster. The foliot was used in very early turret clocks and also in some early domestic clocks made in Continental Europe, but very rarely in British clocks, where the balance was used until superceded by the pendulum.

Both the balancewheel and the foliot were supported on a vertical spindle which also carried the verge flags and was usually termed a staff (see Chapter 2 'The Verge Escapement'). A pendulum makes a much smaller oscillation than either the foliot or the balancewheel. The beat of a foliot or a balancewheel (without a balance spring) is also affected by the force transmitted to it by the escapewheel and by the size of the rotating masses.

Two methods of supporting the upper end of vertical verges were in common use. The oldest is a simple cord attached to the end of the verge staff and held by a cock above it. This style is normally only found in Gothic clocks that are usually only in museum collections, relatively few collectors having clocks of this age.

The word 'potence' (or 'potance') is used in horology to describe a cock that lies between the plates. It derives from a French word for gallows or prop and it has been pointed out that this would be a good description of the cock that clasps the cord attached to the

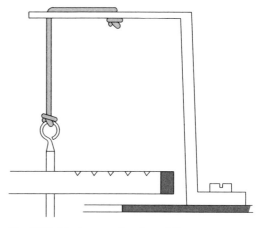

Fig 10/1 Cord suspension for a foliot

196

top of the verge staff.[1] It is an interesting feature, but much too archaic to require much more information (**Fig 10/1**). This is not a good suspension, since any slack in the cord due to changes in weather conditions will cause the verge to lean and beat irregularly.

The second method of supporting the top of the verge staff is a straightforward cock that has a hole for a round pivot on the end of the staff. This method is used in early English balance wheel lantern clocks and also Dutch *stoel* clocks. Though the latter type has a pendulum, it oscillates a horizontal arm attached to a vertical verge.

In the case of both the foliot and the balance wheel the maker has to accommodate the cock within the circle representing the swing of the oscillator, simply because a very large cock would be needed if it was placed outside. A foliot can make a total rotation of no more than about 160 degrees, unless the cock is made so long as to totally span the circle of the foliot.

On the other hand, the balance wheel is provided with a single spoke and is capable of more than three-quarters of a full revolution, before coming close to clashing with the cock, (see **Figs 1/3 & 1/4** in Chapter 1). In practice the swing of the balance must be limited with a banking pin to avoid both flags being disengaged from the crownwheel at the same time. It is important that the balancewheel is attached to the verge staff in a way that ensures that the single spoke is opposite the cock when the escapement is at its midpoint.

The only way that this could have altered since the original making of the clock is if the wheel has been taken off and re-attached incorrectly, or if the verge flags have worn unevenly and then been repaired without taking this into account. The alignment of oscillator and verge flags should be checked since a wrongly placed cock restricts the movement of the balance and interferes with the normal rate adjustment (see Chapter 2, The Verge Escapement).

Whatever the method of supporting the upper end of a vertical verge, the lower one has an adjustable end plate (see Section 2).

Repairing the Foliot Suspension

The repairs that can be made (or need to be made) on a cord suspension are limited to ensuring that the cord is flexible, in good condition and holding the staff upright, and that the cock that holds it is firmly attached to the clock frame. The foot of the cock must be flat and the surface it rests on must also be flat. Very old cocks will be held with a wedge, most of those outside museums have a screw; both devices must be capable of clamping the cock firmly to the frame.

A good material for cord suspensions is polyester, as it is very flexible and stronger than the original.

2 Point or Edge Suspensions

The Bottom Cock or Potence

This device appears in both types of vertical verge and it also provides the support for the lower pivot of the crownwheel in a movement with a horizontal verge fitted with a pendulum. It consists of a cock with a pivot hole, and below it is a piece of hardened and polished steel on which the end of the pivot rests

1   Ernest L. Edwardes *Weight-driven Chamber Clocks of the Middle Ages and Renaissance* (1965), p123

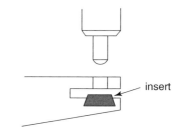

Fig 10/2 Typical bottom pivot for a foliot, balance wheel or crownwheel. The insert is of highly polished dead-hard steel and is often wedge shaped for height adjustment

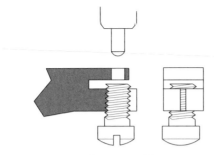

Fig 10/3 Adjustable screw end bearing

(**Fig 10/2**). This is either adjusted for height by means of a wedge or is simply the end face of a screw. In the latter case the threaded hole for the screw is made to grip tightly by means of a saw cut, which may be either vertical (**Fig 10/3**) or horizontal.

This bearing must always be inspected carefully. The face that the end of the lower pivot runs on should not be dimpled, nor should it move during the action of the movement. Stoning the surface is a simple solution to a dimple, but loose end supports can be more awkward. The wedge type usually needs another piece of brass filed to fit underneath the hard steel end 'stone' when the wedging effect has become poor. A screw that is loose in its threaded hole can only be tightened reliably by removing the screw and gently squeezing the end of the cock in a vice.

It may be found that the saw slot that breaks into the threaded hole has become choked with dirt and consequently been forced open slightly. A few strokes with a piercing or jeweller's saw will cure this and probably restore the 'pinch'. If this will not serve, the final solution is to make a new screw, tap the hole to suit it, then harden and polish the end.

The hole is tapped with a standard tap, but the screw is made with a die that is opened up

Fig 10/4 Die adjustment for cutting a tight screw

by tightening the centre of the three screws usually found in the die stock (**Fig 10/4**). This has the effect of spreading the die and cutting an oversize thread. The screw only needs to be tight in its thread, not jammed so firmly that the screwdriver slot is damaged when installing it.

Jewelled Suspensions

All but the cheapest platform escapements have their balances supported in jewelled pivot holes. When the balance swings in a horizontal plane the bottom jewel — or end jewel — forms the suspension. It is precisely the same structure as the support for crownwheels and foliots, but to a different scale and using different materials.

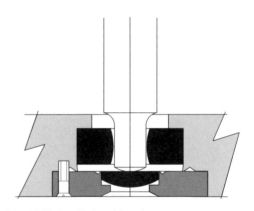

Fig 10/5 Jewelled end bearing

The detail of a typical jewelled bearing is shown in **Fig 10/5**. The end jewel is usually contained in a small brass plate, which in turn is kept in place with a small screw. This bearing is simple for the repairer to examine and also a frequent cause of escapement problems. When examining a platform escapement the screw holding the jewel in place is removed and the jewel turned over so that the flat bearing surface can be examined. There should be no scratches or pits in the area where the end of the balance pivot rests. Any damage to this surface will increase friction.

The simple adjustment of platform escapements has been described in Chapter 6.

Knife-Edge Suspensions

British clocks employing a short pendulum and verge escapement (ie lantern clocks and many bracket clocks) ignored the crutch, and attached the pendulum rod with its small pear-shaped bob to the verge staff itself (**Fig 10/6**).

The reason for using a knife-edge suspension for short pendulums, was to achieve low friction when the pendulum was attached directly to the verge staff or pallet arbor. When pendulums became longer and bobs heavier, the knife edge was not sturdy enough to bear the weight and cut into its bed very quickly. Clockmakers therefore made use of a crutch (suspended from cylindrical pivots) and an independently suspended pendulum without any pivots.

Because friction is directly related to the force on the bearing surfaces, a heavier bob hanging directly on the escapement arbor produces greater friction in a cylindrical pivot and pivot hole bearing. The average weight of pendulum bobs that are hung directly on the verge staff is about about 1½ ounces (50gm).

The knife-edge is often made literally sharp like a knife, which leads to difficulties since it then has a tendency to chip if left dead hard and to turn the edge over if tempered too greatly. There is absolutely no reason why the edge should not be slightly radiused, indeed it is possible that the path of the bob is brought a little closer to a cycloid and consequently there is a slight lessening of circular error (see Chapter 2, pages 19-20). The main point though is that a slightly blunted knife-edge is no worse for timekeeping than a sharp one. The degree of blunting is what would result from stroking a fine Arkansas stone along the edge three or four times.

The best arrangement for a knife-edge suspension is that of a wedge against a flat surface. Unfortunately this leaves the possibility of the verge staff moving to the left or right of true centre as a result of a slight shock, or continuous vibration. Hence restraint of some description has to be used. Banking pins (an obstruction at either limit of the required motion) are not a good idea, as they add a vari-

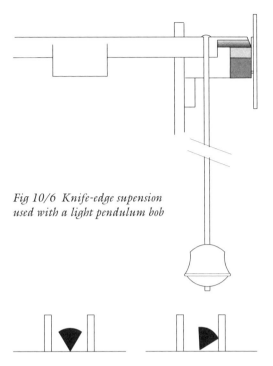

Fig 10/6 Knife-edge supension used with a light pendulum bob

Fig 10/8 Banking pins are not recommended with knife-edge suspensions

able degree of friction, or provide a fulcrum for the knife to kick against (**Fig 10/8**).

The usual solution is to drop the knife-edge into a wide-angled notch with a narrow flat at the apex (**Fig 10/9**), or set the knife into a concave bed. In both cases gravity seats the wedge in the centre and keeps it there. However, it seems probable that the tendency to wander and the effects of the restraint constitute a large part of the errors that occur in this escapement. The knife edge should be hard, there is no virtue in tempering the steel (other than stress-relieving) so long as the

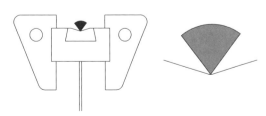

Fig 10/9 Details of knife bed

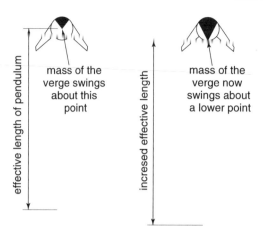

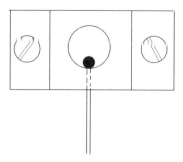

Fig 10/11 Suspension used in some cheap clocks using a small pivot in a large hole

Fig 10/10 The knife-edge should be at the centre of the arbor. If the knife-edge is at the edge of the arbor, not only is the bob lowered, but the mass of the verge staff above the pivot will increase the effective pendulum length for a given beat

knife has a rounded edge (say 0.125mm or 0.005in across).

A rough calculation of the pressure on a brass bed for a knife-edge 3mm (0.125in) long and having a minutely rounded edge results in about 10.5kg/cm² (150lb/in²), which is a very low bearing pressure.

• **Alignment of a Knife-Edge Suspension**
Although the edge of the knife does not have to lie on the centre line of the verge staff (more strength can be built-in if it does not), there are two things that must be borne in mind if the edge is below the centre. Firstly, the mass of the staff will become part of the pendulum, compounding it and making the period of oscillation longer than that indicated by the apparent length of the pendulum rod (**Fig 10/10**). Secondly, it must be remembered that the action of the verge flags must be determined with reference to the knife-edge, rather than the centre of the arbor, or staff.

• **Making or Replacing a Knife-Edge**
Because it is so intimately concerned with the verge escapement as used in British clocks, this subject has been dealt with in Chapter 2, pages 30-37.

Rocking Pin Suspension
A variation of the knife-edge suspension is used in cheap novelty clocks, in particular gravity-wound clocks. In this type of clock the movement gradually drops down a pair of vertical columns, one of which has a rack to drive the movement as the clock descends. This clock typically has a compound pendulum (with one weight above and one below the suspension or fulcrum) with a one-second beat. The forward bearing, and usually also the rearmost one, is a pivot in an oversized hole (**Fig 10/11**). The pivot therefore performs in the same fashion as a knife-edge, rocking on the bottom of the larger hole. The relationship between the pivot and the hole diameter is not critical, but a couple of minutes with a pair of compasses will show that a ratio of less than 1:2 will leave little clearance for the pivot to rock. A. L. Rawlings gives an example in *The Science of Clocks & Watches* of an inverted knife-edge, the point of the wedge pointing upwards and the anvil resting on it.

Black Forest Wire Suspensions
Most Black Forest clocks have a wire suspension that is really a version of the knife-edge. (**Fig 10/12**). An iron staple is driven into a suspension cock with the closed end downwards. Hanging from this is another staple-like loop that has its ends bent over into two circles that enclose the wire of the first loop. The hook of the pendulum is placed on this second staple. Since all the wire used is round in section, the suspension becomes two small

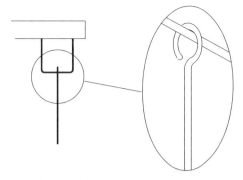

Fig 10/12 Black Forest wire suspension

new   worn

Fig 10/13 The effect of wear on a Black Forest wire suspension

bars that are touching at the point that they cross (**Fig 10/13**). If this point wears, then it becomes a pair of cheeks that fit together closely and develops a lot of friction. Failures in Black Forest clocks associated with the pendulum, are nearly always of this type and the only satisfactory solution is to replace both suspension loops. The arms of each loop should be as nearly equal in length as can be managed, and the inside diameter of the ring on the lower wire loop should be at least 1½ times the diameter of the wire they enclose.

3 Spring Suspensions

The most common form of suspension is the spring, which usually has three components: two brass blocks (top and bottom) and the spring itself (**Fig 10/14**). Longcase suspensions tend to be about 0.007in thick and ¼in wide (0.18mm x 6mm) . Since a longcase pendulum is generally the heaviest one in common use (around 2-5lb) other suspension springs are usually thinner. Good regulators, of course, have much heavier bobs.

Many small clocks, or clocks with small pendulum bobs, have two narrow suspension springs in parallel. This gives the pendulum the stability of a wider spring without the additional stiffness that this would entail.

A spring has to meet a number of conditions to function correctly. Firstly, it must be strong in tension, and a spring 0.007 x ¼in will carry 21lb with a safety factor of six.

Secondly, it should withstand bending. The spring is cantilever mounted and consequently the constant bending moment formula for a beam applies:

$$\frac{M}{I} = \frac{E}{y}$$

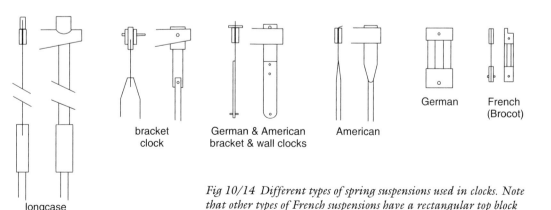

German   French
(Brocot)

bracket   German & American   American
clock   bracket & wall clocks

longcase

Fig 10/14 Different types of spring suspensions used in clocks. Note that other types of French suspensions have a rectangular top block

M = bending moment
I = moment of inertia
E = modulus of elasticity
y = distance from the neutral axis
However, it it is hardly worth doing the calculation, for if the spring is held horizontally it will droop under its own weight with a curvature greater than that imposed by the swinging of the pendulum. Although the strains on the spring will be more complex than this, those imposed by bending it into a curve as the pendulum swings will be very light. Obviously, it is not liable to fail in simple bending.

Thirdly, it must withstand fatigue, due to the constant reversing of stress as the bob swings to and fro. The rule-of-thumb test for fatigue is the ability of the piece to withstand 10 million reversals without showing any evidence of cracks. The author has carried out this test on the suspension for a clock designed for Exeter Museum using a bob of 22lb and with a typical longcase suspension. No failure resulted, but in practice an additional safety factor of two was employed by using two springs in parallel to carry the load. This also increased the stability, of course.

A slight increase in tension will result when the bob is moving fastest, due to centrifugal force, but calculation shows this to be less than 10 per cent in a normal domestic clock. If the safety factors already mentioned are taken into account, then the effect of this is less than the variation in the manufacturing specification of the spring.

The author does not believe he has ever seen a suspension that has failed in operation, unless it has also suffered corrosion, or clumsy handling. It should be appreciated that mounting the crutch or the suspension cock so that a twisting action is applied to the spring should be regarded as clumsy handling. It is totally unnecessary and can create a very high stress in the steel spring.

Lastly the spring must be as flexible as the other requirements will allow. This will depend on the spring's thickness, width and its length. Generally speaking the elastic limit of springs at room temperature does not vary much until one moves out of the range of carbon steels.

Types of Spring Suspension

The construction of a longcase crutch is such that the suspension spring is much longer than that portion of it that is bent as the pendulum swings. In other words, a large part remains straight and this has no bearing on the stiffness of the spring when working. The average longcase clock needs no more than about 1.25in (32mm) of spring to operate correctly. This is an important point, for the length of the normal longcase suspension spring tends to disguise its real stiffness. To judge what this is, flex a short length of the suspension spring — equal to the amount that flexes in practice.

Some clockmakers realised that a long suspension spring is not really necessary, as occasionally a short spring is attached to a vertical extension of the bottom block. An advantage of a long spring is that it acts as a safety measure to protect the escapewheel should the pallets hit the teeth during winding.

Shorter pendulumss have shorter suspension springs: bracket, mantel, and wall clocks have a variety of springs. Top blocks and bottom blocks follow the dictates of the requirements of the back cock. Some blocks are large, some small, some top blocks rest on the cock, some within it, while some are cut away to allow for a Brocot pendulum adjustment. Many lighter suspensions have two parallel strips of spring. This gives stability to the pendulum (resisting 'wobble'), without increasing the stiffness of the spring. If these need replacing it is only necessary to match the original, if available, with the full-size illustrations in clock material suppliers' catalogues.

If there is no evidence of the dimensions of the original suspension, its length can be implied by the position of the crutch on the pendulum. The design of top and bottom blocks can be matched to the cock and pendulum and the thickness guessed at from the weight of the bob. A half-pound bob will need a spring no more than 0.0015in (0.04mm) thick and a total width of ⅛in (3mm), discounting any space between the spring strips.

Many modern replacement suspensions for small clocks now have the top and bottom blocks made of plastic, and the use of these instead of brass ones will not affect the clock. While plastic blocks are certainly not as aesthetically pleasing as brass ones, the method of manufacture ensures that there are fewer residual stresses in the springs, and hence less tendancy for pendulum wobble.

The repairer must ensure that the top block, or the spring — depending on the design of the suspension — is gripped closely, but not tightly, by the backcock (**Fig 10/15**). If either are allowed to rock as the pendulum swings there is a strong possibility of a fault developing.

Making a Replacement Spring Suspension
The spring suspension is a simple device, but it can cause trouble if care is not taken in its manufacture. On the other hand, those suspensions that have two lengths of steel in parallel are difficult to make on a one-off basis, and in any case manufactured replacements are usually available. If it *is* necessary to make such a suspension, the repairer should follow the same procedure as for a single spring, but take great care to make sure that the block that is fastened last is closed down gently and firmly without shifting its position. Otherwise one or other of the springs will bow out, effectively increasing its length — and since both springs are now locked into the top and bottom blocks, it will click in and out as the pendulum swings.

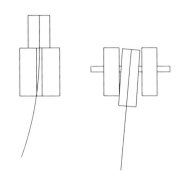

Fig 10/15 The spring should not be loose in the back cock

The cross-section of the steel should be gauged from the remains of the damaged suspension. However if this is missing the following is a rough guide:

longcase	6 x 0.18mm (¼ x 0.007in)
bracket	4 x 0.10mm (⅙ x 0.004in)
English dial	4 x 0.10mm (⅙ x 0.004in)
German wall	4 x 0.05mm (⅙ x 0.002in)
US shelf & wall	3 x 0.03mm (⅛ x 0.0012in)

The spring steel is cut to the correct length as indicated by the distance between the suspension cock and the connection with the crutch. In the case of a longcase clock this will mean that the spring will stretch from the top of the top block and deep enough into the bottom block to place the latter well into the crutch loop and with an almost equal amount of brass protruding above and below it.

• **Making the Top Block**
The top block for many clocks is simply a piece of brass strip bent into a narrow U-shape, and then squeezed onto the end of the spring. The example shown is for a longcase clock, but

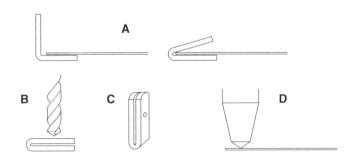

Fig 10/16 Making a new top block for a spring suspension. A Bending the brass strip. B Drilling the top block. C File the lower edges. D Centre punch the spring, stone off the other side and drill to size

the techniques are much the same for any other spring suspension — allowing for the fact that some have bent-strip blocks at top and bottom and some have sawn blocks. The longcase suspension has one of each.

Fig 10/16 shows the sequence of manufacture. The shallow U has both legs filed level just before fastening onto the spring, to ensure that the suspension is properly supported in the suspension cock with no tendency to be forced to lean over to one side.

Frequently the suspension cock does not lie perfectly horizontal when the clock is in its working position. For this reason the top block is often made with a semicircular base so that it swivels on the suspension cock, allowing the top block to maintain a full contact with the cock when the pendulum hangs truly vertical. If they are made square bottomed, care ought to be taken to ensure that when the suspension sits on the cock it makes full contact. It may not lead to any great chance of failure, but it does add an unnecessary risk.

A piece of scrap spring is placed between the arms of the U when it is being squeezed together for filing. This will size the space for the suspension spring. The same scrap is used after filing and drilling the block to clear away the burr and make the job of assembling the block and suspension spring easy.

The top block is drilled by holding it in a vice after the scrap spring has been removed. A drill of 0.75-1.5mm (0.030-0.060in) is sufficient, but it should be matched to the diameter of the material available for the rivet (brass or steel nails are useful). When a hole has been drilled the scrap of spring is hammered back into the gap to cut away the drill swarf. The suspension spring is now inserted and a dot punch used to mark it through the drilled hole in the top block.

The spring is drawn out again, laid on a firm surface and the mark centre-punched to leave a dimple on one side and a lump on the other. If the lump is rubbed with a medium grit emery stone a small hole will be produced that will relieve the crushing point of the drill

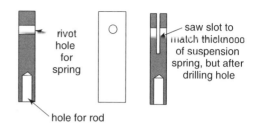

Fig 10/17 Suspension spring bottom block

and allow it to cut through the spring without splitting it. This is far safer than attempting to punch a hole out with a special tool, as spring steel readily cracks when punching unless properly controlled press tools are used. Also the spring can jam on the punch and be quite difficult to remove.

The spring is inserted into the block for the last time and the prepared rivet driven through to fasten it in place. The rivet is then filed smooth.

• **The Bottom Block (Solid)**

The bottom block is made from bar of a thickness to give an easy fit in the slot of the crutch. The hole for the rivet is drilled first (**Fig 10/17**), placing it about 2.5mm (0.1in) from the end, and a piercing or jeweller's saw used to slot the brass ready for the spring. This should be about a 6mm (¼in) deep. The spring must be drilled in the same manner as before, but this time it will have to be marked with a scriber, as a dot punch will not reach through the thicker metal of the block. The rivet is prepared and tested on the block and spring, but not fitted at this point.

The attachment of the pendulum rod, whether using a screw thread, soldered joint or industrial adhesive, is carried out before the spring is fitted so that there is less risk of damaging the spring. The spring should not be held tightly by the bottom block, but should be free so that the weight of the pendulum bob makes it hang vertically. The operations are described in the above order to avoid having the length of the pendulum rod attached to the block while drilling takes place. Of course if the attachment is a screw thread the rod can be detached at any time.

Damaged Suspension Springs

Suspension springs are very prone to kink and crack; any damage to the spring will often cause misbehaviour in the pendulum and cause it to wobble from the vertical. When a light pendulum is hung from a damaged suspension spring the damage can have an effect similar to being 'out of beat', because the energy locked up in the spring at the end of the beat is not equal at opposite ends of the swing. The difference is frequently not sufficient to affect a longcase clock, but a typical American, or Black Forest clock carries a very light bob and any malformation of the suspension spring can be serious.

Some suspension springs are not arranged in parallel, and at least one common pattern has V-shaped springs. This is far more critical in operation than the parallel type — even an almost invisible fault will give rise to a failure that only occurs occasionally and is very difficult to recognise as being due to the suspension. A pendulum hanging on such a suspension will beat steadily until some external event — such as a refrigerator starting up or a heavy footstep close by — occurs at a time when the bob has a minimum of momentum (at each end of the swing) and the resulting slight perturbation is amplified until the clock stops.

Over-Stiff Suspension Springs

Generally speaking the stiffness of a suspension spring is not critical — unless a light pendulum bob is involved. In this case the stiffness of the spring affects the beat of the pendulum and makes the time intervals shorter. It is fairly common in American clocks for the fitting of a new suspension to result in a pendulum which is apparently too short (the clock runs fast), even though the case quite evidently will not accommodate a longer pendulum. This can very often be put down to the use of a modern spring of the same dimensions as the original but using a steel with greater stiffness.

Clocks of this type have bobs that are so light that the spring can be made from the thinnest steel commonly available — usually the 0.0015in (0.04mm) blade of a set of feeler gauges. The limit on 'thinness' is not the duty that the suspension performs, but simply the practical one of handling and fitting it.

Integral Suspension Springs

Not all pendulum rods have a separate suspension. There is an American design that has the rod rolled out at the end to form the suspension spring. The spring is usually led through a slit in the back cock and then bent over the top of the cock to stop it dropping through again. Though it is often the original method, it is not a good one, as it does not allow the pendulum to swing into 'plumb'. A better method is a simple drilled hole through the back cock and suspension spring, and a taper pin to hold it in position. Alternatively the pin may simply pierce the spring and rest on the top of the cock. Both methods are found in this type of suspension.

It is not really worthwhile for a clock repairer to make a replacement, since the suspension is readily obtained from materials suppliers.

The Effects of Temperature on Suspensions

Suspension springs are rarely made from a low expansion material and this must be taken into account when calculating the temperature compensation of pendulums for regulators. However an exception to this is the 400-day clock with a torsion pendulum. A flattened cylindrical pendulum, or a cluster of globes, is hung from a spring that is nowadays made from one of the Invar alloys (Horolovar). The pendulum rotates slowly to and fro, impelled by a rod extending from deadbeat pallets and engaging in a fork towards the top of the spring. The latter twists, imparts a rotating movement to the pendulum and lifts it slightly. At the end of each swing, the weight of the pendulum pulling down on this twisted ribbon, causes the pendulum to reverse its motion and it descends, spinning faster until a maximum is reached with the spring fully extended. The fork receives another impulse and the pendulum begins to rise once more.

Early models have entirely plain pendulums, with no protuberance of the adjustment weights on the upper surface. The movement of mass (needed to alter the period of the pendulum), takes place beneath and within the flattened cylinder. The resulting clock is accurate in timekeeping for a large portion of its 400 day 'going' time. Unfortunately, differences in the driving force of the spring barrel at the beginning and end of the 'wind-up' give a wide variation to the length of time during which impulse is applied, and the efficiency of the escapement alters. In addition, the fact that the clock is not wound (and consequently adjusted for time) each week gives the impression that it is a poor timekeeper.

The author knows of a 400-day clock that has been converted to weight-drive by removing the spring and winding a cord over the outside of the barrel. The cord is led up and to one side over a jockey pulley so that it does not foul the pendulum. The clock works very nicely and keeps good time.

The pendulum of a 400-day clock is nearly isochronous when fitted with a Horolovar suspension spring and, if the tendency to adorn the pendulum with brass balls is avoided, it is not greatly affected by climatic changes

The Crutch Loop

Most longcase clocks, and many other types, have a loop or fork that embraces the sides of the bottom block of the spring suspension. It is important that the inside surfaces that contact the block are not flat — they should be slightly convex — because the block alters its aspect within the loop as the pendulum swings (**Fig 10/18**). It does in fact, lean from side to side, and if the inside surfaces are flat rather than curved, the loop will present an edge to the block when the pendulum is at either end of its swing and have a tendency to 'grab' it.

Because of the bending of the spring as the pendulum moves through its arc, the suspension will shorten very slightly (a straight line will draw its ends in if it is arched in the middle) and consequently the block moves up and down in the loop. Any tightness between loop and block will steal energy from the pendulum.

The ability of the block to slide from the front to the back of the loop must be tested when the pendulum is hanging vertical, and also when it is held over to one side in imitation of its maximum swing. In fact both sides of the maximum swing should be checked, because they may not be similar. When the pendulum is fitted to the suspension and hanging in its normal position the block should not be close to either end of the loop or the fork. In particular, the block must not touch the ends of a closed crutch loop, otherwise the shoulders of one of the pallet pivots may be pushed against the plates and the increased

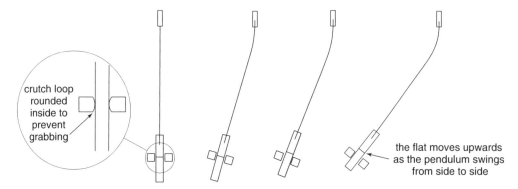

Fig 10/18 As the pendulum swings the lower spring flat changes its aspect with the crutch loop and also moves upwards (shown exaggerated)

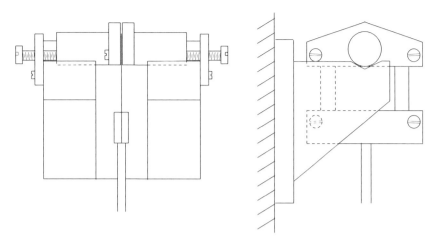

Fig 10/19 Typical suspension for a regulator clock

friction may stop the clock.

Although the block must slide easily in the fork or loop it must not flap. Any free movement of the loop about the block represents wasted energy. The fit should be an easy slide and have no tendency to move the loop backwards and forwards when the block is moved in that fashion.

If the crutch loop does not lie horizontally both from side to side and front to rear it will very probably develop faults. A tilt from side to side will reduce the clearance of the bottom block within the loop and tilting from front to rear produces a strong tendency for the bob to roll or weave about. The lie of the loop should be checked after any adjustment to the beat of the clock.

A dial clock or a bracket clock usually has a slot in the pendulum rod that engages the crutch pin. Before cutting the spring for this type of pendulum the inside of this slot should be examined. If it is at all worn, or has been hacked about by a previous repairer, the spring length should be adjusted so that the pin

misses the damaged part of the slot. If the damage is so extensive that this cannot be done with any certainty, the slot should be filed to produce parallel sides and a new, larger pin made to suit it.

Spring Suspensions for Regulator Clocks
Regulators and other clocks having a very heavy pendulum do not normally have simple blocks at the top and bottom of the springs. A typical suspension is shown at **Fig 10/19**.

Whatever method of support is used at the top of a suspension, whether it is the more usual set of 'chops' (see the drawing), a simple rounded block, or a block and cross pin above (or through) the back cock, it must always be free to swing into the vertical under the weight of the pendulum. This freedom must be limited to the plane at right-angles to the direction of the pendulum swing. Any tendency of the spring to flap backwards and forwards in the cock will lead to periodic variations (poor timekeeping), or even a failure to go.

4 Non-Conductive & Silk Suspensions

Suspensions for Bulle Clocks
Though electric clocks are not dealt with in this book, the non-conductive suspension used in the Bulle clock is considered here for the sake of completeness and as it has a very similar construction to the usual spring suspen-

sion. This clock has a solenoid for its pendulum bob, swinging over and around a curved permanent magnet. Instead of a spring, however, its suspension consists of a top and bottom block with a non-conducting fabric strip gripped between them. Though there is only

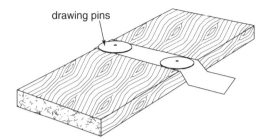

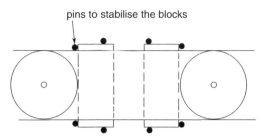

Fig 10/20 Making a new non-conductive suspension

Fig 10/21 The blocks held in position with pins

very little length of fabric visible, about 3mm (⅛in), it is sufficient to make sure that there is no electrical circuit through the suspension. These suspensions need to be checked for stretching of the fabric (the edges stretch and then play no part in stabilising the suspension), and for any material deposited upon it that may make it conductive.

The top and bottom blocks of these suspensions are generally made from plates held together with small screws to clamp the fabric between. Ordinary ribbon from a haberdasher's shop is a suitable material because it has a selvage on both sides — cut fabric will shred and twist. A generous length of the ribbon is stretched over a piece of soft timber with its surface sanded so that it does not snag the ribbon, and held down at each end with drawing pins (thumb tacks) as in **Fig 10/20**.

The screwed plates from each of the blocks are now slid under the ribbon. In order to position these properly — and to maintain the required distance between the top and bottom — each plate is held in place by four small pins (**Fig 10/21**). If the two pins placed across the top of the top block and the bottom of the other encroach on the fabric, holes larger than the diameter of the pins should be made so that they do not affect the tension on the ribbon.

When satisfied that the distance between these plates is correct and that they are truly parallel to each other, the matching plates are put in place and the resulting blocks lightly screwed together. They should grip the fabric tightly enough so that it does not shift easily.

The drawing pins are now removed and the assembly (with the excess tape still attached) held up vertically on a wire that pierces the holding pin hole in the top block while the pendulum is hung on the bottom block.

If the selvages are taut and the tape hangs flat without twisting, the screws may be tightened up and the excess tape cut off. If the edges curl or are of differing lengths then the tape must be drawn through the blocks, favouring one edge or the other until a taut, flat suspension is obtained.

Silk Suspensions

Huygens' suspension for the first pendulum clocks was a cord and this method can be found in French clocks and other small mantel clocks. The description applied normally is 'silk suspension' (**Fig 10/22**). A fine thread is anchored at one end to the top of a suspension cock, allowed to loop down to a hooked-on pendulum rod and then led up through the cock again and thence to an arbor that is used, windlass fashion, to wind up the thread and raise the pendulum. The pendulum is light

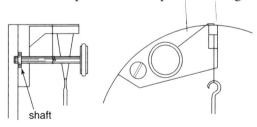

Fig 10/22 A silk suspension. The shaft fits between the plate and the back cock and is tight enough to prevent slip, but easy to rotate by hand

and the thread must be very flexible, but should not be elastic in any way. Button thread is too thick for most pendulums of this type. Sylko machine twist thread of 40 gauge is a very good substitute for silk thread, and a light rub with beeswax is an advantage. Another very useful material, although not generally available, is braided suture thread of the sort used by vetinerary surgeons for external wounds. Silk thread, of course, is ideal, but it will make little or no difference to timekeeping and it is not always easy to find one of

long staple and consequently with no tendency to fluff out.

There are few things that can be wrong with a silk suspension. The winding arbor may be loose and let the pendulum drop down under its own weight. If the clock has not been in use for some time (or has been in the hands of a doubtful repairer), it is wise to check that the inside of the hook has not been roughened by holding, or bending it with pliers. Other than that, it is a very reliable suspension.

5 Crutches

The invention of the pendulum resulted in the verge staff operating in the horizontal plane, rather than vertically as with a balance wheel, and provision was needed to support the pendulum. Some Continental clocks (such as Dutch *stoel* clocks, which were made until the nineteenth century) continued to use a vertical staff with a horizontal projection that engages the pendulum rod

The earliest pendulum arrangement used in a clock is that devised by Christiaan Huygens. The verge staff is fitted with cylindrical pivots at each end and it carries a crutch that transmits the impulse from the escapement to

a pendulum that hangs from cords. This is virtually the same system as that used in pendulum clocks today (**Fig 10/23**). There is very little weight on the pivots, just that of the verge staff (or pallet arbor) and the crutch. As a result the frictional losses are small if the pivot diameter is small — and of course, if there is little weight to carry the pivots *can* be very small in diameter.

Frictional *losses* are related to the diameter of the pivot because of the torque produced by friction at the pivot's radius. *Friction* (for these purposes) is directly related to the weight and the coefficient of friction — area does not affect it.

The smoothness of the pivots of a pallet arbor or a staff, is just as important as that of any other pivot in the movement. It is not absolutely necessary for it to be polished all around, or even for it to be a true cylinder, but the lower semi-cylinder supports the arbor and must have a smooth finish. Since the crutch is often permanently attached to the

Fig 10/23 The Huygens system of moving the escapement via a crutch

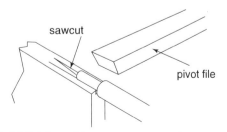

Fig 10/24 Smoothing an escapement pivot

arbor or staff, spinning the piece in a lathe is not a suitable way of repolishing these pivots.

If the crutch is bent out of the way the pivots can be polished by rotating the chuck with one hand while the other applies a pivot file and then a burnisher. If a small piece of scrap brass is held in a vice and a groove made in its thickness at the top (**Fig 10/24**) the pivot can be rested there while using a pivot file and burnisher. The other end of the arbor is held between the finger and thumb of the non-working hand and spun, while the pivot file and burnisher are employed on the damaged surfaces. The shoulders must be attended to as well to ensure that they have a good polished face.

In a longcase clock the friction at the pivot shoulders of the going train accounts for approximately 40 per cent of the frictional losses in that train. There are normally five shoulders in the going train of a weight-driven clock, including the pallet arbor, that may all contribute to this additional source of friction.

Fastening the Crutch

Faults may well develop in a clock as a result of the crutch being loose or misaligned, so the manner in which it is fastened to the pallet arbor is important. The vertical part of the crutch may be attached to the arbor in a number of ways (**Fig 10/25**). It may be riveted into a plain hole, dovetailed into a small block, hard soldered directly. or it may be a friction collar. The latter is intended to allow the clock to be put in beat without bending the crutch upright, and two basic versions of this are illustrated in **Fig 10/26**.

The firmness of the attachment of the crutch must always be tested when servicing an escapement. It is important that there is no relative movement between it and the pallets. To test this the pallets are held in one hand and the crutch in the other and then the attachment checked by twisting them quite firmly. There should be no give at all in those crutches that are riveted or soldered.

A loose crutch may be corrected by additional riveting, thorough cleaning and re-

soldering, or degreasing thoroughly and then using an adhesive such as Loctite.

Crutches that utilise a form of friction attachment will obviously move — they are designed to do so — but they must do so with reluctance, and evenly. If the grip between the friction collar and the pallet arbor varies as the crutch is turned, being tight at one moment and loose at the next, it must be put right. The type of collet that is threaded, split and then screwed onto the arbor rarely gives any trouble unless it has been completely hacked about; the only means of correcting this is to remake it. Since it is unlikely that the repairer will have taps and dies that match the original thread, the arbor must first be softened if necessary and a screw die run down it to produce a good round thread of modern form with no flats.

The collet is always thin walled and will prove difficult, if not impossible, to thread if the natural course of turning the piece first and then drilling and tapping is followed. If the outside diameter of the collet is left larger than the finished dimension, drilling and tap-

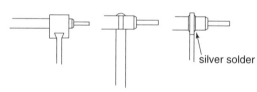

silver solder

Fig 10/25 Methods of fixing the crutch to the pallet arbor

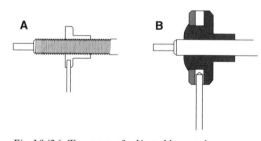

A   B

Fig 10/26 Two types of adjustable crutch:
A Saw–cut along the length to give the screw a tight fit
B The washer fixed to the crutch must have parallel sides to give a friction fit

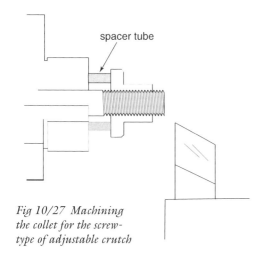

Fig 10/27 Machining the collet for the screw-type of adjustable crutch

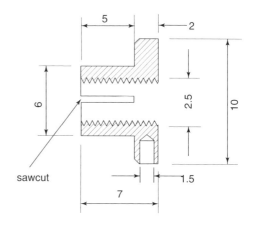

Fig 10/28 The collet of a screw-type of adjustable crutch made from machining brass. The dimensions should be regarded as proportions, rather than actual measurements in millimetres

ping can be dealt with first and then the rough collet screwed onto a piece of scrap steel until it locks against a shoulder or a spacer tube (**Fig 10/27**). A thin wall of about 0.010in (0.25mm) above the diameter of the thread can now be produced by turning the outside of the collet while it is fully supported. This is a useful method of producing any thin walled tube such as a post or a pipe and ensures that the bore is true to the outside.

The shoulder employed here is a short tube trapped between the face of the jaws and the collet. Releasing the jaws of the chuck will allows the unscrewing of this rather delicate piece of brass when the turning is finished. To complete the job it must have a fine saw cut made along its length; suggested proportions are shown in **Fig 10/28**.

The second type of friction collar depends on friction between a shoulder, a washer brazed or made onto the top end of the crutch, and a retaining washer. The assembly is then held together by swaging the parts together, (**Fig 10/29**). The smoothness of the friction fit will depend totally on the washer being the same thickness at all points of its periphery. If it runs thick and thin by a as little as a thousandth of an inch, the grip will vary as the crutch is moved.

Problems occur in old clocks with this type of adjustable crutch when some previous repairer has carried out work on the top of the crutch and has remade the washer end. Un-

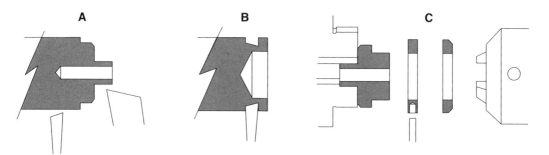

Fig 10/29 Machining a friction type of adjustable crutch. **A** *Machining the collet.* **B** *Parting to ensure a parallel washer.* **C** *Swaging the collet over the second washer using a drill chuck*

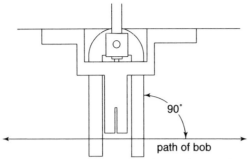

Fig 10/30 The fork of the crutch must be at right-angles to the path of the pendulum bob

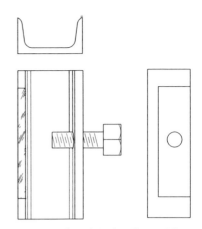

Fig 10/31 Simple tool for bending stiff crutches

less a compressible medium is interposed between the crutch top and the collet, it is almost impossible to make a replacement washer by any method other than turning that will perform correctly. If it is made by facing in the lathe and then parting off without the bar stock being moved in the chuck, the washer will have perfectly parallel faces.

The thickness of the washer is not particularly important — it must of course be consonant with the other dimensions of the collar. It needs to be a little thicker than the upright of the crutch so that it can be soldered to it without solder spreading on to the faces. If this happened the faces would require dressing with a file or emery paper, but they *must not* be touched with a file after parting off. A small hole is drilled in the thickness of the washer to accept the upright, which should be tinned before assembly and heated in situ to make the joint with little or no added solder, to avoid fouling the faces.

The alignment of the fork, loop or pin of a crutch must be at right-angles to its path (**Fig 10/30**). The result of not observing this simple condition is that the movement of the crutch will impart a twisting impulse to the pendulum. Note that it is not sufficient to place the loop or peg at right-angles to the back plate because the pallet arbor itself is often not placed at right-angles to the plate.

Crutch Adjustment
Many crutches have no method of adjustment available to them, other than the bending of

the crutch wire or rod. These include long-case clocks and many French, German and American clocks. Unfortunately many of these are made from material that is too stiff to bend easily. Consequently they should be set as closely in beat as possible before the movement is fitted into the case. Final adjustment must then be made by either rotating the bezel (and hence the movement) in the case of round French clocks, or by packing the movement or seat board to achieve proper balance. When the crutch has a round or square sectioned stem a bending tool (**Fig 10/31**) can be used. It has to be said that is almost always the case that a crutch that is too stiff has been modified by a previous repairer, or corrosion has destroyed the adjustment.

The type of mantel clock that has a wooden

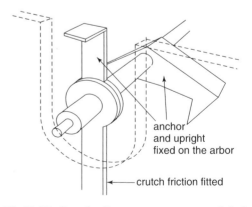

anchor
and upright
fixed on the arbor

crutch friction fitted

Fig 10/32 Crutch adjustment on some mantel clocks

case and a square movement cannot be put in beat by twisting the bezel, as the movement is attached by screws to the inside of the case. Many are provided with a small attachment to the arbor and anchor that engages the sides of an aperture in the back plate. This holds the anchor still while the crutch is moved — or at least that is its purpose, but the idea does not always work in practice (**Fig 10/32**).

Adjustable Crutches

The type of adjustable crutch with a slipping disc or a screwed collet has already been described (pages 209-211) — however there are others.

The crutch is often made in two parts that are joined together with a rivet and washers to form a friction joint; this allows the 'bending' of the crutch by simple pressure on the side (**Fig 10/33**). There are a number of variations on this that provide a finger-adjusted cam or a thin screwed disk which applies this bending in a precisely controlled manner. All are recognisable by the hinged break in their length. The only faults that occur are an increase or decrease in the tightness of the joint. A loose joint may be remedied by the judicious use of a light hammer, but if the joint is too tight the crutch should be removed from the movement and the joint loosened by work-

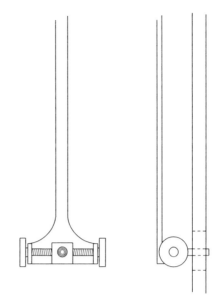

Fig 10/34 Crutch of Vienna regulator with a screw-adjusted peg to set the pendulum in beat

ing it backwards and forwards with penetrating oil. This must not be done in position because there is a strong risk of damaging the pivots of the pallet arbor.

Vienna regulators have a crutch that is provided with a screw adjustment for setting the pendulum in beat (**Fig 10/34**). It is only necessary to turn the screw one way or the other to make the pendulum operate correctly. This style of pendulum and crutch enables the Vienna movement to be detached from the pendulum suspension, the latter being hung directly on the backboard of the case.

The attachment of the crutch pin (that slips through a slot in the pendulum rod) to the horizontal screw is a critical part of this crutch. If it is weak or if the screw itself can slide from side to side within the brass housing, the pendulum will be deprived of part of its impulse.

Offset Crutches

These devices (**Fig 10/35**) have their beat set by adjustment of either the connecting piece (the link that runs horizontally from the

Fig 10/33 Jointed crutch. Care must be taken when setting in beat to ensure that the gap in the fork does not jam on the pendulum rod

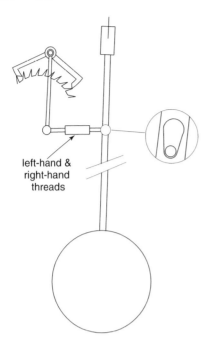

left-hand &
right-hand
threads

Fig 10/35 An offset crutch with a screw-adjusted link from the crutch to the pendulum rod. The end of the link is sometimes fitted into a pear-shaped hole so that the resulting incline relieves the effect of any increased impulse

crutch to the pendulum), or by adjusting screws on the crutch/pallet arbor assembly. It can also be effected by moving the suspension in its support to the left or right. Such a system has the advantage of being easy to adjust for beat while the pendulum is in motion. Though found on Comtoise clocks with anchor escapements (but without the screw adjustment), this type of crutch is rarely found in any other type of clock apart from regulators. It is sometimes attached to the pendulum rod by a peg resting in a pear-shaped hole. This provides a steep incline plane to relieve

the pendulum in the event of an unusually large impulse. It is a simple means of limiting the variations in impulse that affect the pendulum.

Unbalanced Crutches

It is possible to have pallets put out of balance by the bending of the crutch. In other words, the equilibrium of the pallet limbs about the arbor and the mass of the crutch may not balance about a plumb centre line when the load is off the clock. In a movement where this out-of-balance mass is an appreciable fraction of the pendulum mass, the clock will probably fail, even though it apparently beats perfectly.

The crutch of a recoil escapement should be capable of beating when the drive is on and the pendulum is removed. In a longcase clock the crutch will often have to be bent to a different position to achieve this, which means that the pallets have a permanent bias due to being unbalanced. This does not normally affect the longcase clock because of the very great difference in the masses of the bob, the crutch and the pallets. But a French mantel movement is another matter and the pallets should have a much better balance about the arbor centre than a country longcase clock. After many years of maltreatment, the beat adjustment on such a mantel clock may seize up entirely and a subsequent repairer may have had to bend the crutch to obtain a true beat. The result is often an extremely temperamental clock that stops for no apparent reason.

Rocking ships and other *automata* that are operated by the pallet arbor must also be balanced, otherwise the same faults are likely to occur.

CHAPTER 11
Pendulums

1 The Simple Pendulum

The type of pendulum used in most clocks is the simple pendulum. Theoretically it consists of a rod having no mass and a bob, though every practical pendulum rod must have mass. The time in seconds for one beat of a simple pendulum is given by the formula:

$$T = \pi \sqrt{\frac{l}{g}}$$

l = pendulum length in metres or feet
g = acceleration of gravity, 9.81m/sec² or 32.2ft/sec². π = 3.142

A beat is one swing, not a complete oscillation, which is two beats. Table 11/1 gives the values of T and beats per hour for a wide range of pendulum lengths.

Unfortunately a simple pendulum exists only in theory, as pendulum rods must have some mass, and so do the other oscillating parts attached to the crutch and pallet arbor. In consequence it is a complex task to calculate precisely the length of a pendulum. Few clockmakers attempt it, but simply provide enough adjustment to allow for the inaccuracies inherent in using the simple formula. Another assumption is that the distance between the centre of the bob and the under-

| beats/hr | length | | secs |
	inches	mm	
3200	49.55	1258.6	1.12
3600	39.15	994.4	1.00
4000	31.71	805.5	0.90
4400	26.21	665.7	0.81
4800	22.02	559.4	0.75
5200	18.76	476.6	0.69
5600	16.18	411.0	0.64
6000	14.09	358.0	0.60
6400	12.39	314.6	0.56
6800	10.97	278.7	0.53
7200	9.79	248.6	0.50
7600	8.78	223.1	0.47
8000	7.93	201.4	0.45
8800	6.55	166.4	0.41
9600	5.50	139.8	0.37
10400	4.69	119.1	0.35
11200	4.04	102.7	0.32
12000	3.52	89.5	0.30

Table 11/1 Time per beat and beats per hour for pendulums of different length

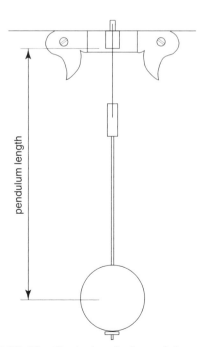

Fig 1/11 The effective length of a pendulum

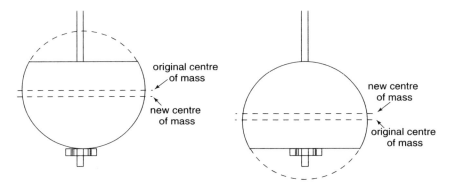

Fig 11/2 The effect on the centre of mass of removing the top or the bottom of a pendulum bob

side of the suspension cock accurately represents the pendulum length (**Fig 11/1**).

No real problem is caused by making these assumptions on a clock with a long pendulum (more than 500mm or 20in), but it is quite different for a pendulum, fitted to a bracket clock for instance, that is only 250mm (10in) from suspension cock to bob centre. Because the mass of the pallets, crutch and rod is substantial, it has the effect of producing a pendulum with a shorter length than a calculation based on the distance from the underside of the suspension cock to the bob centre. Generally this error is in the region of between 12mm (½in) and 25mm (1in). Many old bracket clocks can be seen where the clockmaker has had to carve a hollow in the bottom board to allow the bob to be lowered further than the original design permitted. Nevertheless, not all cases with hollowed-out bottom boards are the result of a clockmaking error; it was sometimes done to keep the case within the proportions dictated by its style.

A simple pendulum can be made to run slower with a given bob diameter by slicing the top or the bottom off the disc. If the top is removed the distance from the suspension cock to the bottom of the bob remains the same, but the centre of mass is lowered. Removing the bottom of a bob raises its centre of mass, but as it now sits lower on the rating nut the overall effect is a greater effective length, and an even slower swinging pendulum, than by reducing the top (**Fig 11/2**).

Two-Part Pendulums
Some mantel clocks have the pendulum bob hung on the rod so that it free to move in the plane of swing (**Fig 11/3**). This does have the effect of protecting the escapement pallets if the clock is moved without care or from over-swinging the pendulum (there are usually banking pins on either side of the rod). The suspension spring must not be allowed a similar freedom, of course.

A number of clocks have similar arrangements for the pendulum rod. Sometimes this is to enable the major part of the rod to be removed from the clock without disturbing the seating of the suspension and the bottom

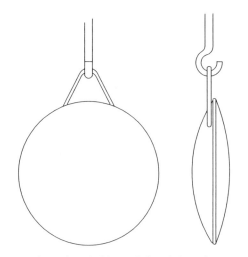

Fig 11/3 A detachable pendulum bob used on some mantel clocks

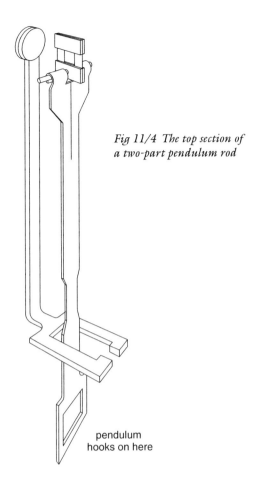

Fig 11/4 The top section of a two-part pendulum rod

pendulum
hooks on here

arc until the escapewheel just comes free of the pallets (when a 'tick' will be heard). Release the pendulum so that it swings to the other side and the next tooth will be cleared with another tick. Repeating the test, by moving the pendulum bob to the other side, should give the same result. This is a more reliable method of testing than simply listening to the swinging pendulum and trying to determine whether the tick is even on opposite swings. In an old clock the drop of the escapewheel teeth on to the pallets is often greater on one side than the other, thus giving unevenness of *loudness* of tick, which can confuse the ear. It is equal *periods* of beat that one is listening for. In addition to which, it is surprising just how often extraneous noise and conversation blur the essential decision.

If the pendulum does not allow the escape pallets to clear the teeth in both directions of the pendulum swing, when it is tested in this way, then the crutch must be adjusted. Suppose that, on moving the bob gently to the right and then releasing immediately it ticks, the swing fails to obtain a tick from the opposite side; then the crutch needs to be moved by the pendulum further to the left than is happening at present. Move the bottom of the crutch to the right either by curving the soft iron stem of the crutch (if it is a longcase clock), or by shifting the crutch on its arbor. The latter may be by having a friction coupling between the pallet arbor collet and the top of the crutch, or by means of screw adjustments.

• **Adjusting 400-Day Clocks**

The suspensions of 400-day clocks are put in beat by twisting the top block clockwise or anticlockwise (**Fig 11/5**). The twisting of the pendulum is observed and its angular position noted when the pallets drop at entry and exit. If the clock is in beat the drop will occur at the same angular distance from the end of the rotational swing for both pallets.

If there is a difference, the top anchorage of the suspension spring is twisted slightly in one direction or the other. The pendulum is twisted slowly by hand until the pallet drops

block within the crutch. The top part of the rod is in fact trapped between the pinning of the top block and the loop of the crutch, and the rest of the rod hooks over a loop at the lower end of the upper part (**Fig 11/4**).

Other multi-part pendulum rods are broken into links (Comtoise clocks for instance), apparently to facilitate transportation.

Putting a Clock in Beat

The term 'in beat' refers to the evenness of the pendulum swing. If the escape pallets are so set that the pendulum has to make a longer swing on one side to clear the escapewheel teeth on that beat, it is said to be 'out of beat'. Energy is wasted in making one pallet swing further than the other, and the clock will stop.

To check that the beat is set correctly, move the pendulum gently to one side of its normal

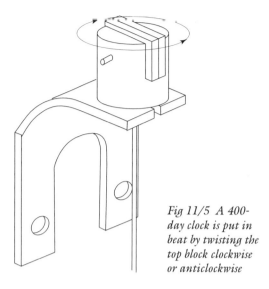

Fig 11/5 A 400-day clock is put in beat by twisting the top block clockwise or anticlockwise

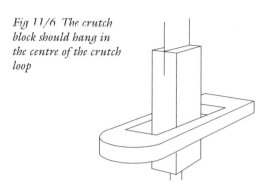

Fig 11/6 The crutch block should hang in the centre of the crutch loop

and is then carefully released. If the return swing then drops the other pallet when the swing is almost completed, the clock is in beat. If it fails to drop or swings considerably after the drop then it is not in beat and twisting of the top anchorage musy continue until the test produces an even beat.

• **Adjustment of Heavy Mantel Clocks**

Putting the mechanism in beat is often a very tedious business on a small movement that is very critical in its working. This is particularly the case with mantel clocks, where there is often very little room to get at the pendulum without having to move the clock from its normal resting place. When these clocks have movements that are held in the case by screws running between the dial bezel and the back bezel, the movement can be left slightly loose in the case while it is put in beat in a more convenient position that has approximately the same level as the final one.

After the beat is correct and the clock has been put into its proper working position on the shelf, the small readjustment that is needed may be made from the front by slightly twisting the dial bezel. It must be emphasized that the correction should only be slight, and if the 12 and 6 positions of the dial are visibly not vertical then the crutch must be altered.

Once the clock is ticking steadily — and in beat — it can be taken down carefully, the fastening screws tightened without shifting the movement so that the clock does not go out of beat the first time it is wound up, and then it is placed back on the mantel-shelf.

In addition to being in beat the clock must also sit so that the pendulum is working in the middle of the crutch loop (**Fig 11/6**). Since many mantel-shelves slope from front to back it may be necessary to use packing under the front or the back of the case to obtain this condition. A mirror can be used to observe the crutch while the packing is placed in position. It is important to ensure that this new adjustment does not disturb those already made and put the movement out of beat again.

It should always be borne in mind that if the clock is very critical, and will not go even if it is only slightly out of beat there is something wrong with it. The escape pallets, the attachment of the crutch and the crutch loop should be checked, and if a heavy pendulum bob is fitted, the back cock must be strong enough to prevent it springing up and down or even from side to side. The firmness of the seat board or other form of mounting is important too. A heavy pendulum will cause a movement to tilt from side to side if it is not physically prevented from doing so by being clamped firmly to a flat seat board and the whole set upon an equally firm support.

2 Pendulum Construction

Since pendulums are often lost or badly damaged it is useful to be able to replace them. Though a large number of designs are available from clockmakers' suppliers, they are not always apposite or of a sufficient quality, and so a number of manufacturing methods are given here.

Lenticular Bobs

Lenticular bobs — round with convex front and rear faces — are the commonest type and can be seen on clocks of all nationalities. Some are made of solid lead, brass or cast iron; some are hollow shells of brass that have been filled with lead or are simply solid lead. Some nineteenth-century longcase bobs are of cast iron faced with a very thin sheet of brass. Others have a lead bob with a quite thick (3mm, 1/8in) cast-brass facing, though the brass facing of the usual longcase bob is much thinner than this.

Pendulum bobs with brass faces need to have a hollow shell (**Fig 11/7**), which can be made in a number of ways. The two parts may be made from sheet brass using metal-beating techniques, pressing or by spinning on the lathe. Metal beating is a practical art that does not benefit from text descriptions and most published accounts only describe spinning. However, pressing is a much simpler method that deserves to be much more widely known.

• Pressing Hollow Shells

There is a very quick method using a wooden former and form die to press out the shell in a limited range of sizes. At first sight the system seems to be flawed, certainly the author had no faith in it when he first heard of it, but despite the lack of control over the sheet metal a very good profile can be obtained from this simple punch and die. Anyone with experience of presswork expects the metal to ruckle around the edge as the centre is drawn down into the hollow die. This is because as the periphery gets shorter there is nowhere but the thickness of the disk for the displaced metal to flow to and there is nothing to hold it flat while this takes place. However within certain limits the metal disk can provide enough stability to overcome the expected ruckling effect around the edges.

The criteria for a successful pressing are:
• For a 100mm (4in) diameter bob the blank should be roughly 1-1.5mm thick (0.04-0.06in).
• The amount of doming is no more than about 10 per cent of the blank diameter.
Hence this method is ideal for longcase bobs.

Pressing a shell does not require a large fly-press, but can be done quite readily with an engineer's vice with jaws 4in wide or larger.

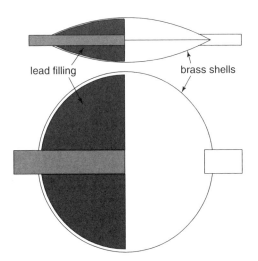

Fig 11/7 Brass-faced pendulum bobs have a hollow shell filled with lead

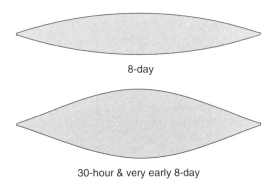

8-day

30-hour & very early 8-day

Fig 11/8 The cross-sectional shape of longcase pendulum bobs

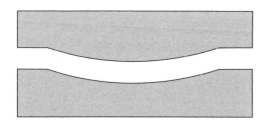

Fig 11/9 Male and female moulds for pressing hollow shells for pendulum bobs

Note that the bobs of early longcase clocks, particularly 30-hour clocks, are deep at the centre, while later ones have faces shaped like a slice off a large sphere (**Fig 11/8**).

A pair of male and female moulds (the punch and die) are turned from two blocks of close-grained hardwood such as beech or medium-density fibreboard (MDF) about 1½-2in thick (**Fig 11/9**). The method of turning a series of steps and then smoothing using a file, as described in the section on spinning (pages 219-220), may be used to make the male mould. For the female mould a woodturning scraper with a rounded end used on a hand rest is best, but the judicious use of metal-turning tools and abrasives would suffice.Use a cardboard template to check the correct cross-sectional shape and although, ideally, the thickness of the brass sheet should be allowed for, this is not important. It is not necessary to allow for any 'spring-back', nor is there any need to have a scratch-free surface, both of which are requisites for spinning. There is no need for great accuracy, normal wood turning measuring instruments are quite good enough.

Cut a disc out of brass sheet using heavy-duty tinsnips (this is much easier than trepanning it out on a lathe), and smooth the edges with a file. The brass should not be too thin; about 1mm (0.04in) thick is satisfactory, but if the metal is too thin it may wrinkle. If the bob is to have a brass shell at the rear as well as the front, then two discs are needed. One of these needs a hole about ½in (12mm) diameter drilled in the centre to allow molten lead to be poured into the finished shell at a

later stage. While most original longcase bobs had a brass facing only on the front, having one on the back as well is simpler for the amateur, as no rear mould is then necessary when pouring the molten lead.

Heat the brass to dull red heat, either on a couple of firebricks or a bed of dry sand, to fully anneal or soften the metal. Quench in water or allow to cool slowly — brass is not affected by rapid cooling in the same way as steel. Clean with emery paper. Make sure that the blank is round and fairly flat.

Place the disc in the die mould, put the punch on top and then squeeze between the jaws of a vice. The whole process only takes about 5-6 minutes, including annealing the brass. It is a very simple process.

It helps if the moulds are somewhat larger than the disc, as there is then no need to centre it accurately if the surface is part of a sphere. If the bob is to be an early type with a non-spherical surface, then the disc needs to be placed centrally, and it helps to hold it in place with masking tape. Very deep bobs may need two attempts with an intermediate anneal, but normal longcase bobs are readily made in one step.

Longcase clock have bobs that would suit this process, but the shells produced have a tapered edge when assembled and soldered. If a bob is required that has a more rounded edge the shells will need a deeper draw at the perimeter and the simple wood punch and die will not do that. It is a spinning job.

• **Spinning Hollow Shells**

Spinning is the process of deforming metal by holding it against a spinning former so they both rotates, and pressing a static tool against the metal to gradually press it over against the former. Spinning is very much more difficult than the method just described, but may be necessary in certain circumstances, such as when the edge of the brass sheet needs to be turned over the edge of the bob.

The lathe used must be at least the size of Myford 7 with a strong frame and headstock, and a 400W (½HP) motor. In general, it is

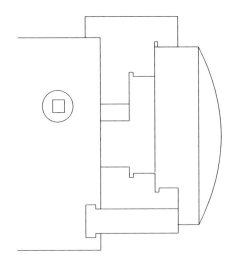

Fig 11/10 A spinning chuck held in the lathe

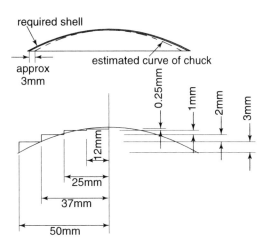

Fig 11/11 A series of steps may be turned to define the curve of the spinning chuck, which should have a slightly tighter curvature than the finished shell

hardly worthwhile spinning a shell for a small bob, anything less than about 3in diameter, because standard bobs are relatively cheap.

The material must either be 70/30 brass or copper (the former is much more usual) and 0.75-1.5mm (0.030-0.060in) thick. Cut discs 6mm (¼in) larger than the finished bob diameter and annealed thoroughly by heating to red heat and quench or allow to cool slowly.

The former used in spinning is called a chuck. If it is intended to make only a few bobs it can be turned out of a hard wood, (beech for instance), but for small production runs an aluminium chuck is necessary. **Fig 11/10** shows both the convex shape of the chuck and its manner of mounting in the lathe. For convenience the curve may be drawn out on a piece of paper and a series of turned diameters that will mark the curve developed from the drawing. **Fig 11/11** shows the series of steps that these will form; it is the inside corner of the step that defines the finished curve. The metal must be faced freehand or a file used to remove the steps and cut the metal back to the corners.

The face should be filed until it is smooth and emery paper used to remove any well defined marks left from filing, because these will be reproduced in the spun metal and, if deep,

will show on the outside of the shell. As the metal will spring away from the chuck after spinning the convex face of the chuck must have a smaller radius than the one desired for the shell. If the depth of the half shell is to be about 12mm (½in), then the depth of the curve on the chuck should be about 6mm (¼in) deeper. A experienced turner may prefer to produce the curve by facing the metal freehand without marking out the curve and turning the steps.

Provision must be made to hold the disc of annealed metal firmly against the chuck for spinning — the driving force for this operation is derived from the friction between the rotating chuck and the annealed disc. A considerable amount of pressure is needed to obtain the drive and, of course, the mating surfaces of the chuck and disc must be free of grease and oil.

A piece of scrap brass that will slip onto the end of a running, or rotating, centre (**Fig 11/12**) will serve to hold the disc to the chuck. To avoid making a noticable mark on the disc where it is clamped, there should be a close match between the inside curve of this clamping piece and the convex curve of the chuck.

The flat disc is held against the chuck with

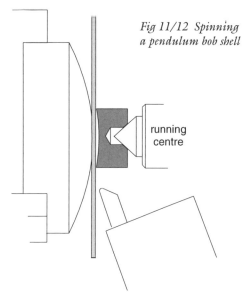

Fig 11/12 Spinning
a pendulum bob shell

running
centre

the clamping piece in place, and the running centre brought up to it until the operator is satisfied that the disc is held reasonably true to its centre. A trial spin of the chuck will ensure that the this has been achieved and then, after locking the tailstock firmly to the lathe bed, the handwheel of the tailstock is turned until the running centre is screwed as hard as possible against the clamping piece.

The tool needed for spinning is a simple piece of brass that presents a vertical radiused corner to the face of the disc. (If more than one shell is to be made using this technique the tool may be made from high-carbon steel and brought to a high polish after hardening and tempering, but for a single shell brass performs quite well.) It should reach above and below the centre line and unlike a turning tool it does not have any rake or front clearance (**Fig 11/13**).

The radius is not important, but if it is too large, the operator will not be able to get close to that part of the disc that is clamped between the chuck and clamping piece, and the finished curve will have a ridge. The tool is locked into the tool post in the normal fashion. Goggles and protective clothing are very necessary, a great deal of lubricant is used during spinning and this will be spun off the edge of the disc.

The lathe is now switched on and the tool advanced to touch the disc as close to the clamped area at the centre as possible. Plenty of oil must be dripped onto the face of the metal from now until the tool is taken away from the metal, otherwise the disc and the tool will weld together and score the surface of the work.

Both hands are employed to turn the handles of saddle and cross-slide simultaneously so that the tool is pressed against the face of the disc and drawn outwards while pressing the rotating metal against the chuck. As the metal is deformed it will buckle and wave strongly and as the tool withdraws from the centre it will be found that the disc successfully resists approaching the chuck closely.

The metal will not take the form of the chuck immediately, frequent passes of the tool from inside to outside must be made, gradually spinning it over at each pass. It will be seen that after a pass or two the metal will not move easily but springs back when the tool is

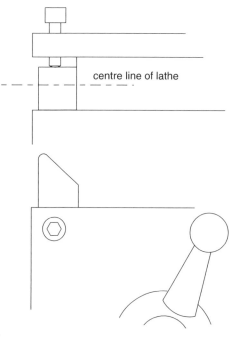

centre line of lathe

Fig 11/13 The spinning tool has a radiussed end which, unlike a turning tool, reaches above and below the lathe centre height

taken away — it has work hardened and must be annealed again. Generally speaking it will be found that a disc for a 4in diameter bob will need annealing four or five times before it is sufficiently curved to form a satisfactory half shell. Even after frequent annealing it is unlikely that the form can be spun to lie closely against the chuck, it will spring back every time. Even in a lathe intended specifically for spinning the metal always springs away from the chuck to a certain extent, this is the reason for making the chuck to a deeper curve than that required.

As metal has been moved from the inside of the shell to the outside, it will be found that the edge of the disc thickens up, it is no longer a true circle, and it will have very uneven edges. After the discs have been spun they should be put back into the lathe and the edges turned. The cuts must be light or the tool will grab the disc and stop it rotating. It helps if the tool is advanced at an angle so

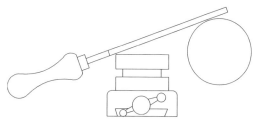

Fig 11/14 Filing the edges of the shell after spinning

that the side touches before the point and if it is ground to have little or no top clearance. If turning proves too difficult, the rim of the discs can be filed by supporting the file on the tool post until it has cut a true circle (**Fig 11/14**). For two-sided bobs both discs must finish at the same diameter.

Filling Pendulum Bobs
• Double-Sided Bobs
The shells must now have two rectangular pieces taken out of their edges into which the

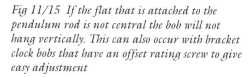

Fig 11/15 If the flat that is attached to the pendulum rod is not central the bob will not hang vertically. This can also occur with bracket clock bobs that have an offset rating screw to give easy adjustment

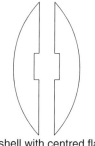

shell with centred flat

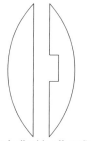

shell with offset flat.

a centred bob
hangs plumb

an off-centre one
does not.

also slightly out of plumb unless
corrected by off-centre rod

flat (the rectangular bar that the bob slides on), is fitted. There are alternative methods of setting the flat into the shells: rectangular spaces of half the flat depth may be filed out of each shell so that the flat engages both equally, or metal may be removed from only one shell. In the first case the flat will be centred between the shells and the bob will hang evenly on the pendulum rod, in the second the bob will be displaced to one side.

This will make little or no difference to most pendulums. However if there is very little horizontal stability imposed by the effective width of the suspension spring, or if the departure of the rod from a true vertical affects the swinging of the pendulum, the first method must be used. There are many examples of pendulum bobs whose centre of mass is displaced from the vertical centre line by using the second method or by employing offset rating screws (**Fig 11/15**).

The shells are assembled with the flat in position and laid down on sand (for stability) on a well-dried brick. It is important that the brick is well dried by placing in an oven at low temperature for several hours. Any moisture within it may well cause flakes of brick to burst off the surface, or even burst the brick completely, when the blow torch is used. Place three or four 'tacks', or blobs, of silver solder spaced around the circumference, and then completely solder the edge of the shell.

Rub French chalk or talcum powder on the flat to prevent molten lead sticking to it (or use a temporary flat of aluminium) and replace the shell, with the flat in place and the central hole uppermost, on the bed of sand (**Fig 11/16**). To prevent the lead flowing out of the join between shell and flat, a little moist bread may be spread around the join. This is a 'tinker's dam' — not spelled 'damn'.

• **Equipment & Protective Clothing**
A few rules should be observed when handling the small amounts of molten lead necessary for making a pendulum bob:
• Goggles should be worn, and gloves are useful — but *only* if the wrist is closed and does not provide a funnel for molten lead.

• The operator should wear an apron that covers the body to the neck and hangs low enough to protect the shoes — there is not sufficient room in a shoe for a foot *and* molten lead. It does not have to be of heavy material unless there is a large quantity of lead to pour and there is real fire risk. A slightly damp heavy cotton one that will deflect any splashes is sufficient in most cases.
• Hair is inflammable, so a head covering is advisable; beards are at least fairly visible but a good head of hair can be well alight before the owner is made aware of it.

The equipment necessary is:
• A source of heat such as a gas torch or gas ring (the latter is more convenient when the molten lead has to be picked up).
• A melting pot or ladle. This must be stable, an old cast iron saucepan is ideal as a ladle is round bottomed and is difficult to support over the heat source.
• A pouring ladle. There is really no substitute for a heavy ladle. A domestic soup ladle is neither large enough, nor made of thick enough metal to stand the reheating that will be necessary if the lead cools while not being poured. A really sturdy stainless-steel catering kitchen ladle is quite satisfactory.

The molten lead is poured into the shell until it is full and then used to top up the level as it cools. If it is not topped up there is every possibility that the lead will rattle in the shell when cool, because lead expands and contracts very much more than brass.

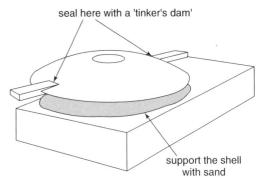

Fig 11/16 The shell supported for filling with lead

When the bob is cool, the flat should tap out with little difficulty (the talcum powder is simply an additional precaution), and the shell can be polished to remove the spinning marks and any scratches.

After removing the flat it should be polished and the edges chamfered so that it slides in the bob without binding. If the bob will not fall under its own weight there is a danger that whoever regulates it in the future will pull it down manually with consequent risk to the suspension spring.

• **Single-Sided or Half-Shell Bob**

This is usually called a faced bob, having a brass or, occasionally, copper facing. It can be made by sinking the flat into a single half-shell so that the flat lies an ⅛in (3mm) below the top edge (**Fig 11/17**). The inside of the shell must be tinned with solder and a soldering iron before pouring the lead. A completely tinned surface is not necessary, but the lead must key to the brass and substantial areas of the inside must be properly covered with solder. Lay the flat in position, using talcum and tinker's dams as before, and lead poured in until is level with the edge and the flat is beneath the surface. Since brass floats on lead the ends of the flat must be weighed down.

It is even more necessary to make sure that the shell is level and cannot tip, because it is open and the lead can pour out over the edge. It should be supported in sand or in some other manner. To make the back of the bob level it will need to be topped up from the ladle as the lead cools.

A final smooth surface can be obtained by melting a small amount of soft solder onto the lead just after it has set. As solder melts at a lower temperature than lead it will only be necessary to waft the flame over it to merge it into the cooling lead. Since solder remains molten at a lower temperature (and has a lower coefficient of expansion), it will set almost dead level and without blow holes. A steel wire brush may be used to dress the lead/solder surface.

• **Solid Lead Bob by Lost-Wax Casting**

For a one-off casting lost-wax is the best

Fig 11/17 When filling a single-sided pendulum bob the open face of the shell must be truly level or the molten lead will pour over the side

method. Candle wax, plaster of Paris and an oven are needed. Lost-wax casting requires a wax form around which plaster can be poured. When the plaster has set the wax is melted out to leave a cavity for the molten metal.

A saucer or the bottom of a basin that is sufficiently rounded inside make useful formers for the wax. Since these will be used to make halves of the final lenticular shape, by adjusting the level of the wax the diameter of the bob can be made smaller than the container, but not larger.

Molten candle wax is poured into the saucer up to a level that will produce the diameter needed, and then allowed to cool. It will make the job easier if it is then cooled in a refrigerator. When it is completely set the wax is tapped out of the saucer or basin, which is then used to make another wax former of the same size.

A brass flat is prepared as before, making sure that it is smooth with no scratches that may make it difficult to remove from the final lead casting. Dusting the surface with talcum is pointless, because it will be removed when the flat and wax forms come together. A temporary flat of aluminium and of exactly the same cross-section as the final one of brass is probably better.

One of the formers is laid, flat side up, in something that will support it (a smaller saucer, sand, etc). Two pieces of wood thick enough to support the pendulum flat at a height that will leave it half sunk into the wax are placed on either side (**Fig 11/18**).

The pendulum flat is now heated to the melting point of the wax and laid across the middle of the wax former and allowed to sink onto the wooden supports. It must only be *just* hot enough to melt the wax, otherwise

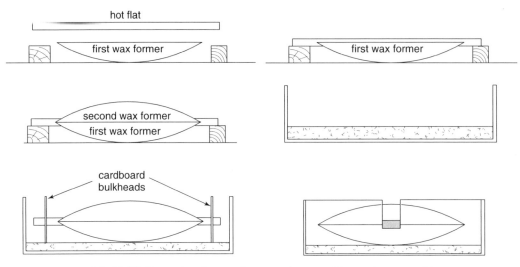

Fig 11/18 Preparing the wax formers prior to making a plaster mould

radiant heat will continue to melt the wax after the flat has stopped sinking. When it has reached the supports, the other form is laid on top and allowed to fall as the wax melts. A little pressure at the finish will press the faces together and express most of the molten wax. What remains will seal the two halves of the former together. A damp cloth may be used to cool off the brass flat and speed the setting of the wax, before placing it back in the refrigerator again.

A cardboard box that is large enough to take the assembly with at least ½in (12mm) thickness of plaster around it is used to support the formers and the outside of the plaster cast. A short length of dowel about 25 x 18mm diameter (1 x ¾in diameter) with clean, flat ends is waxed over its surface. It is necessary to leave the ends of the flat protruding from the sides of the box, or to use two sheets of card that will reach from one side to the other and which can be slid over the ends.

After about half an hour the wax is taken out of the refrigerator. A small amount of plaster about 12mm (½in) deep is poured into the box and, when this is firm, the former and its flat is rested on it with the flat inserted into the holes in the box or the cards. This is to ensure that although the plaster thickness will

be adequate (12mm or so) the flat will protrude when it sets.

When it is certain that the assembly will not sink into the plaster, more plaster is poured around the assembly. When it reaches the top of the former a short dowel is stood upright in the centre and then pouring continues, while holding the dowel firm with one hand. At the finish there should be enough dowel protruding from the plaster for it to be gripped and pulled free when all is set (**Fig 11/19**).

This proceedure is necessary to ensure that the plaster flows underneath the wax former without any air pockets. Alternatively the mould may be partly filled and the wax put in place while the plaster is still soft, if necessary supporting the ends of the flat to prevent the former sinking to the bottom.

The mould is left to set for an hour or so and then turned upside down in a tray that is large enough to contain all the wax inside the mould. Put it into an oven at about 100°C (273°F) to dry out. After about an hour the temperature can be increased to melt out the wax — about 150°C (270°F) should be hot enough to evacuate the mould without filling the room with smoke.

The wax must be taken out of the tray as often as practicable, to reduce the amount of

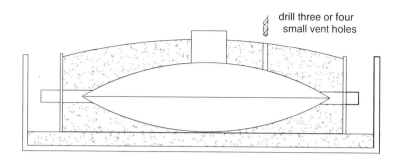

Fig 11/19 The completed plaster mould for making solid lead bobs

drill three or four
small vent holes

potentially flammable material in the oven. **As hot wax vapour is a hazard, being flammable it will form an explosive atmosphere, and must not be allowed to form in any significant quantity. Removal of the molten wax and control of the temperature to no more than 150°C are sensible precautions.**

After about an hour or so remove the mould from the heat and place it somewhere warm and dry until the next day. It is important that the mould is completely dry before molten lead is poured into it, otherwise there is a risk of it spitting out of the mould, or even blowing out with force!

Prepare the mould for casting by drilling a few small holes about 1mm (0.040in) diameter in the upper surface to allow hot gasses and air to leave the cavity as the molten metal flows in. Support the plaster mould on sand, dust the flat with talc and reinserted it and — taking the precautions given earlier — pour lead in slowly through the hole left by the dowel. This forms a 'get' or 'gate' and acts as a reservoir to keep the bob topped up as the lead cools. Any remaining wax will burn off, and the metal is poured slowly to allow the gasses formed to escape over the top of the molten pool. The size of the gate should allow any gas to escape around the stream of molten lead.

It is worth repeating the earlier precautions. Pouring lead is dangerous if tackled without due care. Use goggles and an apron — a cap is a good idea, particularly if you are thin on top. Molten lead will not roll off fast enough to avoid blisters!

When the lead is cold, the plaster may be broken away and the flat should slide out with a tap or two from a light hammer. Brushing with a steel wire brush will produce a smooth bright finish. An application of 'black lead' (graphite paste) or matt black paint is normal for a plain bob. Alternatively the plain, bright lead can be prepared with an undercoat and gold painted or painted to match the dial, which is a traditional treatment for wall clocks with visible pendulums and painted faces.

Solid Brass Bobs

This form of construction is really only suitable for a fairly thick pendulum bob because of the difficulty of holding the blank for machining. Means of holding a thin blank can be devised, such as turning a brass blank with a concave face into which the partially machined bob can be glued or soldered. But thin bobs are generally of small diameter and there is a large range of commercially manufactured ones available.

A blank disc of machining-quality brass, a little larger than the required diameter and about 12mm (½in) thick is needed. Machining brass produces short chips and turns easily. To ensure that the face of the blank is running true and that enough remains outside the jaws to machine a curve on its face (**Fig 11/20A**) place three pieces of drawn brass between the blank and the jaw faces. These must be removed once the chuck jaws have been tightened, for they will probably fly out as soon as the machine is switched on!

This system of machining the bob will leave a short cylindrical section in the middle in-

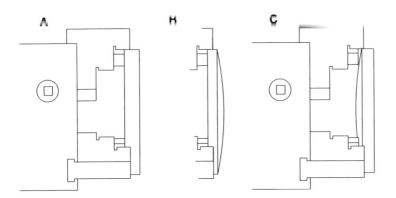

Fig 11/20 Machining a solid brass pendulum bob

stead of bringing the faces of the bob to a sharp edge, but this is not a serious disadvantage. The same machining techniques are used to produce the convex faces as in the earlier description of making a spinning chuck. The curves may be achieved by facing steps onto it in accordance with a drawing, or they may be formed by freehand turning, matching the curve to a card template.

The curve on the face of this bob has little depth — about ³⁄₁₆in (5mm) — and it is not too difficult to wind the facing tool out from the centre while advancing it slowly with the top slide and the right hand. The secret is to start at the centre and draw out. This is self limiting in terms of the depth of metal that can be removed, so that it will be found that the top slide is not applied too enthusiastically. The first attempt will probably result in a series of steps, but a file will take these out, as long as no severe errors have been made. After a little practice the job is very quick and only requires a modest amount of filing to smooth off the face. **Fig 11/20B** shows the first face complete and ready for polishing with emery paper.

In **Fig 11/20C** the blank has been turned around and packing pieces placed between the curved face and the jaw faces again to keep it running true. They will need to be somewhat thicker this time to allow for the metal that has been removed. Again the packing pieces must be taken out before starting the machine. The same procedure as before will complete

the bob and give it the lens shape that is required. Finally it is polished with emery paper.

• **Cutting the Slot for the Flat**

The set up in **Fig 11/21** is a simple one. A piece of steel rod slightly smaller in diameter than the width of the slot to be cut, is held in a tailstock drill chuck. Two saw cuts are made to form the sides of the slot, and to ensure that these are reasonably parallel the lathe chuck must be rotated by 180 degrees between one saw cut and the other. Placing a spirit level firstly on top of and then below two of the jaws, provides an accurate means of controlling this rotation.

With the rod as a guide, a saw cut is made to the full depth of the slot, taking care to keep the saw horizontal. When this cut is completed the chuck is rotated through 180 degrees and a second, similar, cut made. The rod ensures that the slot is the right width, and it is relatively easy to maintain as close an approach to the horizontal as for the first cut. If

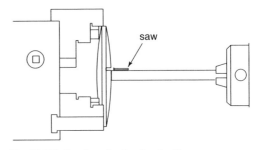

Fig 11/21 Sawing the slot for the flat

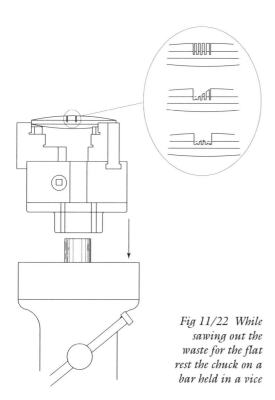

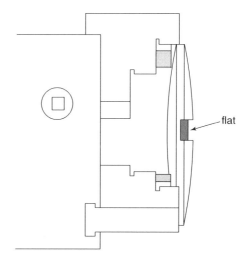

Fig 11/23 *After cutting the slot align the flat horizontally*

Fig 11/22 *While sawing out the waste for the flat rest the chuck on a bar held in a vice*

this is too difficult, a small spirit level may be taped to the saw blade. It will register quite well even though the blade is moving — the fluid is viscous and the cuts do not need to be made with any great vigour.

The cuts should be made about 1.5 mm (1/16in) deeper at the centre of the bob than the depth of the flat that is to be fitted. When the edges and depth of the slot have been defined, the work (still mounted in the chuck) is moved to the bench vice. A piece of rod is turned to fit the bore of the chuck and gripped in the vice jaws. The chuck drops over it and rests on the vice and the rod serves to stop the chuck shifting from its perch (**Fig 11/22**).

The waste metal can be removed by making further saw cuts more-or-less parallel with the first. Using the saw saves a great deal of subsequent filing, so that after a few minutes work the slot should be relatively clean. Finish the slot with a square file until the rod slides easily along it.

Replace the bob in the chuck and use the same distance pieces as before to position it.

Using a light touch the jaws are adjusted until they hold the disc just sufficiently to prevent it dropping out again. The flat is placed in the slot and the chuck rotated until the flat is horizontal (**Fig 12/23**).

Carefully bring the lathe tool close to the surface of the flat and then, while holding the flat securely in the slot, the cross slide is traversed so that the tool point moves parallel to the face of the flat (**Fig 11/24**). If the bob is set correctly the space between tool point and flat will not vary as it is traversed, but any variation will show quite clearly.

Tap the bob light hammer until the face of the flat lies parallel to the path of the tool.

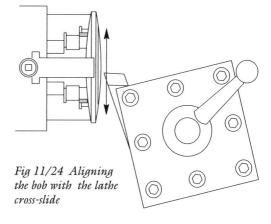

Fig 11/24 *Aligning the bob with the lathe cross-slide*

Fig 11/25 Facing cuts are made until the slot is slightly deeper than the flat

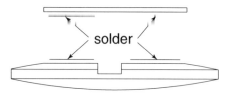

Fig 11/26 The areas of the bob and the disk that are to be tinned

Take care to ensure that this adjustment does not tilt the bob in the other direction and make the cross-section of the slot deeper on one side. Once the correct alignment of the slot is achieved the jaws are tightened to grip the bob firmly. Make a final check on the alignment in case the bob has moved while tightening the jaws, then, after removing the flat, small facing cuts are made until the slot is only very slightly deeper at its deepest point than the thickness of the flat (**Fig 11/25**).

The bob now has a small flat face on one side. The reason for carrying out the machining and filing in this order, is that it is much more difficult to file a slot parallel to a face than to machine the face parallel to an existing slot.

To provide the fourth side to the slot a round blank is cut from 1.5mm (¹⁄₁₆in) thick brass and machined to the same diameter as the small face just produced on the back of the bob. One side of this blank is cleaned and tinned and any excess molten solder wiped away with a piece of cotton cloth.

The face of the bob is tinned too, care being taken to avoid solder entering the slot — preferably by keeping an untinned border about 1.5mm (¹⁄₁₆in) wide on either side of the slot (**Fig 11/26**).

After fluxing the bob and the blank, the tinned surfaces are laid together so that the blank is concentric with the outside diameter of the bob, and heated until the solder melts

and the two parts joined together. A touch of solder (hammered very thin), to the joint will make up for any lack of solder that may be evident. It may be necessary to touch the inside of the slot of the finished assembly with a file to get the flat moving smoothly, but use an old file as solder clogs the teeth and can be difficult to remove completely.

If the flat is loose in the slot the bob can be adjusted by placing it between guarded vice jaws with a brass rod lying parallel to the slot and squeezing slightly to depress the back plate (**Fig 11/27**).

Black Forest Bob

This, the simplest bob of all, consists of a flat brass disc with a spring on the back. The spring needs only to be a piece of brass that has been beaten hard and then soldered at one end to the back of the disc. The pendulum rod is guided by two pieces of the disc turned over at the top and bottom and filed to suit the rod (**Fig 11/28**). Alternatively the blank is curved and a hole drilled at the top and bottom to accept the rod. This jams between the two holes and can be slid up and down by pressing on the back of the disc.

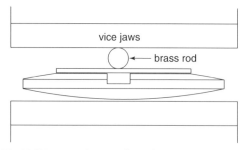

Fig 11/27 Use a brass rod to adjust the fit of the flat after soldering

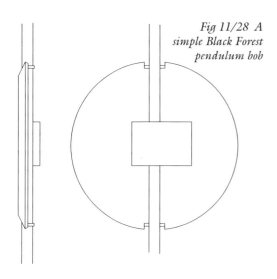

Fig 11/28 A simple Black Forest pendulum bob

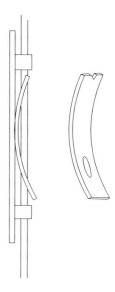

Fig 11/29 A very simple type of pendulum bob

A relatively easy bob to make, that looks fairly good, is an combination of the solid bob and the Black Forest bob. Though original bobs of this type were cast it may be readily fabricated. Make a blank 6mm (¼in) thick and two short brass blocks with a hole drilled in each to suit the rod. The blocks are slid onto the rod, laid onto the back of the disc and silver soldered in place. In addition make a leaf spring with a hole in one or both ends.

(In the one-hole type the opposite end of the spring is notched to rest on the rod.) The pendulum rod passes through both sets of holes, those in the bob and those in the spring and friction is imposed on it by the spring pressing against both the bob and the rod (**Fig 11/29**). No rating nut is used with this or the preceding type of bob, they rely purely on friction.

3 Pendulums — Faults & Comments

In general, without going into the complexities of 'Q' and high-precision regulators (which is outside the scope of this book), the mass of a pendulum bob is not critical. This is the case for clocks with relatively heavy bobs, ie bobs that are significantly more massive than the rod, such as longcase, bracket, and French mantel clocks. Within the limits of the mechanical structure and what seems reasonable to the eye, a clock can have as heavy a pendulum bob as the maker cares to put on it.

A swinging pendulum is kept swinging by the clock movement replacing the energy losses due to bending the suspension spring, friction in the crutch loop and air resistance. The arc of the pendulum varies as the amount of energy passed to it by the crutch varies, but a bob of large mass (and hence large potential and kinetic energy) suffers a smaller percentage change in arc, for a given increase in energy, than a light bob. Since circular error is brought about by changes in arc, it can be seen that a heavy pendulum is better for timekeeping than a light one. The only changes in the energy losses brought about by using a heavy bob are barometric effects (the 'floating' of the bob in air of varying density) and the stress in the spring suspension.

Barometric error for large pendulum bobs is the same as that for small bobs having a similar specific gravity. Changes in the stress of the suspension spring occur in the outer surfaces of the spring — the outer curve has a higher value for tension and the inner one a lowered value for compression.

This seems to be dealing with matters well outside the scope of ordinary regulators, let alone domestic clocks.

However, many small mass-produced clocks have very light pendulums and the relationship between the bob mass and the stiffness of the suspension spring can cause problems.

If a new suspension spring is fitted that is stiffer than the original the pendulum will swing faster than its length indicates, because the spring is adding a significant acceleration to that of gravity. In fact it may be impossible to regulate the clock, because there is not sufficient length in the case to lower the bob any further. The cure is to fit a lighter spring. A piece cut from a 0.0015in (0.04mm) feeler gauge is often ideal. The thickness of the original spring should not be taken as a guide, because if it *is* original it will be made from a steel with less stiffness than an equivalent thickness of modern spring steel — and if it is *not* original, who knows what it is?

A similar problem can occur with short pendulums from fusee movements. These are commonly fitted with brass rods of rectangular section. The rod has a considerable mass when compared with the bob — not as heavy of course, but hefty. Taken in conjunction with the other moving masses of the escapement pallets and crutch, this mass shortens the effective length of the pendulum. In other words a pendulum that is, for instance 10in (254mm) long from the centre of the bob to the underside of the suspension, behaves as if it were only 9in (228mm) long.

Many British bracket clocks have grooves in the bottom of the case that allow the pendulum bob to hang just that little bit lower — not all these are simply the result of maintaining the proportions of the case while using a 'standard' movement. Some are just the result of a clockmaker's error.

CHAPTER 12
Some Useful Techniques

M any of the small jigs and set-ups needed for making escapements have been dealt with in earlier chapers of this book, but there are a few techniques that have not been detailed which are useful for clock repairers. There are many more tools and jigs that specialist restorers make for themselves, but these are unlikely to be of use to those who want to just repair or make escapements. This book does not deal with such tools as punches for extracting plugs from cylinder escapements, setting jigs for jewelled pallets, swing tools for polishing and honing, etc.

Fly Cutting
This is a simple process that employs a single-point tool rotating at high speed to cut tooth forms (gear or escapewheel) in brass discs very easily and cleanly. It is used with a milling attachment on the lathe. In the absence of such an attachment it can be used by rotating the cutter in the chuck and holding the work on the cross-slide. Unfortunately this method has two difficulties: the lathe is generally not rotating fast enough to use the cutter well (3,000-6,000rpm gives good results) and some arrangement has to be made to traverse the blank past (or through) the cutting track of the tool. Neither difficulty is insuperable, but they are merely not as good as a proper milling attachment set-up.

Fig 12/1 illustrates the usual arrangement for milling escapewheels (and of course, other clock gears) on a lathe with a milling attachment. The lathe should have T-slots on the cross-slide so that the fastening of a vertical slide is not a problem. On the vertical slide is a milling spindle or the headstock of a small lathe, the author has used both Sherline and Unimat headstocks and sees no reason why

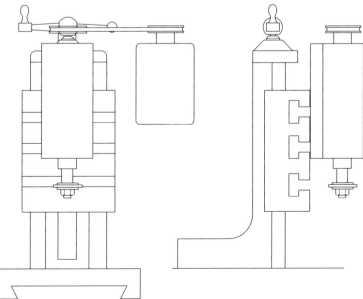

Fig 12/1 Milling attachment for use on a small lathe

233

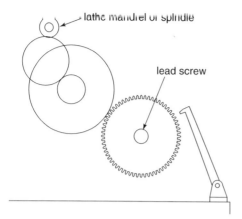

Fig 12/2 Dividing the lathe spindle using change gears

any small lathe that has a swivelling headstock should not perform well enough. The power needed is no more than 150W (½₀HP) and may be as low as 75W (¼₀HP).

In addition to the milling attachment some form of indexing is necessary. If the lathe has gearing between the mandrel and the lead screw that is accessible, it is a simple matter to hinge a hook from the lathe stand and index by gearing and a gear on the end of the lead screw to act as the dividing plate (**Fig 12/2**).

• **Mounting the Gear Blank**
If an escapewheel is to be cut accurately it must

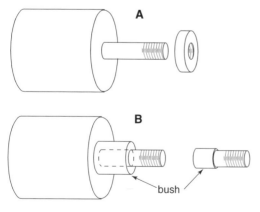

Fig 12/3 Mandrels for holding gear blanks. The spigot of type A is best turned from the solid as an insert might move in use. B uses a brass bush that may be turned down to a very thin walled tube

be mounted accurately, and for this mandrels that can be set up to hold the work concentric with its bore are needed (**Fig 12/3**). Care should be taken to make the mandrel with all its diameters concentric, and be sure that it can be held true in the chuck or collet. As in all turning, it is best to make the mandrel at one setting, having sufficient steel protruding to machine all the diameters, without any need to move the work further out, or turn it round. Machining from the solid bar, rather than inserting a smaller diameter piece on which the wheel is mounted, is preferred.

Large escapewheels (greater than about 30mm diameter) will perform quite satisfactorily with an eccentricity of 0.025mm (0.001in) and a decent three-jaw chuck should be able to achieve this. Smaller wheels, particularly for deadbeat escapements, must be held more accurately. The modification shown in **Fig 12/3B** allows the attachment of a thin brass bush that is turned when the mandrel is ready for the wheel blank. No alteration should be made to the holding of the mandrel after this has been done. The bush is locked with an adhesive and can be removed by heating to about 150°C (300°F).

• **Making the Fly Cutter**
This is a single cutting edge formed on the end of a piece of soft high-carbon steel by turning or filing. The steel is held in a slot that is at right-angles to the axis of rotation. If this slot is off-centre then the tool is automatically given cutting clearances.

Fig 12/4 shows a holder for a fly cutter that is held in the hollow mandrel of a lathe or milling attachment. Most shapes of escapewheel teeth can be very easily filed onto a blank of soft silver-steel (or any high-carbon steel). It is necessary to make sure that the shape is filed to allow clearance at the cutting edges but otherwise it is a simple matter.

Occasionally it is necessary to form the cutter more precisely. **Figs 12/5-7** show set-ups for machining measured angles and radii onto the soft cutter. Note that the clearances are produced automatically by changing the position of the cutter in the holder.

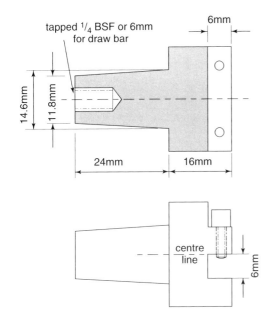

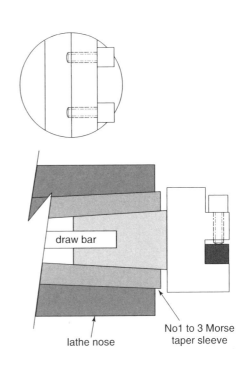

Fig 12/4 Holder for a flycutter. A draw bar (a long bolt) must be used to hold it in the Morse taper of the lathe spindle and a Morse taper sleeve may also be needed

After shaping the cutter it should be checked and then heated to bright red-heat and quenched in oil to harden it. Clean it until bright at the tip, heat to show just the faintest amber colour on the bright metal and quench again to temper the cutting edge.

The holder shown has a short morse taper and is held in the machine mandrel by a long draw bar; it could of course have a parallel shank and be held in a three-jaw chuck. How-ever it is held, the tool holder must not de-flect, otherwise the interrupted cutting of the lathe tool will create a bounce that produces poor cutting edges. The lathe tool shown in **Fig 12/6** is a radius tool for producing pre-cise radii.

Note that the cutting clearances on the cir-cumferential tool surfaces are obtained when the tool is refitted in the holder after being rotated through 180 degrees (**Fig 12/7**).

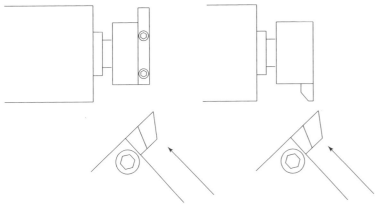

Fig 12/5 The fly cutter is shaped while in its holder. To cut at an angle swivel the top slide

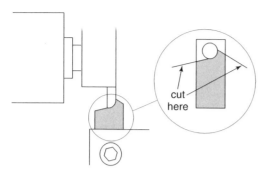

Fig 12/6 A form tool for producing a precise radius

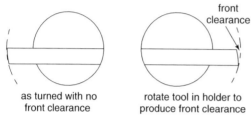

as turned with no   rotate tool in holder to
front clearance   produce front clearance

Fig 12/7 Turning the tool over in its holder gives the necessary clearance

Eccentric Bushes

Many clocks have eccentric bushes for adjustment of the escapement, and also the fly on the striking and chiming trains. These bushes are often damaged, sometimes so badly that the only way in which the movement can be adjusted is to remove the old bush and make and fit another.

• Removing the Bush

Fig 12/8 is a section through part of a typi-

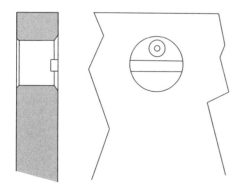

Fig 12/8 An eccentric bush fitted to a French clock

cal French clock plate fitted with an eccentric bush for the pallets. There are two chamfers in the plate: a large one that takes the pressure of the screwdriver blade or spanner and a smaller one that simply prevents the bush falling out of the plate.

As an alternative to the large chamfer the body of the bush and the hole may be made with similar tapers, but this calls for an accuracy that is best obtained by tooling and is not convenient for one-off repairs.

The chamfers should be smooth and made with a tool that will not 'chatter', and a D-bit (**Fig 12/9**) is a simple solution. Note that the flat does not reach the centre line but only close to it so that the metal that is left consists of *slightly* more than a half cone. In this manner the effectiveness of the tool as a cutter is impaired to a degree, imposing a smoothing and burnishing action.

In order to obtain a good match between the chamfer turned on the bush and the one made by the D-bit the bit should be held in the chuck and the side of the turning tool pressed against the cutting edge, before locking it into the tool post (**Fig 12/10**). The bush is turned with the end for the screw slot nearest the chuck. The total depth of the

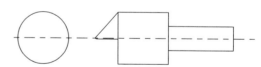

Fig 12/9 D-bit for cutting chamfers and countersinks. Slightly less than half the diameter is removed to form the cutting edge

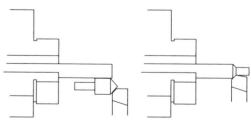

Fig 12/10 Matching the taper of an eccentric bush with that of the D-bit

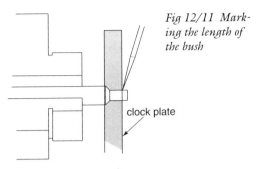

Fig 12/11 Marking the length of the bush

clock plate

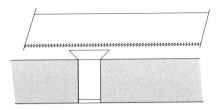

Fig 12/12 Hold the bush in a hole in a plate while cutting the screwdriver slot with a fine hacksaw

chamfer can then be checked by sliding the plate over bush until it is a good fit, not a drive fit. The final over-all length of the bush is gauged by sliding the plate over it and marking the turned surface with a scriber (**Fig 12/11**). The piece is then parted off so that it protrudes above the inside surface of the plate by 0.1mm (0.004in).

The simplest method of making the screwdriver slot is to drill a piece of scrap plate with a hole that is a close fit on the bush, leaving the edges sharp. Then use the plate to hold the bush while a hacksaw makes the slot (**Fig 12/12**). A new blade will cut a better formed slot than an old one.

Fitting the bush is a simple matter of making a very slight chamfer on the inside of the plate, inserting the bush and then beating the inner end with a planishing hammer until the bush has spread to give a tight fit that may be overcome without too much effort with a

screwdriver. Excess metal is dressed off with a fine single-cut file (with the leading edge of the end being stoned smooth first) before polishing the plate.

An alternative method to the screwdriver slot is to file the outer end of the bush to leave a half diameter of the metal standing proud, (**Fig 12/13**) in much the same way as a D-bit is made.

If the bush is made too tight it may be freed by laying the outside of the plate on soft wood and then, using a short, flat ended brass rod, striking the inner end once or twice with a light hammer. The pivot hole is drilled into the bush after it has been fitted.

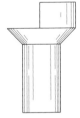

Fig 12/13 A alternative type of head for an eccentric bush

Typical Clock Movements

British striking front work

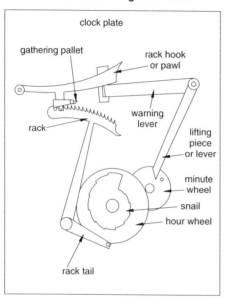

British weight-driven trains

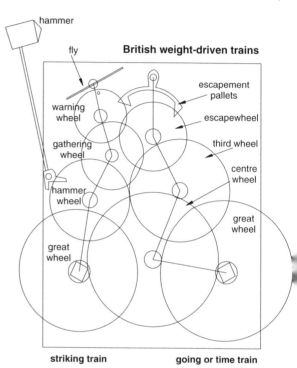

hammer

fly

escapement pallets

warning wheel

escapewheel

gathering wheel

third wheel

centre wheel

hammer wheel

great wheel

clock plate

gathering pallet

rack hook or pawl

warning lever

lifting piece or lever

rack

minute wheel

snail

hour wheel

rack tail

great wheel

striking train   **going or time train**

pinions (small gears driven by a brass
wheel) have the same name as the wheel
on their commonarbor or spindle

Side view of typical movement

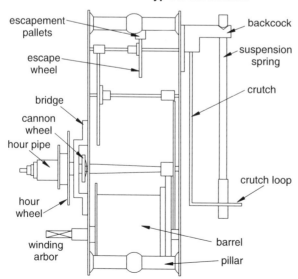

escapement pallets

escape wheel

bridge

cannon wheel

hour pipe

hour wheel

winding arbor

backcock

suspension spring

crutch

crutch loop

barrel

pillar

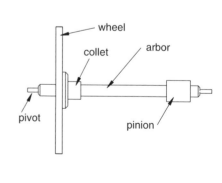

wheel

collet

arbor

pivot

pinion

Additional wheels in 8-day spring-driven trains

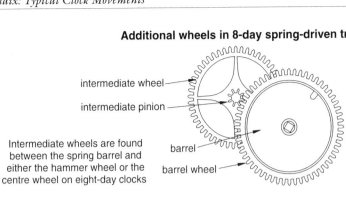

intermediate wheel

intermediate pinion

Intermediate wheels are found
between the spring barrel and
either the hammer wheel or the
centre wheel on eight-day clocks

barrel

barrel wheel

French countwheel striking

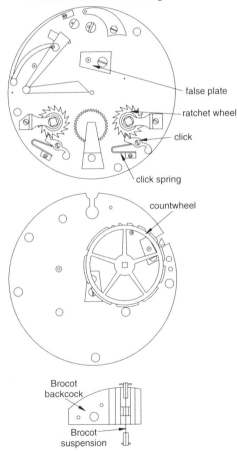

false plate

ratchet wheel

click

click spring

countwheel

Brocot
backcock

Brocot
suspension

French rack striking

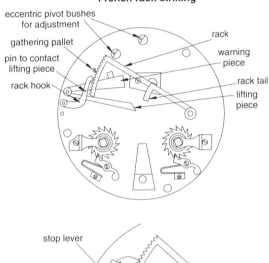

eccentric pivot bushes
for adjustment

gathering pallet

pin to contact
lifting piece

rack hook

rack

warning
piece

rack tail

lifting
piece

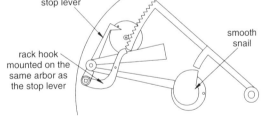

stop lever

rack hook
mounted on the
same arbor as
the stop lever

smooth
snail

Bibliography

Britten, F. J., 1978 *Britten's Watch & Clock Maker's Handbook, Dictionary and Guide* (16th edition revised by Richard Good)

de Carle, Donald, 1946 *Practical Watch Repairing*
1964 *Practical Watch Adjusting*
1968 *Practical Clock Repairing*
1981 *Clock and Watch Repairing* (2nd edition)

Gazeley, W. J., 1956 *Clock and Watch Escapements*
1958 *Watch and Clock Making and Repairing* (2nd edition)

Hope-Jones, Frank, 1940 *Electrical Timekeeping*

'G', *Clock Cleaning and Repairing* 1917 (edited by Bernard E. Jones)

Goodrich, W. L., 1950 *The Modern Clock*

Gordon, G. F. C., 1949 *Clockmaking Past and Present* (2nd edition)

Laycock, William, 1976 *The Lost Science of John 'Longitude' Harrison*

Penman, Laurie, 1984 *Clock design and Construction*
1985 *The Clock Repairer's Handbook*

Rawlings, A. L., 1993 *The Science of Clocks & Watches* (3rd edition, edited by T. & A. Treffry)

Rees, Abraham, 1970 *Rees's Clocks, Watches and Chronometers (1819-20)* (reprint of the horological sections from *The Cyclopaedia; or Universal Dictionary of Arts, Sciences and Literature*)

Saunier, Claudius, 1861 *Treatise on Modern Horology* (reprint 1975)

Index

simple pendulum 215-218
Sinclair-Harding gravity
    escapement 181-182
single-pivot grasshopper
    escapement 192-195
single-sided pendulum bob 225
six-legged gravity escapement
    179-182
sliding contact, avoidance of
    187
small-span anchor pallets 92-
    94, 94
soldering 78
    neutralising acidic flux 46
solid brass pendulum bobs
    227-230
solid lead bob 225-227
span. *See* pallet span
spinning
    chuck 221
    pendulum bobs 220-223
    tool 222
spring steel, drilling 204
spring suspension 210-207
    bottom block 204, 206-207
    making replacement 203-204
    regulator clocks 207
    top block 203-204
    temperature effects 205-206
    types 202-203
'square' anchor escapement
    57, 58-59
    alternative 66-68
steel slips 45, 79
stoel clocks 197
straightening jig 23
suspensions 196-214
    Bulle clocks 207-208
    cord 196
    400-day clock 205-206,
        217
    jewelled 198
    knife-edge 199-200
        alignment of 200
        non-conductive 207-209

rocking pin 200
silk 208-210
spring 201-207. *See also*
    spring suspensions
    vertical verge 196-197
    wire 200-202
suspension springs
    bending 201
    damaged 205
    fatigue 202
    flexiblity 202
    Horolovar 206
    integral 205
    length 202
    over-stiff 205
    stiffness 202, 205
    tension 202
swinging cherub clocks 103

T
tangential pallet contact 95,
    128-129
three legged gravity escape-
    ment 179-182
Thwaites & Reed's six-legged
    gravity escapement 179-180
tic-tac escapement 71-72
'tinker's dam 224
tinning 78
tooth contact before and after
    line of centres 54, 100
torsion pendulum 205-206
triangular-shaped escapewheel
    teeth 82
tripping 173, 176
tube, turning thin walled 211
two-part pendulum 216-217

U
unbalanced crutches 214

V
verge escapement 15-51
    bite of flags 16, 18, 21
    faults and comments 51

flag angle 16-19, 21
flag length 18, 21, 26, 46
geometry 16-19
height of verge 16
making staff and pallets 21-
    28
    flat strip 22
    hardened inserts 27
    separate flags 28
    summary 34-35
    turned staff 27
pallet design 20
pivots 29-37
regional variations 19
repairing broken staff 44
repairing flags 44-50
sequence of events 16
timekeeping 15-16
vertical verge escapements
    suspensions 196-197
    cord 197
    round pivot 197
Vienna anchor escapement 76-
    77
Vienna regulators 167, 187,
    213
Vulliamy-type deadbeat pallets
    104
    adjusting 125-128
    making 120-123

W
wax, precautions with molten
    227
wax chuck 83. *See also* shellac
    chuck
wear
    anchor pallet 54-57
    deadbeat pallet 102
wedge height adjustment 198
weights, typical driving 55
Westminster clock 179
wire suspension 200-202
working arc 187

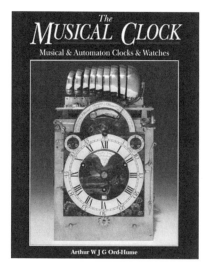
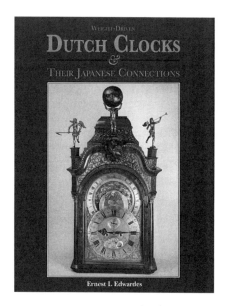

Restoring Musical Boxes & Musical Clocks

By Arthur W. J. G. Ord-Hume

246 x 174mm, 368 pages, 180 illustrations and 184 diagrams, hardback with full-colour dust jacket

How to repair cylinder and disk musical boxes, singing birds, also carillon, organ and dulcimer musical clocks. Includes arranging music for mechanical musical instruments, repinning musical barrels, musical theory, the principles of tuning, a glossary of mechanical and musical terms and index.

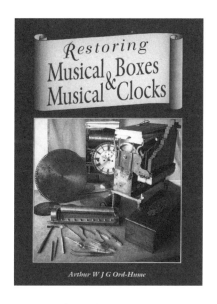

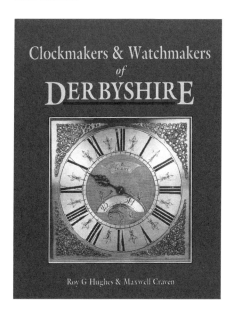

Clockmakers & Watchmakers of Derbyshire

by Roy Hughes & Maxwell Craven

A comprehensive survey of all the known Derbyshire makers of clocks, watches and barometers, from the earliest recorded workers to recent times. There is background information on clockmaking in the county and numerous illustrations. Appendices include case styles for Derbyshire round-dial longcase clocks.

John Whitehurst of Derby: Clockmaker & Scientist 1713-88

By Maxwell Craven

246 x 174mm, 264 pages, 251 illustrations, hardback, full-colour dust jacket

A biography of John Whitehurst FRS, the Derby clockmaker, whose clocks and barometers are highly regarded. This book deals with his scientific work, his clockmaking business and that of its successors. Appendices list his publications, known turret clocks, angle barometers, numbered clocks and apprentices.

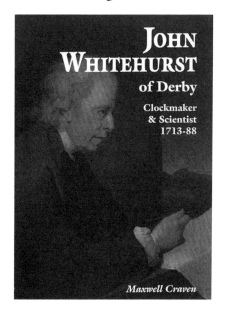

Kent Clocks & Clockmakers

by Michael Pearson

246 x 186mm, 320 pages, 206 black and white illustrations, map, 13 colour illustrations, hard-back with full-colour dust jacket

Kent has a long history of clockmaking, with a clock being installed in Canterbury Cathedral as early as 1292. This book details Kent's early turret clocks, and the history of the county's most influential clockmakers. There is a comprehensive list of over 1,200 clockmakers from the earliest times up to the nineteenth century, while appendices give extracts from local eighteenth-century and early nineteenth-century newspapers relating to clocks and watches, and clockmakers listed by town.

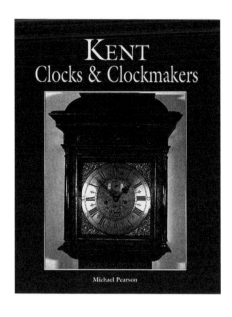

Clockmakers of Northern England

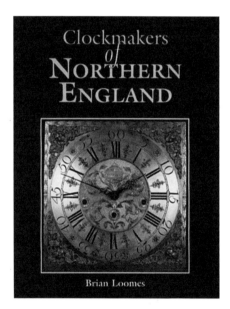

by Brian Loomes

246 x 174mm, 320 pages, 402 illustrations, 5 maps, hardback, full-colour dust jacket

The North of England has a long tradition of clockmaking, many domestic clocks having distinctive regional features. The author records the life and work of the most important, most prolific and best-known clockmakers of the six northernmost counties of England — the old counties of Yorkshire, Lancashire, Cumberland, Westmorland, Durham and Northumberland. This book looks at the earliest clockmakers on a county basis, as well as giving details of some 800 clockmakers from the eighteenth and nineteenth centuries — not only the most important, but also those whose clocks are of particular interest. It is profusely illustrated.